ИЗДАТЕЛЬСТВО · МИР ·

А. А. ПИНСКИЙ

ЗАДАЧИ ПО ФИЗИКЕ

ИЗДАТЕЛЬСТВО «НАУКА» МОСКВА

PROBLEMS
in PHYSICS

A.A. PINSKY

Translated from the Russian

by

Mark Samokhvalov, Cand. Sc. (Tech.)

MIR PUBLISHERS MOSCOW

First published 1980

Revised from the 1977 Russian edition

На английском языке

PREFACE

The two volumes of the "Fundamentals of Physics"*, published in two editions, have been translated into Polish and English and have gained popularity among senior form students of secondary schools where physics is studied at an advanced level, among college freshmen and among instructors and teachers of physics. At the same time, reviews and numerous letters from readers have stressed the need for a system of problems adapted to the theoretical material contained in the book which would enable the reader to consolidate and to check his knowledge of the material studied, and to develop skills in the creative application of the theory to specific physical problems.

This book offers the reader over 750 problems concerning the same subject matter as is treated in the two volumes of the "Fundamentals of Physics". The order of presentation of the theoretical material is also the same.

The availability of a great number of problem books based on the traditional school physics curriculum prompted us to enlarge those sections which are absent from traditional problem books, namely the dynamics of a rotating rigid body, the elements of the theory of relativity and of quantum and statistical physics, of solid-state physics, wave optics, atomic and nuclear physics, etc. Problems dealing with astrophysics illustrate the application of the laws of physics to celestial bodies.

The book contains a few problems requiring elementary skill in differentiating and integrating, as well as some problems to be solved with the aid of numerical methods, which nowadays are being increasingly used.

---

* B. M. Yavorsky and A. A. Pinsky. *Fundamentals of Physics*, v. I and II, Mir Publishers, Moscow, 1975.

As well as the practice exercises there are some rather sophisticated problems requiring a deep knowledge of the theory.

Most of the problems are provided with sufficiently detailed solutions.

Whether a problem book should be provided with detailed solutions, or only the answers should be supplied, is a controversial question. True, the temptation to look into a ready-made solution is quite strong. However we hope that the reader wants to learn to solve the problems himself, and so he will turn to read the solutions only in extreme circumstances. On the other hand, having in mind that the majority of readers will work with the book on their own, we feel obliged to offer them help when they are unable to cope with a problem. Note that the solutions provided are not always the only ones possible. We shall be grateful to any reader who suggests more elegant or original solutions.

Reference data required for the solution of the problems is presented in the appendices. They augment the data contained in the corresponding chapters of the series "Fundamentals of Physics".

The collection of problems may serve as an aid for students preparing for examinations in physics. It may be used in physico-mathematical schools or for extra-curricular work in physics. The problems will be useful to students studying to become physics teachers, to students at technical colleges, and to physics teachers in schools, technical schools and secondary vocational schools.

The author expresses his sincere gratitude to Prof. N. N. Malov and Prof. B. M. Yavorsky and also to Yu. A. Selesnev, Ya. F. Lerner and M. M. Samokhvalov. Their valuable remarks enabled the author to make corrections to the manuscript.

A. A. Pinsky

CONTENTS

Tables

SOME PRACTICAL HINTS

1. Before you attempt to solve the problems contained in some chapter, study the corresponding chapters of the "Fundamentals of Physics". Bear in mind that the most frequent reason that you cannot solve a problem is that your knowledge of the theory is not profound enough or is too formal.

2. Think about assumptions which could simplify the solution. For instance, when calculating forces in dynamics, one usually assumes them to be constant, while in the theory of oscillations they are taken to be quasi-elastic. Processes in gases are usually considered to be quasi-static, the elements of electrical circuits linear, the waves sinusoidal, etc. When necessary, the violation of these conditions is specially mentioned; in some cases it is evident from the particulars of the problem (a solenoid with a ferromagnetic core, a modulated wave, etc.).

3. Try to draw a schematic diagram or a sketch; this always makes consideration of the problem easier. Sometimes it pays to show the evolution of one's thinking on the diagram by partitioning it, or by introducing successive simplifications (for instance, when determining internal forces, or when designing compound circuits). Remember, a good diagram is half the success in solving a problem.

4. In most cases the problem should be solved in a general form with all the relevant quantities denoted by corresponding symbols and the calculations made using symbols. Don't let it trouble you if some of the quantities are not specified in the statement of the problem—they will either cancel out, or their values may be found in the appendices to this book, or in the "Fundamentals of Physics". Do not be scared by mathematical operations—the ability to perform them freely is an element of the mathematical knowledge indispensible to the student of physics.

Note that it is not always convenient to solve the problem in a general form. Sometimes the price of generality is an excessive volume of calculations. In such cases the problem should be solved directly with numbers substituted for the relevant physical quantities.

5. Having obtained the solution in a general form try to make sure it is a sensible one. To do this, sometimes dimensional analysis may be helpful, sometimes—the analysis of particular or limiting cases, or a comparison with a similar problem already solved is needed. For example, having solved a problem in dynamics which takes account of the forces of friction you may compare the result with that of a similar problem without friction, a relativistic calculation can be compared with a similar calculation in Newtonian mechanics, etc.

6. If the problem contains numerical values the final answer should be numerical as well. Do not underestimate calculations. In practice we are always interested in the numerical values of the quantities sought and only rarely in their expression in terms of other quantities.

All data, including those derived from the tables, should be expressed in the same system of units (as a rule, in the SI system) with the numerical data written in the standard form, i.e. in the form of $a \times 10^n$ where $1 \leqslant a < 10$. All values should be specified to the same accuracy.

7. All calculations (including those in the majority of problems involving the use of numerical methods) should be performed with the aid of a slide rule, the use of which guarantees reasonable accuracy. In the cases when the initial data are specified to two significant digits, the results of the calculations should be rounded off to the same number of digits.

Only a few problems on the theory of relativity, wave optics, atomic spectra, etc. involve calculations requiring an accuracy of four or five digits. For these mathematical tables should be used.

8. Having obtained an answer compare it with the one given at the end of the problem book. Do not be disappointed if your answer does not coincide with the author's. Both answers might be two different forms of the same expression. For instance, the expressions

$$\frac{\sin \alpha - \mu \cos \alpha}{\sin \alpha + \mu \cos \alpha} \quad \text{and} \quad \frac{\sin (\alpha - \varphi)}{\sin (\alpha + \varphi)}$$

coincide if one puts $\mu = \tan \varphi$. If you are unable to find ways of transforming one form of the answer into the other, make a numerical calculation using both formulas, and if the results coincide, your solution obviously may be taken to be correct.

9. After you have obtained the correct answer it is a good idea to look at the solution offered in the problem book. Should the solutions turn out to be different, try to find out which is the best. It will be all to the good if your solution is simpler, shorter and more elegant than that of the author. However, one should not preclude the possibility of errors accidentally compensating each other, so that the answer obtained is only formally correct. Such an analysis of the solution is very helpful and instructive.

10. When you are unable to solve the problem right away, don't hurry to read the solution supplied. Make a new study of the respective theoretical material, paying attention to the finer points. Experience shows that a repeated study of the theory with a definite goal in mind is very effective and ensures quick success when a second crack at the problem is attempted.

However, repeated study of the theory still may not help in solving the problem. This should not be a cause for gloom and despair. This problem book contains many creative and difficult problems, and it is not to be wondered at that you will not be able to cope with them all single-handed. In such a case try to make a detailed analysis of the solution supplied by the author. Perhaps after that you will be able to find a new solution. Experience shows that detailed study of some of the ready-made solutions is also very instructive and helps to raise the level of knowledge and to stimulate creative abilities.

Here's a concrete example of the way the above recommendations should be applied.

Problem. A small mirror with a mass of 9.0 mg is suspended from a thin quartz filament 4.0 cm long. A powerful laser flash is emitted in a direction perpendicular to the mirror, so that the system is deflected from the vertical by a certain angle. Calculate this angle knowing the energy of the laser flash to be 1.0×10^2 J.

Solution will be performed by stages.

1. The deflection of the system is caused by the momentum the light transmits to the mirror upon reflection. Accelerated to a definite velocity the mirror rises to a definite height. In this case the kinetic energy of the mirror is transformed into its potential energy in the gravitational field. Consequently, to solve the problem one must know the expression for the momentum of the light flash, and the laws of conservation of momentum and of energy.

2. To solve the problem, introduce several simplifying assumptions. To begin with we shall neglect the mass and

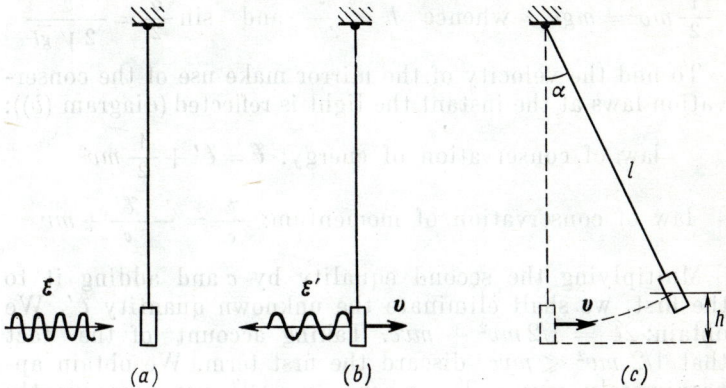

Fig. 1.

the elasticity of the filament, the friction at the suspension and air resistance. Then we shall assume the mirror to be a perfect reflector (neglecting the absorption of light). Finally, because the mirror's velocity is small we shall perform all the calculations approximately, using Newtonian mechanics.

3. It will be helpful to draw a schematic diagram depicting the dynamics of the process (Fig. 1). Here diagram (a) shows the state of the system before the light falls on the mirror, (b) at the moment the light is reflected and (c) the deflection of the mirror together with the filament by the angle sought. The stages of the solution are also clear from the diagrams.

4. Denote the energy of the laser flash by $\mathscr{E}$, its momentum $p = \mathscr{E}/c$, the velocity of light by c, the mirror's mass by m,

its velocity at the moment of recoil by v, the height it rises by h, the length of the filament by l and the angle of deflection by α.

It may be seen from the diagram that

$$h = l - l \cos \alpha = l\,(1 - \cos \alpha) = 2l \sin^2 \frac{\alpha}{2}$$

It follows that in order to find the angle of deflection one must find the height to which the mirror rises. To do this use the law of conservation of energy:

$$\frac{1}{2}\,mv^2 = mgh, \quad \text{whence} \quad h = \frac{v^2}{2g} \quad \text{and} \quad \sin\frac{\alpha}{2} = \frac{v}{2\sqrt{gl}}$$

To find the velocity of the mirror make use of the conservation laws at the instant the light is reflected (diagram (b)):

law of conservation of energy: $\mathscr{E} = \mathscr{E}' + \dfrac{1}{2}\,mv^2$

law of conservation of momentum: $\dfrac{\mathscr{E}}{c} = -\dfrac{\mathscr{E}'}{c} + mv$

Multiplying the second equality by c and adding it to the first, we shall eliminate the unknown quantity $\mathscr{E}'$. We obtain: $2\mathscr{E} = 1/2\,mv^2 + mvc$. Taking account of the fact that $1/2\,mv^2 \ll mvc$, discard the first term. We obtain approximately $mvc = 2\mathscr{E}$, whence $v = 2\mathscr{E}/mc$; consequently

$$\sin\frac{\alpha}{2} = \frac{\mathscr{E}}{mc\,\sqrt{gl}}$$

5. Dimensional analysis convinces us of the plausibility of the answer:

$$\left[\sin\frac{\alpha}{2}\right] = \frac{\text{J}\cdot\text{s}}{\text{kg}\cdot\text{m}\,\sqrt{\text{m}\cdot\text{s}^{-2}\cdot\text{m}}} = \frac{\text{J}\cdot\text{s}^2}{\text{kg}\cdot\text{m}^2} = 1$$

i.e. the sine turns out to be dimensionless, which was to be expected.

6. In the calculations write out all the data to two significant digits expressing them in SI units:

$$m = 9.0\,\text{mg} = 9.0 \times 10^{-6}\,\text{kg}$$

$$g = 9.8\,\text{m/s}^2$$

$$\mathscr{E} = 1.0 \times 10^2 \, \text{J}$$
$$c = 3.0 \times 10^8 \, \text{m/s}$$
$$l = 4.0 \, \text{cm} = 4.0 \times 10^{-2} \, \text{m}$$

Substitute the numerical values into the final formula:

$$\sin \frac{\alpha}{2} = \frac{\mathscr{E}}{mc \sqrt{gl}} = \frac{1.0 \times 10^2}{9.0 \times 10^{-6} \times 3.0 \times 10^8 \sqrt{9.8 \times 4.0 \times 10^{-2}}} =$$
$$= 5.9 \times 10^{-2}$$
$$\frac{\alpha}{2} = 3°24', \quad \alpha = 6°48'$$

PROBLEMS

Part One

MOTION AND FORCES

1. Kinematics of a Particle

1.1. Two particles move along the x-axis uniformly with speeds $v_1 = 8$ m/s and $v_2 = 4$ m/s. At the initial moment the first point was 21 m to the left of the origin and the second 7 m to the right of the origin. When will the first point catch up with the second? Where will this take place? Plot the graph of the motion.

1.2. The initial distance between two particles is 300 m. The particles head towards each other at speeds of 1.5 m/s and 3.5 m/s, respectively. When will they meet? Where will the meeting take place? Plot the graph.

1.3. A car left a city travelling uniformly at a speed of 80 km/h. It was followed 1.5 hours later by a motorcycle whose speed was 100 km/h. How much time elapsed after the car left the city before the motorcycle caught up with it? Where did this take place? Plot the graph.

1.4. The speed of a swimmer with respect to the water is v, the speed of the stream is u. In what direction should the swimmer move to reach the opposite point on the other bank of the river? How long will he swim if the width of the river is l?

1.5. What should be the angle at which a swimmer should swim to reach point C from point A (Fig. 1.5)? The speed of the swimmer v, the speed of the stream u, and the angle β are all known.

1.6. At what angle to the stream should a swimmer swim to reach the opposite bank as soon as possible?

1.7. The speed of a motor launch with respect to the water is $v = 7$ m/s, the speed of the stream $u = 3$ m/s. When the launch began travelling up-stream, a float was dropped from it. The launch travelled 4.2 km up-stream, turned about and caught up with the float. How long is it before the launch reaches the float again?

1.8. A motorcyclist started up, rode for 20 s with an acceleration of 1.5m/s², then 2 min at a constant speed, and, finally, braked uniformly for 15 s and stopped. Find the maximum speed, the deceleration during braking and the distance covered by the motorcyclist (graphically).

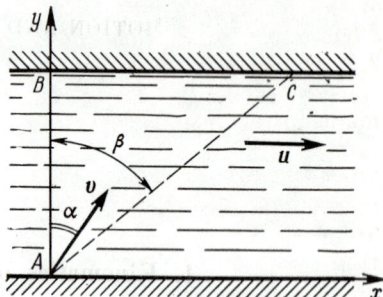

Fig. 1.5.

1.9. Prove that for a motion with a uniform rectilinear acceleration

$$2a(l - l_0) = v^2 - v_0^2$$

1.10. A shell leaves the barrel of a gun at a speed of 800 m/s. The barrel is 2.0 m long. Find the average acceleration.

2. Force

2.1. Find the spring constant k of a system made up of two springs joined in series.

2.2. Two parallel forces F_1 and F_2 acting in the same direction are applied to a rigid body.

Prove that

(a) the magnitude of the resultant force is equal to the sum of magnitudes of the forces being added;

(b) the resultant force is parallel to the forces being added and acts in the same direction;

(c) the resultant force passes through the centre of the parallel forces, i.e. through the point which divides the distance between the points of application of both forces into sections inversely proportional to the magnitude of the forces.

2.3. Find the position of the centre of a system of parallel forces applied to a rigid body.

2.4. Find the position of the centre of two unequal antiparallel forces. The distance between the points of application of the forces F_1 and F_2 is a.

2.5. Find the spring constant of a system made up of two springs joined in parallel.

2.6. A weight of mass m is suspended from a cord so that one section of it makes an angle α_1 with the horizontal and the other

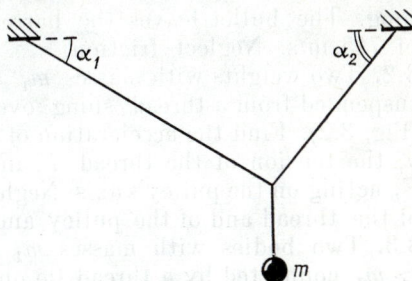

Fig. 2.6a.

—an angle α_2 (Fig. 2.6a)*. Find the tension of these sections of the cord.

2.7. A weight of mass m is suspended from a hinged bracket

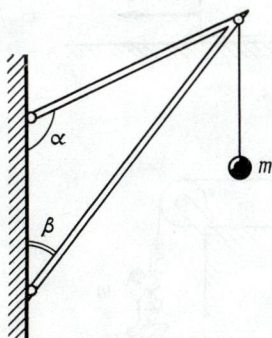

Fig. 2.7a.

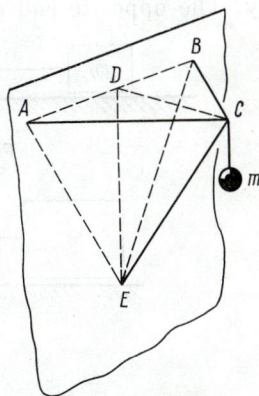

Fig. 2.8a.

(Fig. 2.7a). Find the forces in the rods making up the bracket.

2.8. A weight of mass m hangs from a bracket (Fig. 2.8a); $AB = AC = BC = EC = a$; $DE = a/2$. Find the forces in the rods.

* Figure numbers correspond to the numbers of problems. Letter "a" implies graphical presentation in the Solutions.

3. Particle Dynamics

3.1. Find the average pressure of the gases in the barrel of a gun if the calibre (the diameter) of the bullet is 7.62 mm, its mass is 9.1 g and the barrel is 610 mm long. The bullet leaves the barrel at a speed of 715 m/s. Neglect friction.

3.2. Two weights with masses m_1 and m_2 are suspended from a thread slung over a pulley (Fig. 3.2). Find the acceleration of the system a, the tension of the thread F and the force F_p acting on the pulley's axis. Neglect the mass of the thread and of the pulley and friction.

3.3. Two bodies with masses m_1 and $m_2 >$ $> m_1$ connected by a thread lie on a smooth table. A force Q is first applied to the larger and then to the smaller of the bodies (Fig. 3.3). Is the tension of the thread in both cases the same?

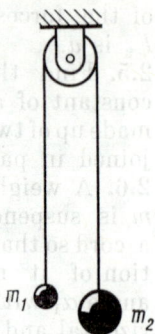

Fig. 3.2.

3.4. A monkey of mass m clings to a rope slung over a fixed pulley. The opposite end of the rope is tied to a weight of

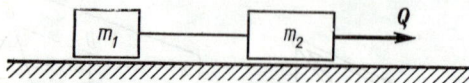

Fig. 3.3.

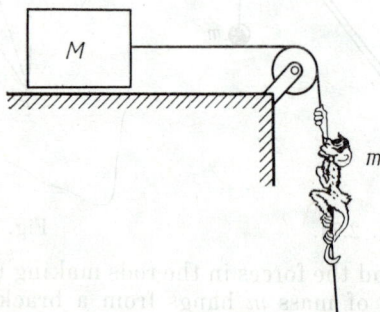

Fig. 3.4.

mass M lying on a horizontal plate (Fig. 3.4). Neglecting friction find the acceleration of both bodies (relative to the plate) and the tension of the rope for the three cases:

(1) the monkey does not move with respect to the rope;

(2) the monkey moves upwards with respect to the rope with acceleration b;

(3) the monkey moves downwards with respect to the rope with an acceleration b.

3.5. A block of mass M lies on a plane inclined at an angle α to the horizontal. A weight of mass m is connected to the block by a thread slung over a pulley (Fig. 3.5a). Find the acceleration of the weight and the tension of the thread. Friction, the mass of the pulley and of the thread are to be neglected.

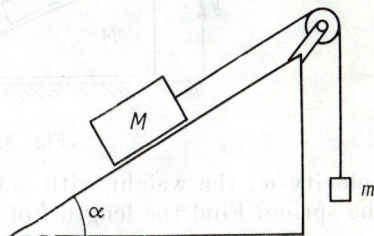

Fig 3.5a.

3.6. A rod of mass m_2 rests on a wedge of mass m_1 (Fig. 3.6a). Guides allow the rod to move only in the direction of the y-axis and the wedge only in the direction of the x-axis. Find the accel-

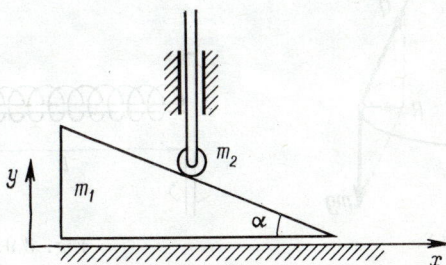

Fig. 3.6a

erations of both bodies and the reaction of the wedge. Neglect friction.

3.7. A block of mass m is placed on a wedge of mass M (Fig. 3.7a). Find the accelerations of the block and the wedge in the reference system fixed to the table, and the reaction. Friction is to be neglected.

Analyse the limiting case when the wedge remains stationary.

3.8. Find the period of revolution of a conical simple pendulum whose thread of length l makes an angle α with the vertical (Fig. 3.8).

3.9. An undeformed spring with the spring constant k has length l_0. When the system (Fig. 3.9) rotates at an angular

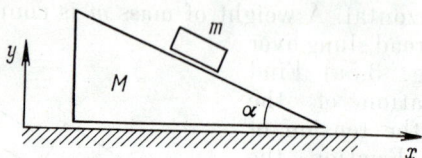

Fig. 3.7a.

velocity ω, the weight with mass m causes an extension of the spring. Find the length l of the rotating spring.

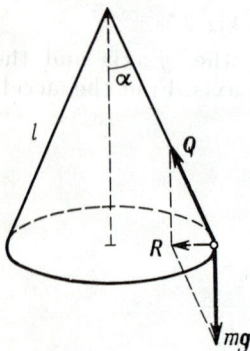

Fig. 3.8.

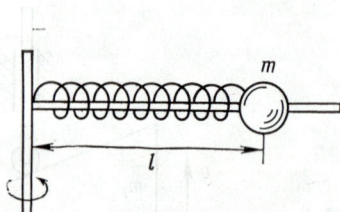

Fig. 3.9.

3.10. A plane flies at a constant speed of 200 m/s in a horizontal path with radius of curvature equal to 5 km. What is its angle of bank?

3.11. A plane flying at a constant speed of 300 m/s makes a wingover* in the vertical plane with the radius 1.3 km.

---

* A flight manoeuvre in which a plane is put into a climbing turn until nearly stalled after which the nose is allowed to fall while the turn is continued until normal flight is attained in a direction opposite to that in which the manoeuvre was entered. Also called a Nesterov loop.

Find the change in weight in the upper and the lower points of the loop.

3.12. A particle is thrown with an initial speed v_0 at an angle α to the horizontal. Find the radius of curvature r at the highest point of its path, and its ratios to the maximum height H and to the distance L of the particle's flight.

3.13. The equation for a parabola is of the form $x^2 = 2py$, where the parameter $p > 0$. Find the radius of curvature of the parabola at each point.

3.14. Prove that the tangent line to the parabola $x^2 = 2py$ at an arbitrary point makes an angle α with the x-axis whose

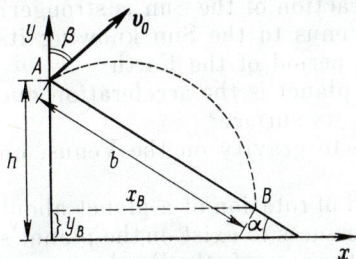

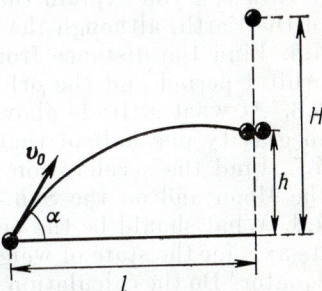

Fig. 3.15.   Fig. 3.16.

tangent is equal to the x-coordinate of the point divided by the parameter p (i.e. $\tan \alpha = x/p$).

3.15. The surface of a hill is inclined at an angle α to the horizontal (Fig. 3.15). A stone is thrown from the summit of the hill at an initial speed v_0 at an angle β to the vertical. How far from the summit will the stone strike the ground?

3.16. A body falls freely from some altitude H Fig. 3.16). At the moment the first body starts falling another body is thrown from the Earth's surface, which collides with the first at an altitude $h = H/2$. The horizontal distance is l. Find the initial velocity and the angle at which it was thrown.

3.17. Before the discoveries of Galileo the common opinion was that the greater the mass of a body is the faster it falls. Try to prove logically, using the fact of additivity of mass, that all bodies, independent of their mass, must fall in the same way. You will be repeating Galileo's reasoning. (Galileo used *reductio ad absurdum*).

4. Gravitation. Electrical Forces

4.1. Find the mass of the Earth from its polar radius and the free fall acceleration at the pole.

4.2. Find the mass of the Earth knowing the orbital period and the radius of the Moon.

4.3. Find the mass of the Sun knowing the average distance from the Earth to the Sun (the astronomical unit) and the orbital period of the Earth.

4.4. Compare the forces with which the Sun and the Earth act on the Moon.

How can you explain the fact that the Moon is a satellite of the Earth, although the attraction of the Sun is stronger?

4.5. Find the distance from Venus to the Sun knowing its orbital period and the orbital period of the Earth.

4.6. At what altitude above a planet is the acceleration due to gravity one half of that at its surface?

4.7. Find the acceleration due to gravity on the Venus, on the Moon and on the Sun.

4.8. What should be the period of rotation of a planet about its axis for the state of weightlessness to exist on the planet's equator? Do the calculation for the case of the Earth.

4.9. Two small balls with masses of 0.5 g each hang on threads 0.8 m long each tied to a common hook. What charge has been acquired by the system if, as a result, an angle $2\alpha = 12°$ has been established between the threads?

4.10. Two equal positive charges are placed at two corners of a square, the other two corners having negative charges of equal magnitude. Find the field intensity in the centre of the square in the two cases.

4.11. A charge q is uniformly distributed over the surface of a ring-shaped conductor of radius a. Find the field intensity on the axis of the conductor at a distance x from the plane of the conductor.

4.12. The molecule of water may, as a first approximation, be considered as a dipole with an electric moment $p = 6.1 \times 10^{-30}$ C·m. Estimate the force of attraction between two water molecules.

4.13. An electric field of intensity E is set up between two parallel plates of length L. An electron beam enters the field at an angle $\alpha > 0$ to the plates and leaves it at an angle

$\beta < 0$ (Fig. 4.13). Find the initial velocity of the electrons. The force of gravity is to be neglected.

4.14. Two plane-parallel plates $l = 2$ cm long serve as the control electrodes of a cathode-ray tube. The distance from the control electrodes to the tube's screen is $L = 30$ cm.

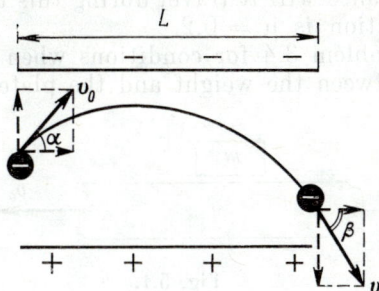

Fig. 4.13.

An electron beam enters midway between the plates parallel to them at a velocity of $v_0 = 2 \times 10^7$ m/s. What is the

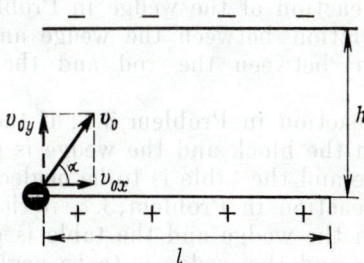

Fig. 4.15.

electric field between the electrodes if the beam's displacement on the screen is $d = 12$ cm?

4.15. The length of plane-parallel electrodes is l, the distance between them is h. An electric field of intensity E is set up between them. An electron enters the field close to the lower plate at an initial speed v_0 and at an angle α to the plates (Fig. 4.15). What should the field intensity be for the electron to pass between the electrodes without striking either of them? For what angles α is this possible?

5. Friction

5.1. A stationary body of mass m is slowly lowered on to a massive platform $(M \gg m)$ moving at a speed $v_0 = 4$ m/s (Fig. 5.1). How long will the body slide along the platform and what distance will it travel during this time? The coefficient of friction is $\mu = 0.2$.

5.2. Solve Problem 3.4 for conditions when the coefficient of friction between the weight and the plate is μ.

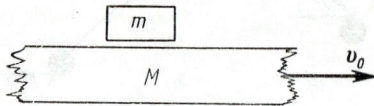

Fig. 5.1.

5.3. Find the acceleration of the block in Problem 3.5 for conditions when the coefficient of friction between the block and the inclined plane is μ.

5.4. Find the reaction of the wedge in Problem 3.6, if the coefficient of friction between the wedge and the table is μ, the friction between the rod and the wedge being negligible.

5.5. Find the reaction in Problem 3.7, if the coefficient of friction between the block and the wedge is μ. Friction between the wedge and the table is to be neglected.

5.6. Find the reaction in Problem 3.7, if the coefficient of friction between the wedge and the table is μ. Friction between the block and the wedge is to be neglected.

5.7. A block lies on a wedge with the slope angle α. The coefficient of static friction between the bar and the wedge is $\mu < \tan \alpha$. What should be the acceleration of the wedge to prevent the bar from sliding down?

5.8. A disk rotates at 70 r.p.m. in a horizontal plane. How would you place an object on the disk so that it would remain on it? The coefficient of static friction between the object and the disk is $\mu^{\text{stat}} = 0.44$.

5.9. In the motorcycle stunt called "the wall of death" the track is a vertical cylindrical surface of 18 m diameter. What should be the minimum speed of the motorcyclist to prevent him from sliding down? The coefficient of friction is $\mu \leqslant 0.8$. Take the motorcycle to be a point mass.

5.10. A spherical bowl of radius R rotates about the vertical diameter. The bowl contains a small object whose radius vector in the course of rotation makes an angle α with the vertical (Fig. 5.10a). What should be the minimum angular velocity ω of the bowl in order to prevent the object from sliding down, if the coefficient of static friction is μ^{stat}?

5.11. A motorcyclist rides at a speed of 90 km/h. What is the radius of curvature of the bend the motorcyclist can make, if the coefficient of friction between the rubber tyre and the asphalt is 0.65? What is the motorcyclist's inclination to the horizontal?

5.12. A glass ball of 4.0 mm diameter falls in a glycerine solution ($\rho_0 = 1.21 \times 10^3$ kg/m³, $\eta = 5.02 \times 10^{-2}$ Pa·s). The density of the glass is $\rho = 2.53 \times 10^3$ kg/m³. Find the steady-state speed and the initial acceleration. Make an approximate estimate of the time in which the ball attains the steady-state speed, and the distance the ball travels during this time.

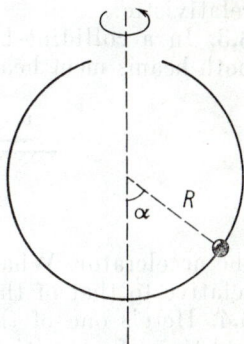

Fig. 5.10a.

5.13. With the aid of numerical calculation find the instantaneous values of the acceleration and the speed of the falling ball in the previous problem and plot the graph. Choose an interval of time equal to $\Delta t = 0.02$ s.

5.14. Estimate the steady-state speed of settling of dust particles in a room $l = 2.8$ m high and the time of settling. The minimum diameter of a dust particle is $2r = 0.06$ mm. The viscosity of air at 20 °C is $\eta = 1.8 \times 10^{-5}$ Pa·s, the density of the dust particles is $\rho = 2 \times 10^3$ kg/m³.

5.15. Estimate the speed at which hail falls if the diameter of a hailstone is $2r = 5$ mm, and its density is $\rho = 8 \times 10^2$ kg/m³.

5.16. When you have learned to integrate, find the dependence on time of the instantaneous velocity of the ball in Problem 5.13.

6. Theory of Relativity

6.1. Making use of the principle of relativity prove that the lateral dimensions of an object do not change with a change in the reference frame.

6.2. Estimate the relative error in calculations when the classical law of addition of velocities is used instead of the relativistic.

6.3. In a colliding-beam proton accelerator the protons of both beams meet head on at a speed of $0.99000c$ relative to

Fig. 6.4.

the accelerator. What is the speed of a proton of one beam relative to that of the other?

6.4. Here's one of the "disproofs" of the relativistic law of addition of velocities. Suppose two objects initially at the same point start moving relative to the Earth in opposite directions (Fig. 6.4). The total distance covered by the objects is

$$\Delta l = \Delta l_1 - \Delta l_2 = v_1 \Delta t - (-v_2 \Delta t) = (v_1 + v_2) \Delta t$$

Hence, the speed of approach $u = \Delta l / \Delta t = v_1 + v_2$.

We obtained the classical law of addition of velocities and not the relativistic one. Where lies the error in such reasoning?

6.5. The velocity of light in a stationary medium is $u = c/n$ where c is the velocity of light in vacuum and n is the refractive index of the material (see §63.1). Find the velocity of light in the medium moving at a constant speed relative to the source of light.

6.6. In the Fizeau experiment two light beams travel head on, one along a stream of fluid, the other in the opposite direction (Fig. 6.6). If the length of each tube is l, the velocity of the fluid v and its refractive index n, what will be the difference between the travel times of the light beams?

6.7. What will be the distance a pion (pi-meson) travels before it decays, if its speed is $v = 0.99c$ and its intrinsic lifetime is $\tau_0 = 2.6 \times 10^{-8}$ s? What would be the transit

distance if there is no relativistic time dilation? The distance
is measured in the laboratory reference frame.

6.8. Find the intrinsic lifetime of a particle if its velocity
is below the light velocity in vacuum by 0.2% and the distance it travels before decaying is about 300 km.

6.9. At what speed must a particle move for its rest mass to
be trebled?

6.10. Find the expression for the density of a body in an arbitrary inertial frame of reference.

6.11. At two points of an inertial reference frame separated by
a distance along the x-axis of
$l = x_2 - x_1$ two events take place
simultaneously. Find the time
interval between the events in an
arbitrary inertial reference frame.

6.12. An electron is accelerated
in an electric field of intensity
$E = 3.0 \times 10^6$ N/C. Find the
speed of the electron after 1.0 ns.
What would be the speed of
the electron, if its mass is independent of speed?

Fig. 6.6.

6.13. A force acts on a particle
moving at a relativistic speed in a direction perpendicular
to its path. How will the particle move? Express the force
in terms of the speed and of the radius of curvature of the
path.

6.14. When you have learned to differentiate trigonometric
functions, try to prove that in the relativistic case the formula $F = ma$ does not hold, even if m is taken to be the
relativistic mass.

6.15. Introduce the following definition: the length of a
moving rod is the product of its speed and the time interval
between the moments when its two ends pass a static clock.
The proper length is determined in a similar way with the
aid of a clock moving at the same speed along a static rod.
Find the relation between the length of a moving rod l and
its proper length l_0.

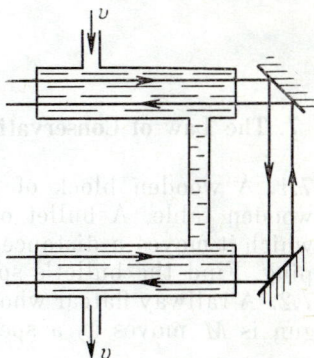

Part Two

7. The Law of Conservation of Momentum. Centre of Mass

7.1. A wooden block of 5.0 kg mass lies on a horizontal wooden table. A bullet of 9.0 g mass hits the block after which it moves a distance 25 cm across the table before stopping. Find the bullet's speed.

7.2. A railway flatcar whose mass together with the artillery gun is M moves at a speed V along the x-axis (Fig. 7.2).

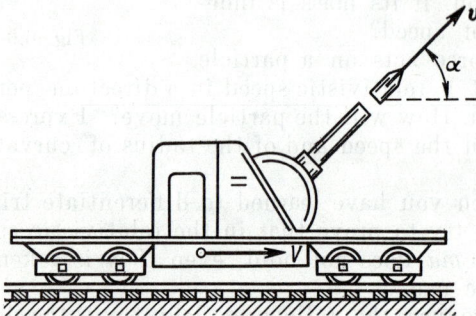

Fig. 7.2.

The gun barrel makes an angle α with this axis. A projectile of mass m leaves the gun at speed v (relative to the gun) in the direction of the flatcar's motion. Find the speed of the flatcar after the gun has been fired. What should the speed of the flatcar be for it to stop after the firing? Neglect friction.

Put $M = 10$ tons, $m = 120$ kg, $V = 6.0$ m/s, $v = 900$ m/s, $\alpha = 30°$.

7.3. The mass of a boat is $M = 80$ kg, the mass of a boy is $m = 36$ kg. The boy moves from the stern to the bows of the boat. What distance does the boat move, if its length is $l = 2.8$ m? At such low speeds the water resistance may be neglected.

7.4. Find the initial acceleration of a rocket if its initial mass is 40 metric tons, the exhaust velocity of gases is 4 km/s and the fuel consumption 200 kg/s.

7.5. The initial mass of a missile is $M_0 = 160$ tons, the exhaust velocity is 4 km/s. After 90 tons of fuel have burnt out the first stage with a mass of 30 tons is detached. Next additional 28 tons of fuel are burnt. What is the final speed of the second stage?

What would be the speed of a single-stage missile with the same mass of fuel?

7.6. When you have learned to integrate, derive the Tsiolkovsky formula.

7.7. Why do astronauts experience an increase in overload as the spaceship is accelerated? Assume the fuel consumption to be constant.

7.8. A carriage closed on all sides stands on rails. Can the passengers inside the carriage cause an oscillatory motion of the carriage? Friction with the rails should be neglected. The mass of the carriage should be assumed to be commensurate with that of the passengers.

7.9. Prove that the centre of mass of a uniform triangular plate coincides with the point of intersection of its medians.

7.10. Find the center of mass of a uniform plate shown in Fig. 7.10a.

7.11. Find the center of mass of a plate shown in Fig. 7.11. Put $R = 5.00$ cm, $r = 3.00$ cm.

7.12. Using numerical methods find the center of mass of a semicircle. To facilitate computation put $R = 1.00$.

7.13. Using numerical methods find the center of mass of a hemisphere.

7.14. Using numerical methods find the center of mass of a right circular cone with the height $h = 1$ and its generatrix making an angle α with the height.

7.15. Using integral calculus solve the Problems 7.12,

7.13, and **7.14** analytically.

7.16. The third Kepler law was derived in § 9.4 for the case of a planet mass being much smaller than that of the Sun,

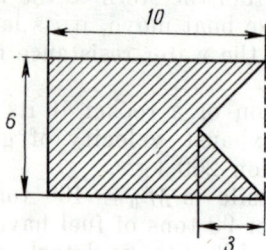

Fig. 7.10a.

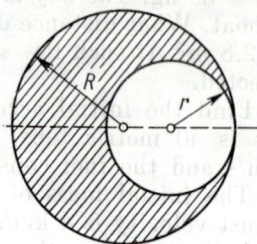

Fig. 7.11.

so that the Sun could be considered to be stationary. Derive this law for the case of two bodies rotating about their centre of mass.

8. Total and Kinetic Energy

8.1. Find the rest energy (the proper energy) of an electron, a proton, and a neutron.

8.2. Find the velocity of a particle whose kinetic energy is equal to its rest energy.

8.3. Find the kinetic energy and the momentum of an electron whose speed is $0.92c$.

8.4. The kinetic energy of a proton is 10 GeV. Find its momentum and velocity.

8.5. The kinetic energy of electrons in the Kharkov and the Erevan linear accelerators is 10 MeV. Find the speed of the electrons.

8.6. What is the error when the classical expression for the kinetic energy is substituted for the relativistic expression? Calculate for $u_1 = 0.1c$; for $u_2 = 0.9c$ and for $u_3 = 0.99c$.

8.7. The midship section of a launch is $S = 4$ m², the power of its engine is $P = 300$ h.p., the efficiency is $\eta = 25\%$. What is the maximum speed of the launch? Put $C = 0.5$.

8.8. A winch powered by an engine of specified power P pulls a weight up an inclined plane (see Fig. 3.5a, p. 21). The plane makes an angle α with the horizontal, and the coefficient of friction is μ. For what angle of inclination will the speed of the weight be a minimum?

8.9. A hydraulic monitor emits a jet of water at a speed of 100 m/s. The water flow rate is 144 m³/h. Find the power of its pump if its efficiency is 75%.

8.10. An electron with zero initial velocity is accelerated in an electric field of intensity E. Find the velocity of the electron after it has travelled a distance l. Do the calculations for the classical and for the relativistic case. Show that for a weak field the relativistic formula becomes the same as the classical formula.

8.11. For an ultra-relativistic particle $(pc \gg \mathscr{E}_0)$ its total energy may be assumed to be equal to the product of its momentum and of the velocity of light in vacuum, i.e. $\mathscr{E} = pc$. Determine the error arising from this assumption.

9. Uncertainty Relation

9.1. Assuming that in a hydrogen atom the electron rotates about the nucleus in a circular orbit, estimate the radius of this orbit.

9.2. What kinetic energy must an electron have to be able to penetrate the nucleus? The dimensions of a nucleus are of the order of 10^{-15} m.

9.3. Assess the kinetic energy of conduction electrons in a metal in which their concentration is of the order of 10^{29} m^{-3}.

9.4. According to modern ideas, a pulsar is a star made up almost entirely of neutrons.* Assuming the mass of the pulsar to be equal to that of the Sun $(2 \times 10^{30}$ kg) and its radius to be of the order of 10 km, estimate the kinetic energy of the neutrons.

10. Elementary Theory of Collisions

10.1. A block with the mass of 2.0 kg lies on a smooth horizontal table. A bullet with the mass of 9.0 g flying at a speed of 800 m/s at an angle of 30° to the horizontal hits the

---

* The possibility of such a state of matter was first suggested by L. D. Landau, Member of the Academy of Sciences of the USSR, in 1932. See, for example, the paper "On the sources of stellar energy", Doklady Academii Nauk SSSR, v. 17, p. 301 (1937) (in Russian).

block and sticks in it. What is the speed and the direction
of the resulting motion of the block?

Does the apparent loss of the vertical component of its
momentum contradict the law of conservation of momentum?

10.2. A radon nucleus with an atomic mass of 216 emits an
alpha-particle with an atomic mass 4 and a kinetic energy
8 MeV. What is the energy of the recoil nucleus?

10.3. A smooth ball hits a smooth wall at a certain angle.
The collision is elastic. Prove that the angle of reflection
is equal to the angle of incidence.

10.4. A ball moving parallel to the y-axis undergoes an
elastic collision with a parabolic mirror $y^2 = 2px$. Prove

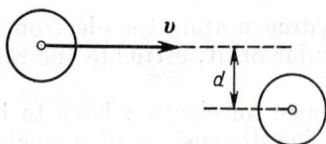

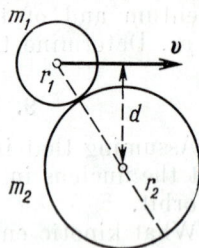

Fig. 10.7a.   Fig. 10.8a.

that no matter where the point of impact lies, it will arrive
at the mirror's focus F. Find the position of the focus.

10.5. Prove that as a result of an elastic collision of two
nonrelativistic particles of equal mass the scattering angle
will be 90°.

10.6. A relativistic proton with kinetic energy K collides
with a stationary proton. Assuming the collision to be elastic
and the energy to be partitioned equally between the particles, find the scattering angle. Calculate for the cases $K =
= 500$ MeV and $K = 10$ GeV.

10.7. A disk of radius r moving on perfectly smooth surface
at a speed v undergoes an elastic collision with an identical
stationary disk. Express the magnitude and the direction
of the velocity of each of the disks after the collision as a
function of the impact parameter d (Fig. 10.7a). Calculations to be made only for the nonrelativistic approximation.

10.8. Solve the previous problem assuming the mass of the moving disk to be m_1 and its radius r_1, and the corresponding magnitudes of the stationary disk to be m_2 and r_2 (Fig. 10.8a).

10.9. Calculate the pressure exerted by a flux of particles striking a wall at an angle α to its normal. Consider the case of elastic collisions. The particle concentration is n.

10.10. Estimate the sail area of a sailing boat moving at a constant speed in the direction of the wind assuming its midship section to be $S_0 = 1.0$ m^2, the coefficient $C = 0.1$, the boat's speed $v_0 = 3.0$ m/s, and the wind velocity $v = 6.0$ m/s.

10.11. A ball is thrown horizontally at a speed v_0 from the top of a hill whose slope is α (to the horizontal). Assuming the ball's impact on the hill's surface to be elastic find the point where it will hit the hill the second time.

11. Potential Energy. Potential

11.1. Prove that in a uniform field the work is independent of the path.

11.2. When you have learned to integrate exponential functions, try to derive formulas (18.6), (18.10), and (18.12).

11.3. Assume the potential energy of an object to be zero if the object is infinitely distant from the Earth. Write the expression for the potential energy of the object at an arbitrary point above the Earth.

What is its potential energy on the Earth's surface?

11.4. Assume the potential energy of an object to be zero if the object is on the Earth's surface. Write down the expression for the potential energy of the object at an arbitrary point above the Earth.

What is its potential energy at an infinite distance?

11.5. Calculate the energy of a dipole. What is the meaning of a minus sign?

11.6. The dipole moment of a hydrogen chloride molecule is 3.44×10^{-30} C·m, the separation of the dipole is 1.01×10^{-10} m. Estimate the energy liberated in the course of formation of 1 kg of hydrogen chloride from the starting materials, if the number of molecules in 1 kg is 1.6×10^{25}.

11.7. Find the potential of the electric field in the first Bohr orbit of a hydrogen atom (see Problem 9.1).

3*

11.8. Find the sum of the kinetic and the potential energies of an electron in the first Bohr orbit. Explain the meaning of the sign of the total energy (see Problem 9.1).

11.9. Find the momentum and the velocity acquired by an electrically charged particle which has travelled through a potential difference $\varphi = \varphi_1 - \varphi_2$. Take the initial velocity of the particle to be zero. Do the calculation both for the nonrelativistic and the relativistic cases.

11.10. Find the potential difference for which the error in the value of the momentum for the previous problem calculated using the nonrelativistic approximation does not exceed 5%. Do the calculations both for the electron and for the proton.

11.11. In the ultra-relativistic case the momentum of a particle accelerated by a potential difference φ is found with the aid of the formula $p = e\varphi/c$, this value being expressed in units of MeV/c, where c is the velocity of light in a vacuum. Express this unit in the SI system. Find out for what potential differences the use of this formula leads to an error of less than 5%. Do the calculations both for the electron and the proton.

12. The Law of Conservation of Energy in Newtonian Mechanics

12.1. The ballistic pendulum is a block of 3.0 kg mass suspended from a thread 2.5 m long. A bullet with the mass of 9.0 g hits the block and sticks in it, the result being a deflection of the system by an angle of 18° (Fig. 12.1). Find the bullet's speed.

12.2. A body of 5 kg mass is raised vertically to a height of 10 m by a force of 120 N. Find the final velocity of the body using two methods: Newton's second law and the law of conservation of energy. The initial speed is zero.

12.3. Solve Problem 5.1 using the law of conservation of energy.

12.4. A weight is suspended from a thread of length l. What is the initial speed that has to be imparted to it at the lowest point to make it complete a full revolution? The mass of the thread is to be neglected.

12.5. Solve the same problem for the case of a weight suspended from a thin rod of negligible mass.

12.6. A weight of mass m hangs on a thread. The thread is deflected by an angle α_0 and let go. Find the tension of the thread as a function of the angle α.

12.7. A small disk of mass m lies on the highest point of a sphere of radius R. A slight push makes the disk start sliding down. Find the force of pressure of the disk on the sphere as a function of the angle its radius vector makes with the vertical. Where does the disk lose contact with the sphere? Friction is to be neglected.

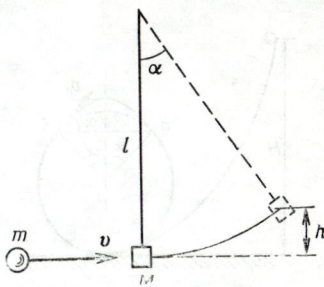

Fig. 12.1.

12.8. A cyclist rolls down a "devil's loop" track from a height H. Find the pressure of the cyclist on the track as a function of the angle the radius vector makes with the vertical. Do the calculations also for the case when the cyclist rolls down from the minimum height.

12.9. A small object loops a vertical loop in which a symmetrical section of angle 2α has been removed (Fig. 12.9). Find the maximum and the minimum heights from which the object, after loosing contact with the loop at point A and flying through the air, will reach point B. Find the corresponding angles of the section removed for which this is possible.

12.10. The point of an elliptical orbit closest to the Sun is called the perihelion, and the point most distant from it is called aphelion (Fig. 12.10). Denoting the distance from the perihelion to the Sun by r_0, and the velocity of the planet at the perihelion by v_0, find the radius of curvature of the orbit at the perihelion and at the aphelion, the distance from the aphelion to the Sun, and the velocity of the planet at the aphelion.

Prove that the motion of a planet in an elliptical orbit is only possible, if its total energy is negative.

12.11. Prove that if a space vehicle travels along a parabolic path with the Earth (or some other planet) at its focus, the total mechanical energy of the vehicle is zero.

12.12. Solve Problem 3.6 using the law of conservation of energy.

12.13. Solve Problem 3.7 using the laws of conservation of energy and momentum.

12.14. A space vehicle of 1 tonne mass is to take off from the Moon and fly to the Earth. Find the amount of fuel required. Compare the result with the amount of fuel needed to send

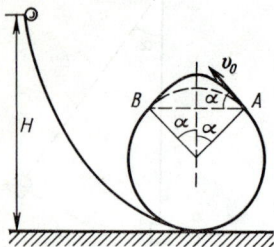

Fig. 12.9.

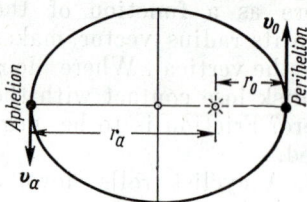

Fig. 12.10.

an identical vehicle from the Earth. Assume the rocket to be a single-stage vehicle.

12.15. A star with a mass of more than three times that of the Sun contracts so much upon cooling that it is not able to radiate; neither material particles nor light are able to overcome its gravitational field. Find the radius of such an object (a "black hole").

13. The Law of Conservation of Energy

13.1. Two identical lumps of ice collide head on. What must their speed be for their complete sublimation to take place as a result of an inelastic collision? The initial temperature is $t_0 = -30$ °C. Radiative losses are to be neglected.

13.2. A lead bullet penetrates a board, its speed being reduced as a result from 400 m/s to 200 m/s. What fraction of the bullet will melt? Neglect the heating of the board. The initial temperature is about 30 °C.

13.3. The intensity of solar radiation reaching the illuminated side of the Earth each second is $J = 1.36$ kW/m². Find the decrease in the internal energy and the mass of the Sun per second. How long will it take for the Sun's mass to decrease due to radiation by 10%? The volume of the Sun is to be assumed to remain constant.

13.4. A nonrelativistic particle collides inelastically with an identical stationary particle. What is the kinetic energy of the body thus formed? What happened to the rest of the kinetic energy?

13.5. A particle with rest mass M_0 splits up into two identical fragments which fly apart in opposite directions at speeds of $0.90c$. Find the rest mass of each fragment.

13.6. A relativistic particle collides inelastically with an identical stationary particle. What are the internal and the kinetic energies of the resulting object? The kinetic energy of the particle before the collision is $K = e\varphi$ where φ is the potential of the accelerating electric field. Do the calculations for protons with kinetic energies of 10 GeV and 76 GeV.

13.7. Find the kinetic energy that must be imparted to a positron for a proton-antiproton pair to be obtained as a result of its collision with a stationary electron.

13.8. Solve the previous problem assuming the collision to take place in a colliding-beam accelerator in which the electrons and positrons meet head on with equal velocities.

13.9. Compare the efficiency of a colliding-beam accelerator with that of an accelerator in which the particles strike a target made up of identical stationary particles.

13.10. What should be the energy of a conventional accelerator for it to be able to do the work of a colliding-beam accelerator of 200 MeV? Do the calculations both for electrons and for protons.

14. Rotational Dynamics of a Rigid Body

14.1. A force couple is the term used for a system of two equal antiparallel forces; the arm of the couple is the shortest distance between the forces. Prove that the torque is equal to the product of the magnitude of the force and the arm no matter what is the position of the point with respect to which the torque is determined.

14.2. Solve Problem 2.2, applying to the system two force couples having torques equal in magnitude and opposite in sign.

14.3. Find the torque on the shaft of an electric motor of 20 kW power if its rotor turns at 1440 r.p.m.

14.4. The torsion modulus of a spiral spring is 2 N·m/rad. The spring is turned 10 times. What is the work done?

14.5. Find the moment of inertia of a disk about an axis passing through a point on its circumference perpendicular to its plane.

14.6. The mass of a disk with a circular hole cut in it (Fig. 14.6) is m. Find its moment of inertia about an axis passing through point A perpendicularly to the disk's plane.

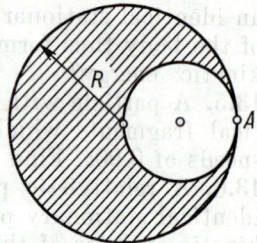

Fig. 14.6.

14.7. When you have learned to integrate, derive the formula for the moment of inertia of a disk.

14.8. Derive, making use of an integral, the formula for the moment of inertia of a sphere about its diameter.

14.9. Derive, making use of an integral, the formula for the moment of inertia of a right circular cone about its height.

14.10. Solve Problem 14.8 using numerical methods.

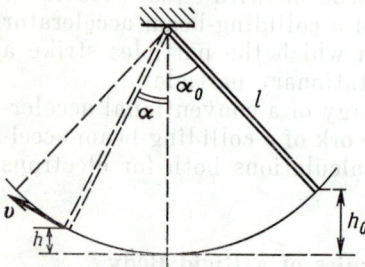

Fig. 14.12.

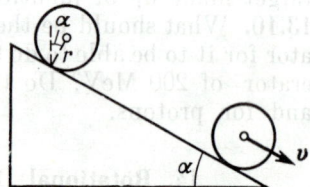

Fig. 14.13.

14.11. Solve Problem 14.9 using numerical methods.

14.12. A uniform rod of length l can rotate without friction about an axis passing through its upper end (Fig. 14.12). The rod is deflected by an angle α_0 and let go. Find the speed of the lower end of the rod as a function of the angle α.

14.13. A solid cylinder with base radius r is placed on top of an inclined plane of length l and slope angle α (Fig. 14.13).

The cylinder rolls down without slipping. Find the speed of the centre of mass of the cylinder at the bottom of the plane, if the coefficient of rolling friction is k. Can rolling friction be neglected? Do the calculation for the following conditions: $l = 1$ m, $\alpha = 30°$, $r = 10$ cm, $k = 5 \times 10^{-4}$ m.

What would be the speed if, in the absence of friction, the cylinder slides down?

14.14. Solve Problem 14.13 for a thin-walled solid cylinder of the same radius and mass.

14.15. A solid flywheel of 20 kg mass and 120 mm radius revolves at 600 r.p.m. With what force must a brake lining be pressed against it for the flywheel to stop in 3 s, if the coefficient of friction is 0.1?

14.16. A flywheel with moment of inertia 0.86 kg·m² and a cylinder of 5 cm radius of negligible mass are fixed to a common shaft (Fig. 14.16). A thread is wound around the cylinder, and a weight of 6.0 kg mass is attached to it. What time will the weight take to fall 1 m? What will be its final speed? Assume the initial speed to be zero.

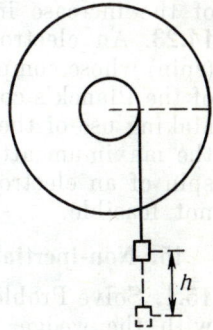

Fig. 14.16.

14.17. Solve Problem 3.2 assuming the moment of inertia of the pulley to be I and its radius to be r.

14.18. Solve Problem 12.7 assuming a ball of mass m and of radius r to roll down from the top without slipping. Neglect energy losses due to rolling friction.

14.19. A man stands in the centre of a Zhukovskii turntable (a rotating platform with frictionless bearings) and rotates with it at 30 r.p.m. The moment of inertia of the man's body with respect to the axis of rotation is about 1.2 kg·m². The man holds in his outstretched hands two weights of mass 3 kg each. The distance between the weights is 160 cm. What will be the change in the speed of rotation of the system, if the man lets his hands fall so that the distance between the weights becomes 40 cm? The moment of inertia of the turntable is 0.6 kg·m², the change in the moment of inertia of the man's hands and the friction are to be neglected.

14.20. A man of 80 kg mass is standing on the rim of a circular platform rotating about its axis. The platform with the man on it rotates at 12.0 r.p.m. How will the system rotate, if the man moves to the platform's centre? What work will the man perform in changing his position? The mass of the platform is 200 kg and its radius is 1.2 m.

14.21. Suppose the Sun contracts (collapses) to a pulsar. Estimate the minimum radius of the pulsar and its period of rotation. The period of revolution of the Sun about its axis is 25.38 days (1 day = 24 hours).

14.22. Compare the kinetic energies of rotation of the pulsar and of the Sun (see Problem 14.21). What is the source of the increase in kinetic energy?

14.23. An electron has an intrinsic angular momentum (spin) whose component in an arbitrary direction is one half of the Planck's constant, i.e. $L_z = \hbar/2 = 5.25 \times 10^{-35}$ J·s. Making use of the fact that the speed of light in vacuum is the maximum attainable, prove that a model in which the spin of an electron is due to the rotation about its axis is not feasible.

15. Non-inertial Frames of Reference and Gravitation

15.1. Solve Problem 5.7 in the frame of reference connected with the wedge.

15.2. Solve Problem 5.8 in the rotating frame of reference connected with the disk.

15.3. Solve Problem 5.9 in a rotating frame of reference.

15.4. Solve Problem 3.8 in a rotating frame of reference.

15.5. Solve Problem 3.9 in a rotating frame of reference.

15.6. What is the angular velocity of rotation of a star at which the matter starts to escape from its equator? In calculating make use of a reference frame fixed to the rotating star. Compare with Problem 14.21.

15.7. A drop of fat in milk has a diameter of the order of 0.02 mm. Estimate the time it takes to separate cream in a centrifuge at room temperature ($t \approx 20$ °C), if the depth of the vessel is 20 cm, the rotation radius 80 cm and the speed 600 r.p.m. Compare with the time needed to separate cream in the gravitational field.

15.8. A centrifugal governor is of the form shown in Fig. 15.8. The mass of each weight is m, the spring constant is k. Will this device work in conditions of weightlessness? What is the dependence of the angle α on the speed of rotation of the system? What is the maximum speed for which the device is designed if the maximum contraction of the spring is 10% of its original length?

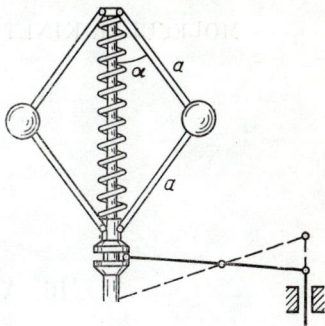

Fig. 15.8.

15.9. Prove that the surface of a liquid in a rotating vessel assumes the form of a paraboloid of rotation.

15.10. Making use of the principle of equivalence explain the origin of weightlessness in a spacecraft orbiting the Earth (or some other planet).

15.11. What should be the angular velocity of rotation of a spacecraft about its axis for the astronaut to feel effects similar to those of the Moon's gravitational field, where the free fall acceleration is one sixth of the Earth's? Take the spacecraft's diameter to be 6 m.

15.12. In October 1971 an atomic clock was placed on a "Boeing 747" flying at an altitude of 10 km at a velocity of 1000 km/h eastwards. An identical clock, with time-keeping accuracy of 1 ns (1 nanosecond $= 10^{-9}$ s) remained on the Earth. The plane was in flight 60 h, after which a comparison was made of the clocks' readings. What was the difference in the readings of the clocks in the plane and on the Earth? What were the contributions of the plane's elevation and its speed of flight?

15.13. Find the gravitational shift in frequency on the Sun, on a white dwarf, and on a pulsar. Assume the masses of all three types of stars to be the same and equal to 2×10^{30} kg; the radius of the Sun to be 7×10^5 km, of the white dwarf 10^3 km, and of a pulsar 10 km.

15.14. Our solution of Problem 12.15 was incorrect; we made use of the formula for the escape velocity derived from nonrelativistic expressions for the kinetic and the potential energies. Try to derive a formula for the radius of a black hole from relativistic considerations.

Part Three

MOLECULAR-KINETIC THEORY OF GASES

16. An Ideal Gas

16.1. Prove that the magnitude of the hydrostatic pressure is proportional to the height of the column of liquid (or gas) and is independent of the vessel's shape.

16.2. Making use of the expression for the hydrostatic pressure, derive an expression for the magnitude of the Archimedes force.

16.3. What is the value of the unit of pressure 1 mmHg (torr) on the Moon? On Venus? Use data from Problem 4.7.

16.4. In Stern's experiment (1920) silver atoms emitted by a heated filament passed through a slit and were deposited on the cooled wall of an outer cylinder (Fig. 16.4). When the system was rotated at high speed there was a deflection of the slit's image. The apparatus was first rotated in one direction and then in the opposite direction, and the distance between the deflected images was measured. Find this distance if the radius of the internal cylinder is 2.0 cm and of the external one 8.0 cm. The speed of rotation is 2700 r.p.m. and the filament temperature 960 °C.

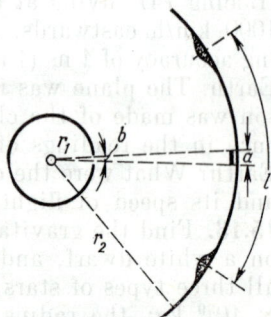

Fig. 16.4.

Estimate the errors of measurement, if the width of the slit is 0.5 mm.

16.5. At what speed must the rotor of Lammert's machine rotate for gas molecules with velocities of 700 m/s to pass through the slits? What velocity spread will be recorded in the experiment? Take the distance between the disks to be 40 cm, the angle between the slits to be 20° and the angular width of the slit to be 2°.

Estimate the error in the experiment.

16.6. The temperature of the Sun's external layer (the photosphere) is about 6000 K. Why don't hydrogen atoms, the main component of the photosphere, leave the Sun's surface?

16.7. The height of the photosphere is much less than the Sun's radius. Equating gravitational and pressure forces try to estimate the height of the photosphere assuming it to be made up entirely of atomic hydrogen.

16.8. The density of the photosphere assessed with the aid of optical methods is 2×10^{-4} kg/m³. Find the average gas pressure in the photosphere and the mean free path of hydrogen atoms.

16.9. Knowing the mass and the radius of the Sun one may find the average density of the Sun's material. Estimate the pressure and the temperature of the gas in the middle of the radius assuming, for the sake of simplicity, that the density is constant and that the acceleration due to gravity at this point is one half its value at the surface. What is the proton concentration at this point?

16.10. Explain the reason why the Moon cannot retain its atmosphere. Take into account that during a lunar day its temperature rises above 100 °C.

16.11. A vacuum has been created in a radio tube, i.e. a state of gas where the mean free path of its particles exceeds the characteristic dimensions of the vessel. Assuming the tube's length to be 5 cm and it to be filled with argon, estimate the density and the pressure of the gas at room temperature (20 °C).

16.12. Find the lifting force of a balloon of 2×10^4 m³ capacity filled with helium at the surface of the Earth and at an altitude of 10 km above sea level. The balloon's envelope is open underneath. For data on the properties of the Earth's atmosphere see § 26.10, Table 26.3.

16.13. Find the molecular formula of ammonia, if its density at the pressure of 780 mmHg and the temperature of 20 °C is 0.736 kg/m³.

16.14. Dalton's law is formulated as follows: *the total pressure of a mixture of ideal gases is equal to the sum of the partial pressures of these gases.* The partial pressure is the pressure of a given gas as if it alone occupied the whole vessel. Prove this law.

16.15. A gas container of 20 l capacity contains a mixture of 10 g of hydrogen and 48 g of oxygen. After the mixture is ignited by a spark the gas formed is heated to 300 °C. Find the pressure of the gas.

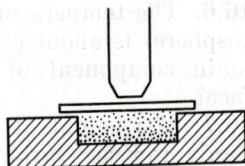

Fig. 16.17.

16.16. Assuming air ($M = 29$ kg/mole) to be composed mainly of oxygen and nitrogen, find the percentage composition of these gases in the atmosphere.

16.17. In 1908-1910 Perrin determined the Avogadro number. He did it by observing the distribution of tiny gumboge gum balls in water with the aid of a short-focus microscope (Fig. 16.17). By adjusting the focus of the microscope to observe a definite layer he was able to count the number of particles in each layer. In one of the experiments the following data were obtained:

Height of the layer above the tray's bottom, μm	5	35	65	95
Number of particles in the layer	100	47	23	12

Knowing the ball's radius to be 0.212 μm, the density of gumboge gum to be 1.252×10^3 kg/m³, the density of water at 27 °C to be 0.997×10^3 kg/m³ find the Avogadro number.

16.18. A gas rotates in a centrifuge. Taking into account that the field of centrifugal forces of inertia is equivalent to a gravitational field, write the expression for the barometric distribution in the centrifuge.

16.19. Centrifuging may be used for the separation of isotopes. To do this a mixture of two gases is placed inside a cylindrical vessel rotating at a high speed. Because of the action of centrifugal forces, the isotope concentration near the cylinder wall will be different from that in the centre.

Compare the concentrations of the light and the heavy uranium isotopes near the centrifuge walls, if the diameter of the cylinder is 10 cm, the rotation speed is 2.0×10^3 r. p.s., the temperature of uranium hexafluoride is 27 °C. For concentrations in normal conditions see § 25.6.

Find the enrichment factor in the mixture of the heavy isotope near the walls of the vessel. The term enrichment factor applies to the quotient obtained by dividing the concentration ratio during rotation by the initial concentration ratio:

$$x = \left(\frac{n_2}{n_1} \right) : \left(\frac{n_{02}}{n_{01}} \right)$$

16.20. How many times in succession should the light fraction be separated in the centrifuge to obtain a mixture containing 80% of light uranium isotope?

16.21. We have obtained the barometric distribution for the case of an isothermal atmosphere; indeed, in § 26.10 we assumed the temperature to be the same at every point. Actually, in the real atmosphere the temperature drops with altitude. It may be demonstrated that if the decrease in the temperature with the altitude is linear, i.e. if $T = T_0 (1 - \alpha h)$, the barometrical formula assumes the form

$$\frac{p}{p_0} = \left(\frac{T}{T_0} \right)^{mg/\alpha k T_0}$$

Prove that if α is small this formula reduces to the formula for the barometric distribution in an isothermal atmosphere.

16.22. Try to derive the barometrical formula for an atmosphere in which the temperature decreases linearly with the altitude.

16.23. Measurements carried out by the Soviet "Venus" space-probes with the aid of their landing modules have shown that from an altitude of 50 km above the surface of Venus the temperature of the planet's atmosphere changes linearly as the altitude decreases. Using the data given below prove that this layer of the atmosphere consists mainly of carbon dioxide gas.

Altitude above surface h, km	50	42	37	15	0
Pressure p, atm	1	3.3	6	37	90
Temperature t, °C	80	160	200	360	485
T, K	353	433	473	633	758

17. The First Law of Thermodynamics

17.1. A vessel contains helium, which expands at a constant pressure when 15 kJ of heat is supplied to it. What will be the variation of the internal energy of the gas? What is the work performed in the expansion?

17.2. A cylinder contains 0.15 kg of hydrogen. The cylinder is closed by a piston supporting a weight of 74 kg (Fig. 17.2). What amount of heat should be supplied to lift the weight by 0.6 m? The process should be assumed isobaric, the heat capacity of the vessel and the external pressure should be neglected.

17.3. For monoatomic gases $\gamma = 1.66 \pm \pm 0.01$. Find specific heats of helium and of neon.

17.4. For most diatomic gases at room temperatures $\gamma = \pm 1.40 \pm 0.01$. Find the specific heat of nitrogen in these conditions.

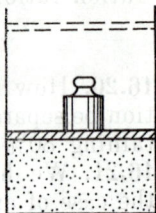

Fig. 17.2.

17.5. A cylindrical vessel of 28 cm diameter contains 20 g of nitrogen compressed by a piston supporting a weight of 75 kg. The temperature of the gas is 17 °C. What work will the gas do, if it is heated to a temperature of 250 °C? What amount of heat should be supplied to it? What distance will the weight be raised? The process should be assumed isobaric; the heating of the vessel and the external pressure should be neglected.

17.6. Upon expansion, the pressure of a gas rose linearly (Fig. 17.6). What work did the gas perform? By how much did its

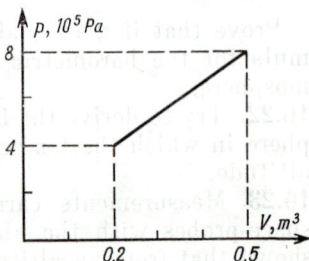

Fig. 17.6.

internal energy increase? What quantity of heat has been supplied to it? The gas was monoatomic.

What was the molar heat of the gas in this process? Compare with the specific heats at constant pressure and at constant volume.

17.7. The initial gas pressure is 6×10^5 Pa and the volume 1 m³. Expansion at constant temperature leads to its volume being increased two-fold. Using numerical methods calculate the work of expansion of the gas.

Compare with the formula in § 27.6 and estimate the error.

17.8. When you have learned to integrate derive the formula to calculate the work of expansion of a gas at constant temperature.

17.9. A gas has been subjected to an isochoric-isobaric cycle *1-2-3-4-1* (Fig. 17.9a). Plot the graph of this cycle in the *p-ρ*, *V-T* and *p-T* coordinates.

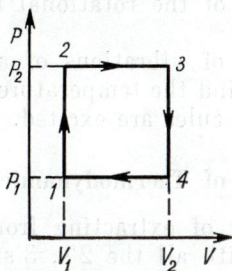   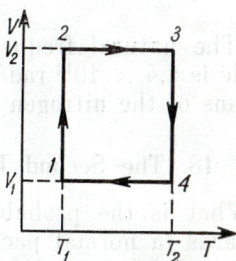

Eig. 17.9a.   Fig. 17.10a.

17.10. A gas has been subjected to isothermal-isochoric cycle *1-2-3-4-1* (Fig. 17.10a). Plot the graph of this cycle in *p-V*, *p-ρ*, and *p-T* coordinates.

17.11. When you have learned to integrate derive the Poisson formula for an adiabatic process.

17.12. Express the relations between the pressure and the temperature and between the volume and the temperature in an adiabatic process.

17.13. The initial pressure of air is 4.0×10^5 Pa, the initial volume is 2.0 m³. The gas was compressed adiabatically so that its volume decreased to a quarter of its original volume. Find the final pressure. Compare with the pressure that would result from a similar compression of the gas at a constant temperature.

Which process requires the greater work to be performed in compressing the gas?

17.14. The initial pressure of neon is 2.0×10^5 Pa, the initial volume is 0.4 m³. The gas expanded adiabatically so that its volume increased three times. Find the final pressure. Compare with the pressure that would result from an expansion at constant temperature. In which process does the gas perform more work upon expansion?

17.15. Find the degree of compression of air if its temperature rises from 15 °C to 700 °C upon compression. Assume the compression process to be adiabatic.

17.16. The distance between the atomic centres in a nitrogen molecule is 1.094×10^{-10} m. Find the moment of inertia of the molecule and the temperature at which molecular collisions cause the state of the rotational motion to change.

17.17. The natural frequency of vibrations of a nitrogen molecule is 4.4×10^{14} rad/s. Find the temperature at which vibrations of the nitrogen molecules are excited.

18. The Second Law of Thermodynamics

18.1. What is the probability of extracting from a pack of 36 cards (a normal pack with all the 2's, 3's, 4's, and 5's removed) (a) a spade card; (b) a red card; (c) a queen of any suit?

18.2. What is the probability of extracting from a pack of cards (a) a court-card; (b) a red court-card?

18.3. What is the probability of extracting two aces in succession from a pack as in Problem 18.1 (a) if the ace

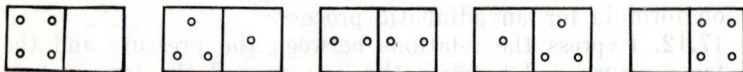

Fig. 18.4.

extracted first is returned to the pack; (b) if the ace extracted first is not returned?

18.4. Find the mathematical and the thermodynamical probabilities of the five possible distributions of four balls in two halves of a vessel (Fig. 18.4), assuming them to be distinguishable.

18.5. Try to generalize the result of the previous problem to include the case when one part of the vessel contains k out of n balls ($k \leqslant n$) in conditions when

(a) the probabilities of a ball being in the left-hand and the right-hand parts of the vessel are different;

(b) the probabilities of a ball being in either part of the vessel are equal.

18.6. Plot the graphs of the functions C_6^k and C_8^k*. (Choose the scale of the x-axis so that the graphs can be conveniently compared. For instance, for $n = 6$ you can use the scale 1 : 13 mm and for $n=8$ the scale 1 : 10 mm.)

18.7. A vessel of capacity V_0 contains n molecules. Calculate the probability of all the molecules assembling in a part of the vessel $V < V_0$.

18.8. Prove the theorem converse to the one of § 28.8: if in the course of the heat exchange between two bodies contained in a closed and an adiabatically isolated system the entropy rises, then the heat transfer will be in the direction from the heated body to the cold one.

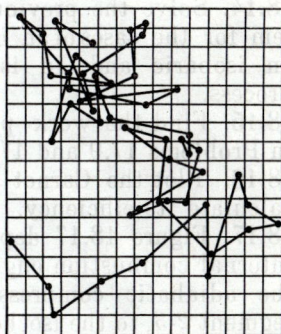

Fig. 18.9.

18.9. Figure 18.9 shows the results of a series of observations of a migrating Brownian particle. The observations were made at intervals of 30 s, the temperature of water was 25 °C, the radius of a Brownian particle is 4.4×10^{-7} m. Measuring the "steps" of the particle in the scale specified, find the square of the r.m.s. displacement for a given time, and calculate the Boltzmann constant and the Avogadro number. The scale is as follows: 1 mm on the graph corresponds to a displacement of 1.25 μm.

18.10. Plot the T-S diagram (i.e. the entropy vs temperature dependence) (a) for an adiabatic process; (b) for an isothermic process.

---

* In this book, as in "Fundamentals of Physics" by B. Yavorsky and A. Pinsky, the notation C_n^k is used for $\binom{n}{k}$, i.e. the number of combinations of k objects from n.

18.11. How can you calculate the amount of heat received (or delivered) by a system, using the T-S diagram?

18.12. Express the amount of heat received by a system in the course of isothermic expansion in terms of temperature and entropy.

18.13. When you have learned to integrate, calculate the change in entropy in the course of an arbitrary quasi-static process.

18.14. Solve the previous problem for the cases of an isochoric, an isobaric and an isothermic process.

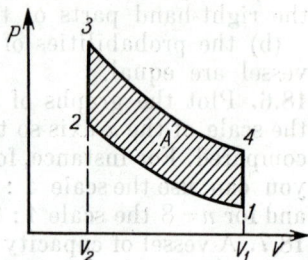
Fig. 18.17.

18.15. Find the work per cycle in Problems 17.9 and 17.10.

18.16. Plot the Carnot cycle in the T-S coordinates and calculate its efficiency.

18.17. Figure 18.17 depicts an idealized cycle of a petrol internal combustion engine. The segment 1-2 corresponds to the adiabatic compression of the combustible mixture; segment 2-3, to the isochoric combustion of fuel in the course of which the working fluid receives an amount of heat Q; segment 3-4 corresponds to the adiabatic expansion of the working fluid; segment 4-1, to the isochoric exhaust of spent gases. Express the engine's efficiency in terms of the gas compression ratio $x = V_2/V_1$.

18.18. The compression ratio of an automotive petrol engine is about $1 : 7$. Assuming the Poisson constant for the air-fuel mixture to be 1.38 find the maximum efficiency of this engine and compare it with the actual efficiency, which does not exceed 25%.

18.19. Making use of the results of Problems 17.8 and 18.7 try to find the connection between the entropy and the thermodynamical probability.

19. Fundamentals of Fluid Dynamics

19.1. Oil flows in a pipeline at a speed of 0.8 m/s. The oil flow rate is 2×10^3 tons/h. Find the diameter of the pipeline.

19.2. The internal diameter of a nozzle is 2 cm. It emits a jet of water at a speed of 18 m/s. Find the excess pressure in the fire-hose, the diameter of which is 6 cm.

19.3. To measure the flow rate in a gas pipeline a narrowing is made in it and the pressure difference between the wide and the narrow parts of the pipe is measured (Fig. 19.3). Find the gas flow rate, if its density is 1.4 kg/m^3, the diameter of the pipe is 50 mm, the diameter of the narrowing is 30 mm and the pressure difference is 18 mm of water. The compressibility of the gas is to be neglected.

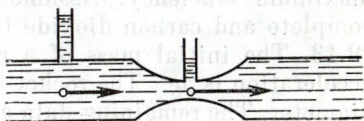

Fig. 19.3.

19.4. Derive the Bernoulli equation for an incompressible liquid flowing in an inclined tube of variable cross section in a gravitational field.

19.5. Water flows out of a wide vessel through a small orifice. Express the flow velocity as a function of the height of the column of liquid.

19.6. Using the Bernoulli equation for a compressible flow derive the relation between the velocity of the flow at a given point and the local sound velocity.

19.7. An explosion creates a shock wave. Find the initial velocity of the wave front when the air pressure is 200 times the atmospheric pressure, assuming that the front of the shock wave may be regarded as a discontinuity in the density. Take into account that at such pressures $\gamma = 1.8$.

19.8. The volume of air decreased to one third of its original value as a result of shock compression. How many times did the pressure of air and its temperature increase? Compare with the variation of these quantities as a result of quasi-static adiabatic compression.

19.9. A jet plane flies at an altitude of 1 km at a speed twice that of sound. How far away will the plane be from an observer when he first hears it coming?

19.10. Show that shock compression of a gas causes its entropy to rise.

19.11. The steam temperature in a boiler is 600 °C, the pressure is 200 atm. The steam is ejected from a Laval nozzle. Find the velocity and the temperature of steam in the critical cross section. To avoid the condensation of steam as it leaves the nozzle, its temperature should exceed 100 °C. What is the maximum speed at which the steam leaves the nozzle?

19.12. The velocity of combustion products ejected from the nozzle of a rocket is 2.0 km/s and the temperature is 600 °C. Find the temperature in the combustion chamber and the maximum efficiency. Assume the fuel combustion to be complete and carbon dioxide to be ejected from the nozzle.

19.13. The initial mass of a rocket is 30 tons, the initial acceleration is $3g$. The rocket has four nozzles each of 20 cm diameter. The remaining data are the same as in the previous problem. Find the initial fuel consumption (together with the oxidant), the density and the pressure of the gas ejected from the nozzle.

19.14. A passenger plane flies at an altitude of 8 km at a speed of 900 km/h. The speed is measured with the aid of a Pitot-Prandtl tube. Find the pressure difference in the differential manometer. For data relating to the atmosphere see § 26.10, Table 26.3.

19.15. Find the speed of a motor launch, if the water in the Pitot-Prandtl tube has risen to a height of 1.8 m.

19.16. What excess pressure should a pump set up in an oil pipeline, if the distance between the pumping stations is 50 km? What is the pump's power? The pipeline should be assumed smooth, and the data of Problem 19.1 should be used.

19.17. May the continuity equation be used in the analysis of a pipeline? What about the equation of momenta and the Bernoulli equation?

Part Four

MOLECULAR FORCES AND STATES
OF AGGREGATION OF MATTER

20. Solids

20.1. An aluminium cube with 1 cm edge is subjected to hydrostatic stress. What force acts on each face if the decrease in the volume is 1 percent?

20.2. Hooke's law is valid for the elastic extension (or compression) of a rod. This law may be written down, by analogy with the formula of the previous problem, by substituting Young's modulus E for the bulk modulus K. Write this formula and express the rigidity of the rod in terms of its dimensions.

20.3. A steel cable is made up of 120 wires each of 1 mm diameter. The rope's length is 4 m,

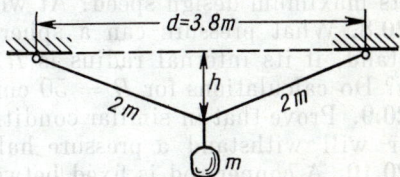

Fig. 20.3.

the distance between the suspension points is 3.8 m (Fig. 20.3). A weight of 1 tonne mass is suspended in the middle of the rope. What will be the rope's elongation? What weight will cause the rupture of the rope? The rope is made of soft steel.

20.4. Imagine an infinitely long one-dimensional ionic crystal—a chain of alternating positive and negative ions with a distance a between them (Fig. 20.4). Find the force with which one half of the chain acts on an arbitrary ion and compare the result with the force F_0 acting between the two adjacent ions. Calculation accuracy should be better than 0.001.

20.5. Find the breaking stress of an ionic crystal neglecting the effect of all the ions except the nearest neighbours. Do numerical calculations for a sodium chloride crystal in which the distance between the centres of neighbouring ions (the lattice constant a) is, according to data obtained with the aid of X-ray structural analysis, equal to 2.81 Å. Do the same for a lithium fluoride crystal, in which $a = 2.01$ Å.

Fig. 20.4.

20.6. The theoretical values for the rupture strength obtained in the previous problem exceed by tens of times the rupture strength of good steels and by many thousands of times the rupture strength of real ionic crystals. What is the explanation for this?

20.7. A steel flywheel is made in the shape of a solid ring of 40 cm external and 30 cm internal diameter. What is its maximum design speed? At what speed will it fly apart?

20.8. What pressure can a spherical steel container withstand, if its internal radius is R and the wall thickness is d? Do calculations for $R = 50$ cm, $d = 5$ mm.

20.9. Prove that in similar conditions a cylindrical container will withstand a pressure half as great.

20.10. A copper rod is fixed between two supports. Its temperature was raised by 50 °C. What is the resulting stress in the rod?

20.11. A steel cylinder was cooled in liquid nitrogen (72 K) and fitted without play into a nickel-chrome steel shell at room temperature (20 °C). The internal radius of the shell is 25 mm and the external radius is 35 mm. Neglecting deformation of the cylinder find the stress in the shell and the nature of its deformation.

20.12. Water penetrated into a crack in a rock and froze there. What is the resulting pressure?

20.13. To determine the volume expansion coefficient of kerosene, one end of a U-tube filled with it was held at 10 °C, and the other at 80 °C. The level of liquid in one tube was 280 mm and in the other 300 mm. Find the coefficient.

20.14. What is the number of atoms in an elementary cell of a simple cubic lattice?

20.15. What is the number of atoms in an elementary cell of a face-centered cubic lattice?

20.16. What is the number of atoms in an elementary cell of a closely packed hexagonal lattice?

21. Liquids

21.1. The viscosity of mercury decreases with the rise in temperature (Table 21.1a). Check whether relation (34.10) is valid for mercury. Calculate the activation energy.

Table 21.1a

Temperature t, °C	Viscosity η, mPa·s	Temperature t, °C	Viscosity η, mPa·s
0	1.681	50	1.407
10	1.621	60	1.367
20	1.552	70	1.327
30	1.499	100	1.232
40	1.450		

21.2. To what height will water in a capillary of 0.8 mm diameter rise? Assume the contact angle to be zero.

21.3. A capillary of 0.8 mm diameter is immersed in water, and rises 2 cm above the water. To what height will the water rise in it? How can the result be made consistent with the result of the previous problem?

21.4. There were 100 droplets of mercury of 1 mm diameter on a glass plate. Subsequently they merged into one big drop. How will the energy of the surface layer change? The process is isothermal.

21.5. To pump liquid out of a vessel which is not wetted by it into a vessel wetted by it one may make use of surface tension forces (a capillary pump). What will be the speed of flow of petrol in a capillary of 2 mm diameter and of 10 cm length? The experiment is conducted in conditions of weightlessness.

21.6. Compare the effectiveness of a capillary pump for water at low and high temperatures.

21.7. Liquid in a capillary rises to a height h. What column of liquid will remain in the capillary, if it is filled in a horizontal position and then placed in a vertical position? Assume the capillary to be sufficiently long.

21.8. Find the height to which a liquid rises between two long parallel plates, a distance d apart.

21.9. A drop of water of 0.2 g mass is placed between two well cleaned glass plates, the distance between which is 0.01 cm. Find the force of attraction between the plates.

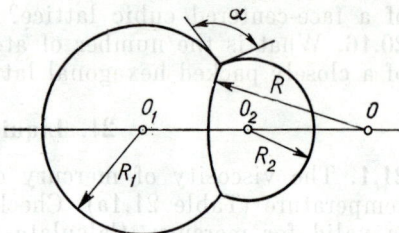

Fig. 21.10.

21.10. Two soap bubbles with radii of curvature R_1 and R_2, where $R_2 < R_1$ are brought into contact as shown in Fig. 21.10. What is the radius of curvature of the film between them? What is the contact angle of the films?

22. Vapours

22.1. Making use of Table 35.1 check the validity of the Mendeleev-Clapeyron equation for the case of saturated water vapour. Can saturated vapour be assumed to be an ideal gas?

22.2. Isn't the result of the previous problem in contradiction with the fact that the ideal gas isochore in p-T coordinates is represented by a linear graph, while the isochore of saturated vapour is nonlinear (see § 35.3, Fig. 35.2)?

22.3. A cylinder closed by a piston contains 8 g of water vapour at a temperature of 55 °C. The vapour is compressed isothermally. What will be its volume when dew begins to appear?

22.4. A cylinder closed by a piston contains 3.5 g of water and 2.9 g of water vapour at a temperature of 40 °C. The gas expands isothermally. What will be the volume corresponding to complete evaporation of water?

22.5. The air temperature is 18 °C, the dew point is 7 °C. Find the absolute and the relative humidities of the air.
22.6. During the day the air temperature was 25 °C, the relative humidity was 68%. At night the temperature fell to 11 °C. Will dew precipitate? If the answer is positive, what will be the precipitation per cubic metre of air?
22.7. 5 m³ of air with a relative humidity of 22% at 15 °C and 3 m³ of air with a relative humidity of 46% at 28 °C have been mixed together. The total volume of the mixture is 8 m³. Find the relative humidity of the mixture.
22.8. Making use of the values of the critical parameters of water (§ 35.5) check whether those parameters satisfy the ideal gas law. Explain the result.
22.9. Table 22.9 contains the values of the density of liquid

Table 22.9

Temperature t, °C	Density of liquid ρ, kg/m³	Density of vapour ρ, kg/m³	Vapour pressure p, MPa
0	914	96	3.47
10	856	133	4.48
20	766	190	5.70
25	703	240	6.41
30	598	334	7.16
31	536	392	7.32
31.25	497	422	7.38
31.35	464	464	7.39

carbon dioxide, as well as the pressure and the density of its saturated vapour. Find the critical parameters of this substance. Plot the density vs temperature graphs.

23. Phase Transitions

23.1. What amount of work is performed when 1 kg of water turns into steam at 100 °C? How much energy is spent to break the bonds between the molecules?
23.2. If you sling a thin wire loop around a block of ice and attach to it a weight of several kilograms then after some time the wire will pass through the block of ice, but the block remains intact (Fig. 23.2). Explain this phenomenon.
23.3. 0.2 kg of water vapour at 100 °C is admitted into a

mixture consisting of 5 kg of water and 3 kg of ice. What will happen? Neglect radiative losses.

23.4. Solve Problem 23.3 assuming that 1.1 kg of water vapour was admitted into the mixture.

23.5. 0.5 kg of ice at −15 °C is thrown into a litre of water at room temperature (20 °C). What will happen? Neglect losses.

23.6. Solve Problem 23.5 assuming the amount of water to be 3 l.

23.7. Pure water can be supercooled down to −10 °C. If a small ice crystal is thrown into, it immediately freezes. What fraction of water will freeze? The system is adiabatically isolated.

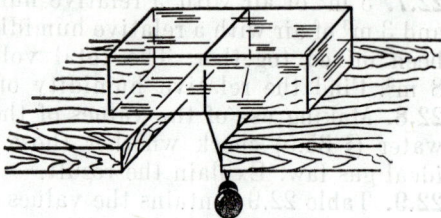

Fig. 23.2.

23.8. Water is boiling in a kettle on an electric hot-plate of 800 W power. Find the steam outflow velocity, if the cross section of the spout is 0.9 cm² and the pressure at the output is normal. The efficiency of the hot plate is 72%.

23.9. Ice at 0 °C is enclosed in an adiabatic shell and is compressed to a pressure of 600 atm. It is known that an increase in the pressure of 138 atm causes the melting point of ice to drop by 1 K. Assuming the phase diagram in this part to be linear, find the fraction of the ice that is going to melt.

23.10. To determine the quality of thermal insulation of a Dewar vessel, it is filled with ice at 0 °C. 42 g of ice have melted in 24 h. Usually liquid nitrogen at 78 K is kept in this flask. Assuming the quantity of heat entering the flask to be proportional to the difference in the internal and the external temperatures of the vessel, find the amount of liquid nitrogen that is going to evaporate in 24 h. The ambient temperature is 20 °C, the heat of vapourization of liquid nitrogen at normal pressure is 1.8×10^5 J/K.

23.11. The triple point of carbon dioxide (CO_2) corresponds to a pressure of 5.18×10^5 Pa and a temperature of 216.5 K. In what temperature range can liquid carbon dioxide be obtained? In what conditions does sublimation take place?

Part Five

24. A Field of Fixed Charges in a Vacuum

24.1. Estimate the upper limit of the error made in calculating the force of interaction between charged spherical conductors with the aid of the Coulomb law. The radii of the spheres are r_0, the distance between their centres is r. Carry out the calculations for $r \geqslant 20r_0$.

24.2. Two electric charges $q_1 = q$ and $q_2 = -2q$ are placed at a distance $l = 6a$ apart. Find the locus of points in the plane of the charges where the field potential is zero.

24.3. Prove that the units of field intensity N/C and V/m are identical.

24.4. An oil droplet of 0.01 mm diameter floats in equilibrium between two horizontal plates the distance between which is 25 mm. What is the charge of the droplet, if the equilibrium corresponds to a voltage of 3.6×10^4 V across the plates?

24.5. In §§ 18.3 and 18.7, 18.8 we have obtained the expression for the potential of the field of a point charge using numerical methods. When you have learned to differentiate, prove that formula (18.25) leads to the expression for the field intensity of a point charge known from the Coulomb law.

24.6. When you have learned to integrate, derive formula (18.25) from the familiar expression for the field intensity of a point charge.

24.7. A charge q is uniformly distributed on a ring-shaped conductor of radius a. Find the field potential in an arbitrary point on the conductor's axis a distance x away from the plane in which the conductor lies. Using the relation between the potential and the field intensity, find the field intensity at this point. Compare with Problem 4.11.

24.8. A dipole is placed in the field of a point charge, the distance between the dipole and the field source being much greater than the dipole separation. Find the force acting on the dipole and the torque, if the dipole is arranged:

(a) perpendicular to the line of force;

(b) in the direction of the line of force.

24.9. Two capacitors with capacitances C_1 and C_2 are connected in parallel. Find the resultant capacitance.

24.10. The same capacitors are connected in series. Find the resultant capacitance.

24.11. Several identical capacitors were connected in parallel and charged to a voltage φ_0. Subsequently they were reconnected in series with the aid of a switch. What will be the voltage across the terminals? Will the energy of the system change?

24.12. Draw the diagram of a switch which enables a parallel connection of a capacitor battery to be changed to a series one and vice versa.

24.13. A sphere carries a uniformly distributed electric charge. Prove that the field inside the sphere is zero.

24.14. Prove that the field on the surface of a sphere carrying a uniformly distributed electric charge is equal to that which would have been established, if the entire charge were concentrated in the centre of the sphere.

24.15. Find the electric field at an arbitrary point of a sphere carrying a charge uniformly distributed over its volume.

24.16. Find the capacitance of a spherical capacitor. Prove that for small distances between the spheres the capacitance may be calculated with the aid of the formula for a plane capacitor.

Estimate the error made by doing this.

24.17. Suppose that an electron may be considered to be a ball of radius a carrying an electric charge e uniformly distributed over its surface. It may be shown that outside this ball and on its surface the field will be the same as that of an equal point charge; inside the ball the field is zero. From these considerations find the energy of the electron's field. Assuming it to be equal to the electron's rest energy estimate the radius of this ball (double this quantity is called the classical radius of the electron).

Compare with Problem 14.23.

24.18. A spherical shell of radius R carries a uniformly distributed charge q. The electrical forces arising cause the ex-

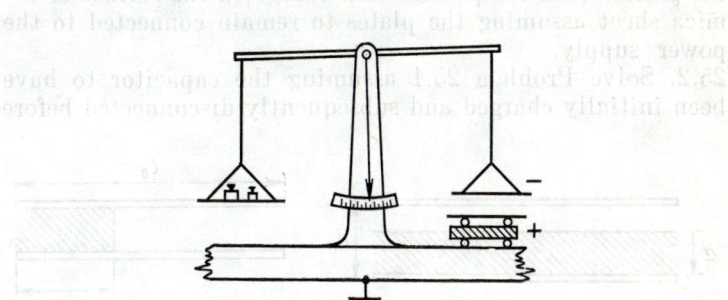

Fig. 24.20.

pansion of the shell. Find the mechanical stress in the shell.

24.19. The radius of a soap bubble is 5 mm. What charge should be imparted to it to make it begin to swell?

24.20. The lower plate of a plane capacitor lies on an insulating plane. The upper plate is earthed through scales (Fig. 24.20). The scales are balanced. What additional weight should be placed on the left-hand pan to maintain the balance, if a voltage of 5000 V is applied across the plates? The distance between the plates is 5 mm and the area of the plates is 80 cm².

Fig. 24.21.

24.21. Two identical capacitors are charged to different potentials φ_1 and φ_2 relative to the negative earthed electrodes. The capacitors are then connected in parallel (Fig. 24.21). Find the potential of the battery after the connection was made and the change in the energy of the system.

25. Dielectrics

25.1. The distance between the plates of a plane capacitor*
is 10 mm, the voltage is 10 kV. A sheet of mica of the same
dimensions as those of the plates is then inserted between
the plates. Find the polarization charge on the surface of the
mica sheet assuming the plates to remain connected to the
power supply.
25.2. Solve Problem 25.1 assuming the capacitor to have
been initially charged and subsequently disconnected before

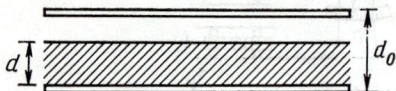

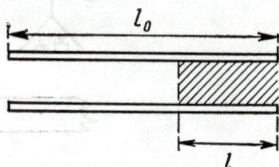

Fig. 25.4.   Fig. 25.5.

the mica sheet is inserted in it.
25.3. Find the capacitance of a capacitor, if it is made up of
120 sheets of paraffined paper 0.1 mm thick, interspaced
with aluminium foil sheets of
5 cm × 3 cm dimensions.

In what range of voltages
can such a capacitor work?
25.4. Find the capacitance of
a capacitor if the area of its
plates is S, the distance between
the plates is d_0 and a dielectric
sheet of the thickness $d < d_0$
is inserted into the capacitor
(Fig. 25.4).
25.5. Find the capacitance of
a capacitor in which the space
between the plates is partly
filled with a dielectric (Fig. 25.5).

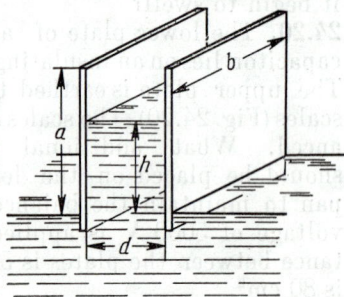

Fig. 25.7.

25.6. A water droplet is placed in the field of a point charge
of 10^{-5} C. How far from the droplet must the charge be for
the electric forces to overcome the force of gravity? The

---

* In all problems involving plane capacitors fringe effects are
to be ignored.

radius of the droplet is much less than the distance between the droplet and the charge.

25.7. A large vessel is filled with a liquid. Two vertical plates touch the surface of the liquid (Fig. 25.7). The dimensions of the plates are a and b, the distance between them is d. The plates have been charged by applying a voltage φ_0 and then disconnected from the voltage source. To what height will the liquid rise? Ignore capillary effects.

25.8. Solve Problem 25.7 assuming that the plates remain connected to the voltage source.

25.9. The electric susceptibility of water vapour is strongly dependent on temperature:

Temperature t, °C	120	150	180	210
Pressure p, mmHg	565	609	653	698
Electric susceptibility χ_e	4.00×10^{-3}	3.72×10^{-3}	3.49×10^{-3}	3.29×10^{-3}

Plot a graph and find the temperature dependence of the electric susceptibility. Calculate the dipole moment of a molecule of water.

25.10. The dielectric permittivity of gaseous argon at standard conditions is 1.00054. Find the dipole moment of an argon atom in an electric field of 10 kV/m. Compare with the dipole moment of a water molecule.

26. Direct Current

26.1. A circular ring made of copper wire of 0.1 mm diameter and 60 cm long is connected as shown in Fig. 26.1. Find the resistance of the circuit. What should the length of the shorter section $AB = x$ be for the resistance of the circuit to be 0.2 ohm?

26.2. Find the resistance of the wire figure shown in Fig. 26.2a. The wire is uniform, made of aluminium of 0.4 mm diameter. The length of the side of the square is 20 cm.

26.3. A five-pointed regular star (Fig. 26.3) has been soldered together from uniform wire. The resistance of the section EL is r. Find the resistance of the section FL.

26.4. The wire star of the previous problem is connected to the circuit at points F and C. Find the equivalent resistance.

26.5. A cube is soldered together from identical pieces of

wire each of a resistance r. It is connected to the circuit at
the corners lying on opposite ends of a body diagonal
(Fig. 26.5a). Find the equivalent resistance.

26.6. The instrument used to measure resistance is the
Wheatstone bridge with a slide resistance—a wire of high
resistivity of length L (Fig. 26.6). Here R is a calibrated
resistance, R_x the unknown resistance. By moving the sliding contact, the current in the galvanometer is made to

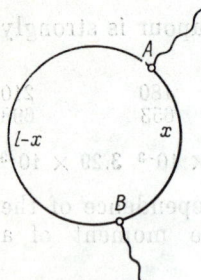

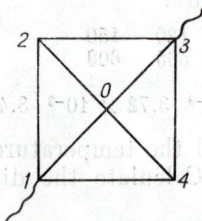

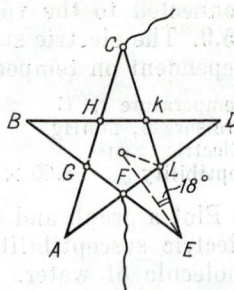

Fig. 26.1.   Fig. 26.2 a   Fig. 26.3.

drop to zero. Making use of this condition (of bridge balance),
find the resistance being measured.

26.7. What is the condition for the error in measuring resistance on a Wheatstone bridge to be a minimum? How can
it be achieved?

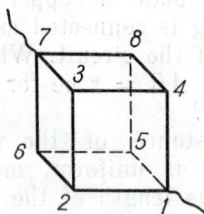

Fig. 26.5a.

26.8. A current of 100 A flows in a conical copper conductor
with dimensions as shown in Fig. 26.8. Find the current
density and electric field intensity at the end faces of the
conductor.

26.9. When you have learned to integrate find the resistance of the conductor of the previous problem and the voltage across it.

26.10. The e.m.f. of one accumulator is e, its internal resistance is r. Find the e.m.f. $\mathscr{E}$ and the internal resistance

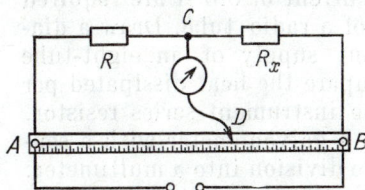

Fig. 26.6.

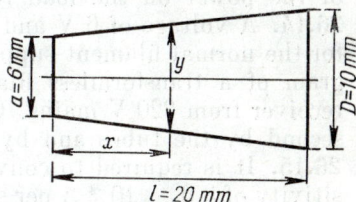

Fig. 26.8.

R_i of a battery of n accumulators connected (Fig. 26.10):

(a) in series;

(b) in parallel;

(c) in m series-connected groups of k accumulators, $m < n$, $k = n/m$, where the accumulators are connected in parallel.

26.11. 200 alkaline accumulators are to be charged by a dynamo generating a voltage of 230 V. The e.m.f. of each

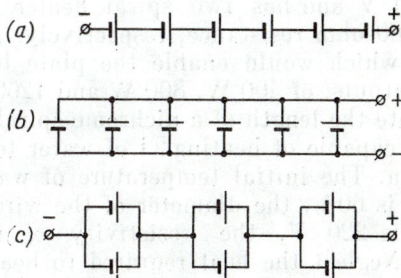

Fig. 26.10.

accumulator is 1.4 V, the internal resistance 0.01 ohm, the charging current 30 A. Suggest the circuit diagram and calculate the resistance of the rheostat.

26.12. A power supply with an e.m.f. $\mathscr{E}$ and internal resistance r is connected to a variable resistance R. Find the dependence of the total power generated by the supply and of the power delivered to the external circuit on the load resistance.

26.13. Determine the load resistance for which the power delivered to the circuit is a maximum. Graph the dependence of the power on the load resistance.

26.14. A voltage of 6 V and a current of 0.3 A are required for the normal filament supply of a radio tube. Draw a diagram of a transformless filament supply of an eight-tube receiver from 220 V mains. Compare the heat dissipated per second by the tubes and by the instrument series resistor.

26.15. It is required to convert a galvanometer with a sensitivity of 3.0×10^{-4} A per scale division into a multimeter: a voltmeter for voltages of 10 V, 100 V and 1000 V and an ammeter for currents of 100 mA and 5 A. Draw the circuit diagram and calculate the resistor block. The scale comprises 50 divisions.

26.16. How many 220 V bulbs of 300 W power each may be installed in a building, if the mains voltage is 235 V and the wiring is done using aluminium wire of 6 mm diameter? The power line is a two-wire line, and the distance from the mains terminal to the building is 100 m.

26.17. A hot plate with regulated power is designed for a voltage of 220 V and has two spiral heater elements of 120 ohm and 60 ohm resistance, respectively. Devise a circuit diagram which would enable the plate to operate at three power-outputs: of 400 W, 800 W and 1200 W.

26.18. Calculate the length of a nichrome spiral for an electric hot plate capable of heating 2 l of water to the boiling point in 8 min. The initial temperature of water is 20 °C, the efficiency is 60%, the diameter of the wire is 0.8 mm, the voltage is 220 V, the resistivity of nichrome is 10^{-6} ohm·m. Neglect the heat required to heat the kettle.

26.19. The current in a conductor of 40 ohm resistance increases linearly from 5 A to 25 A in 10 s. How much heat is liberated in it during this time? Solve the problem using two methods: (a) numerical calculation; (b) integration.

26.20. When you have learned to integrate, try to derive a formula for the instantaneous current from a capacitor discharged through a resistor.

26.21. The voltage stabilizer S is a device whose idealized characteristic is depicted in Fig. 26.21. The voltage stabilizer is connected in series with a normal resistor R to the power supply whose e.m.f. is $\mathcal{E}$. Neglecting the internal resistance of the power supply find the current in the circuit and the voltage drop across the voltage stabilizer and the resistor.

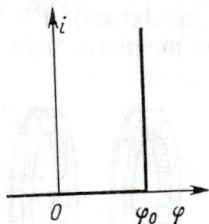

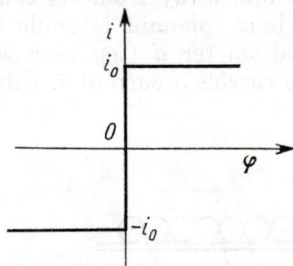

Fig. 26.21.   Fig. 26.22.

26.22. Barretter B is a conductor whose idealized characteristic is shown in Fig. 26.22. The barretter is connected in series with a resistor of resistance R to a power supply of e.m.f. $\mathcal{E}$. Find the current in the circuit and the voltage drop across the barretter and the resistor. Neglect the internal resistance of the power supply.

27. A Magnetic Field in a Vacuum

27.1. Here's another paradox from the theory of relativity. Let a spring be perpendicular to the speed of the reference frame. Acted upon by the force F_0 the spring extends by a length $l_0 = F_0/k$. As is well known, transition from one reference frame to another leaves the lateral dimensions unaltered (see Problem 6.1), therefore $l = l_0$. Isn't this in contradiction with the fact that as a result of such a transition the lateral force changes in accordance with the law $F = F_0 \sqrt{1 - v^2/c^2}$?

27.2. A proton beam in an accelerator moves at a speed of $0.990c$ relative to the accelerator. Compare the force of interaction between the protons with the Coulomb force.

27.3. Making use of the principle of relativity prove that the intensity of the transverse electric field of moving charges exceeds that of their Coulomb field.

27.4. A circular coil of 200 mm diameter is made of 100 turns of thin wire and carries a current of 50 mA. Find the magnetic field induction in the centre of the coil and on the coil's axis 100 mm away from its centre.

27.5. A long solenoid is made by closely winding turns of wire of diameter d (together with insulation) (Fig. 27.5). The wire carries a current i. Find the magnetic field induc-

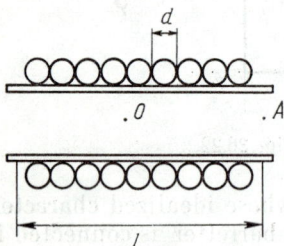

Fig. 27.5.

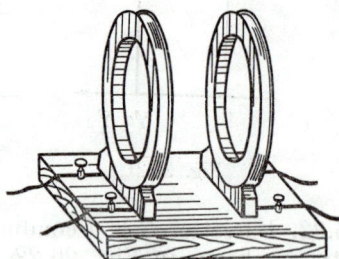

Fig. 27.6.

tion in the centre O and on the end A of the solenoid. Carry out the calculation for $d = 0.1$ mm, $i = 5$ A.

27.6. Helmholtz coils consist of two thin flat coils placed as shown in Fig. 27.6. Compare the magnetic field intensities in the centre of each coil with that in the midpoint of the axis and prove that inside the Helmholtz coils the field is almost uniform. Take the distance between the coils to be equal to one half of the radius.

27.7. The horizontal component of the Earth's magnetic field is 16 A/m. Calculate the dimensions of the Helmholtz coils designed to compensate the Earth's magnetic field, if the current in a coil is 200 mA and the number of turns in each winding is 50.

27.8. A thin ring of 10 cm radius carries a uniformly distributed charge. The ring rotates at a constant speed of 1200 r.p.m. about its axis passing through the centre of the ring perpendicular to its plane. Find the charge carried by the ring, if the magnetic field induction in its centre is 3.8×10^{-9} T.

27.9. A surface charge density of 10^{-2} C/m^2 has been created by friction on a glass disk of $h = 5$ mm thickness and $R = 50$ mm radius. The disk rotates at 1.6 r.p.s. Find the magnetic field intensity at the centre of the disk.

When you have learned to integrate, find the magnetic moment and the ratio of the magnetic moment to the angular momentum.

27.10. A magnetic field is established by a circular current i of radius a. Find the magnetic field gradient (i.e. the derivative of the magnetic field induction vector) in the direction of the circular current's axis at a point whose distance from the centre of the turn is x.

28. Charges and Currents in a Magnetic Field

28.1. An alpha-particle moves in a uniform magnetic field with an induction of 1.2 tesla (T) in a circle of 49 cm radius in the plane perpendicular to the lines of force. Find the speed and the kinetic energy of the particle.

28.2. Solve Problem 28.1 for a muon. What are its speed and kinetic energy?

28.3. A charged particle moving in a uniform magnetic field penetrates a layer of lead and thereby loses one half of its kinetic energy. How does the radius of curvature of its path change? Carry out calculations for both a relativistic and a nonrelativistic particle.

28.4. Find the period of revolution of an electron having a kinetic energy of 1.5 MeV in a magnetic field with induction 0.02 T. The electron moves in a plane perpendicular to the lines of force.

28.5. An electron accelerated in an electric field of 20 kV enters a uniform magnetic field with induction 0.1 T. Its velocity vector makes an angle of 75° with the magnetic field vector. Find the shape of the path.

28.6. Show that it makes little sense placing the dees of a cyclotron into a uniform magnetic field. Specify a rational shape of the pole pieces capable of focusing a particle beam in the centre of the dees.

28.7. The electron beam in the device shown in Fig. 28.7a is deflected upwards by a transverse magnetic field. The field is effective along a length $l = 20$ mm, the distance of the deflection system from the screen being $L = 175$ mm. The magnetic induction is 10^{-3} T, the anode voltage is 500 V. Find the deflection of the electron beam on the screen.

28.8. What electric field should be set up in the device discussed in the previous problem to return the electrons to the centre of the screen?

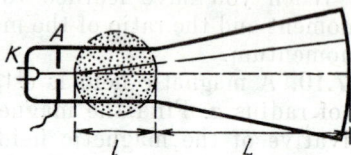

28.9. In the Dubna heavy-ion cyclotron neon ions are accelerated to an energy of 100 MeV. The diameter of the dees is 310 cm, the magnetic field induction in the gap is 1.1 T, the accelerating potential is 300 kV. Find the degree of ionization of a neon atom, the total number of revolutions of an ion in the process of its acceleration and the frequency of the change in polarity of the accelerating field.

Fig. 28.7a.

28.10. The diameter of the magnet of the Serpukhov synchrotron is 472 m. The protons enter the accelerating chamber with an energy of 100 MeV and leave it with an energy of 76.5 GeV. Find the initial and the final magnetic induction in the gap and the accelerating field frequencies.

28.11. A uniform electric field of 1 MV/m and a uniform magnetic field of 10^{-2} T were set up in some region of space. The electric field strength vector is perpendicular to the magnetic induction vector. A muon beam moves in a direction perpendicular to both vectors and passes without being deflected by the combined action of both fields. What is the velocity of the particles?

Can the charge of the particle and its sign be determined in this experiment?

28.12. The velocity filter of a mass spectrometer employs an electric field strength of 1.0×10^2 V/m and a perpendicular magnetic induction of 2.0×10^{-2} T. The induction of the deflecting uniform magnetic field which is perpendicular to the beam is 9.0×10^{-2} T. Ions with similar charges and with mass numbers 20 and 22 pass through the filter and make a 180° turn in the deflecting field (Fig. 28.12). What is the distance between the points S_1 and S_2?

28.13. In the Bainbridge mass spectrometer (Fig. 28.13) the distance between the velocity filter (selector) exit and the entrance slit of the detecting device (collector slit) is fixed and equal to $l = 400$ mm. The magnetic induction in both sections of the device is the same, being equal to 5.00×10^{-2} T. When the electric field in the velocity filter

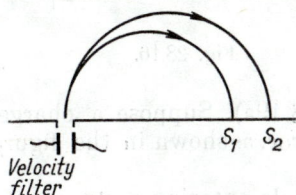

Fig. 28.12.

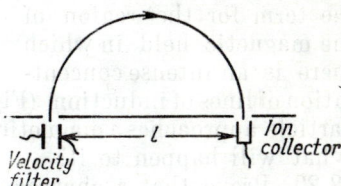

Fig. 28.13.

is varied continuously the anode current peaks are observed at field strengths of 1.20×10^4 V/m and 1.60×10^4 V/m. Assuming the ions to be singly charged, identify them (i.e. find the element to which they belong).

28.14. The moving coil of a galvanometer 4 cm long and 1.5 cm wide, made of 200 turns of thin wire, works in a magnetic field with induction of 0.1 T. The plane of the coil is parallel to lines of induction. Find the torque acting on the coil when a current of 1 mA flows in it.

28.15. The moving coil of a galvanometer made of 200 turns of thin wire is suspended from an elastic thread. The area of the coil is 1 cm², it coincides in direction with the lines of induction of a magnetic field with induction of 15 mT. When the current of 5.0 μA is passed through the coil it turns through 15°. By what angle will the coil turn with a current of 7.5 μA? What is the torsion modulus of the thread?

28.16. Find the force of interaction between two current-carrying coils, the distance between the centres of which is much greater than their linear dimensions (Fig. 28.16).

28.17. The parameters of two small identical current-carrying coils are as follows: the radius of winding is 20 mm, the number of turns is 10^3, the current is 0.5 A, the distance between the coils is 300 mm. What is the force of interaction between the coils?

28.18. Suppose that an electric charge moves in a magnetic field in a plane perpendicular to the lines of induction. Prove that the orbital magnetic moment of the circulating charge is directed against the field.

28.19. "Magnetic mirror" is the term for the region of the magnetic field in which there is an intense concentration of lines of induction (Fig. 28.19a). Suppose a charged particle approaches a magnetic mirror, as shown in the figure. What will happen to it?

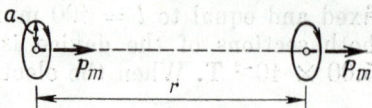

Fig. 28.16.

28.20. Prove that a charged particle entering a strong uniform magnetic field experiences specular reflection, if its speed is below some limiting value (the "magnetic mirror" principle, Fig. 28.20). Find the kinetic energy of the electrons which experience specular reflection, if the electron beam is

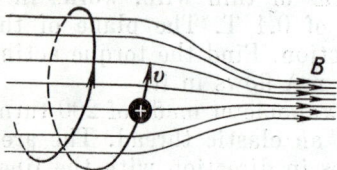

Fig. 28.19a.

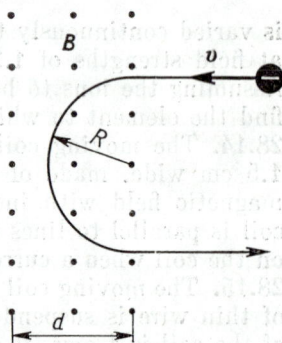

Fig. 28.20.

perpendicular to the "magnetic mirror". The magnetic field with an induction $B = 0.1$ T is established in a large region, the thickness of the "magnetic mirror" is $d = 10$ cm.

29. Magnetic Materials

29.1. A bismuth ball of 5 mm radius is placed in a magnetic field with an induction 2×10^{-5} T. What is the magnetic moment of the ball? What is its direction? The magnetic susceptibility of bismuth is $\chi_m = -1.76 \times 10^{-4}$.

29.2. Solve a similar problem for the case of a tungsten ball. The magnetic susceptibility of tungsten is $\chi_m = 1.76 \times \times 10^{-4}$.

29.3. The magnetic moment of a gadolinium atom is 7.95 μ_B (μ_B is the Bohr magneton). Gadolinium crystallizes in a face-centered cubic lattice with lattice constant of 3.2 Å. Find the saturation magnetization. Take into account that an elementary cell of a face-centered lattice contains four atoms (see Problem 20.15).

29.4. The temperature of a paramagnetic material is 30 °C, the atomic concentration is 10^{27} m^{-3}, the atomic magnetic moment is two Bohr magnetons. Estimate by what number the number of atoms with magnetic moments oriented in the direction of the field exceeds the number of atoms with magnetic moments oriented against the field, if the field induction is 1.2 T.

How will the result change, if the substance is cooled to the temperature of liquid nitrogen (-195.8 °C)?

29.5. Find the magnetization of the substance under the conditions of the previous problem.

29.6. Show, that it is impossible to explain the nature of ferromagnetism on the basis of the interaction of magnetic dipoles.

29.7. Estimate the energy of the exchange interaction of electron spin magnetic moments in iron domains.

29.8. Calculate the deflection of the beam of atoms from its axis in the Stern-Gerlach experiment for the following parameters of the apparatus: the length of pole pieces is 3.5 cm, the magnetic field gradient is of the order of 10^2 T/m. In the experiment silver atoms flying out of a "molecular oven" at a temperature of 730 °C were deflected. The projection of the magnetic moment of a silver atom on the direction of the magnetic induction vector is equal to a Bohr magneton.

29.9. The initial magnetization curve of technically pure iron is shown in Fig. 29.9a. Making use of the graph find the magnetic permeabilities of this material at magnetic fields strength of: 50 A/m; 75 A/m; 100 A/m; 200 A/m; 500 A/m; 1000 A/m; 1500 A/m.

Plot the graph of the dependence of the magnetic permeability on the magnetic field. Making use of the graph estimate the field at which the magnetic permeability is at its max-

imum (μ_{mex}), and the approximate value of the latter.
29.10. Table 29.10 gives the coordinates of some of the points of the asymptotic hysteresis cycle of a ferromagnetic material. Plot the hysteresis loop. (The recommended scale is 10 mm = 100 A/m and 10 mm = 0.20 T.) Find the coer-

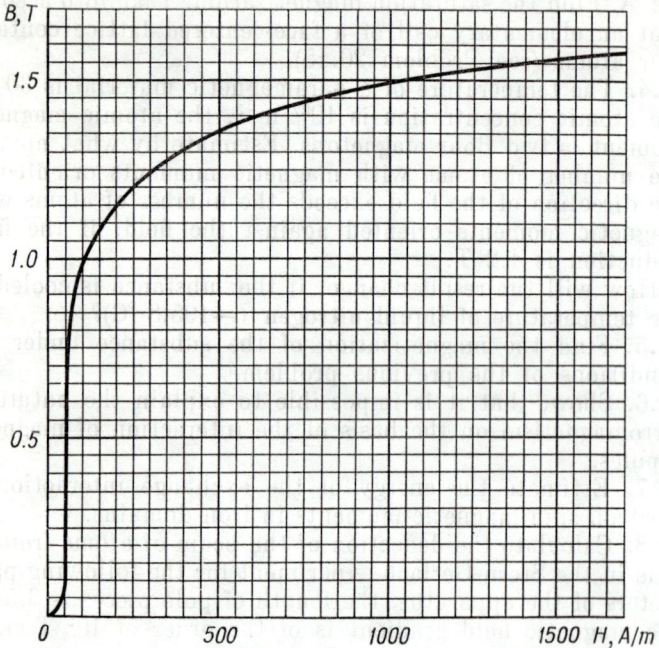

Fig. 29.9a.

cive force and saturation induction from the graph. Calculate the saturation magnetization and remnant magnetization M_r.
29.11. For several practical applications the so-called "differential" magnetic permeability $\mu' = \frac{1}{\mu_0} \frac{dB}{dH}$ and not the usual magnetic permeability $\mu = B/\mu_0 H$ is the parameter of interest. Here $\frac{dB}{dH}$ is the derivative of the field induc-

Table 29.10

Magnetic field strength H, A/m	Magnetic induction B, T		Magnetic field strength H, A/m	Magnetic induction B, T	
	lower branch of the loop	upper branch of the loop		lower branch of the loop	upper branch of the loop
0	−0.23	0.23	500	0.92	1.15
100	0	0.46	600	1.10	1.19
200	0.23	0.69	700	1.20	1.24
300	0.46	0.92	800	1.26	1.26
400	0.69	1.08			

tion with respect to the field intensity, i.e. the slope of the graph in Fig. 29.9a. For the purpose of practical calculations one can assume $\mu' = \dfrac{1}{\mu_0} \dfrac{\Delta B}{\Delta H}$, where ΔB and ΔH are chosen so small that the respective segment of the graph may be regarded as a straight line. Find the approximate values of the differential magnetic permeability for the same values of the magnetic field strength as in Problem 29.9.

30. Electromagnetic Induction

30.1. A plane with a wing span of 18 m flies horizontally at a speed of 800 km/h. The vertical component of the Earth's magnetic field strength is about 40 A/m. Find the voltage across the tips of the wings.

Will a light bulb connected to the wing tips glow?

30.2. A conductor of length l and mass m can slide without friction, but with an ideal electrical contact, along two vertical conductors AB and CD connected through a capacitor (Fig. 30.2). Perpendicular to the plane of the figure a uniform magnetic field of induction B is set up. Find the voltage across the capacitor plates as a function of h.

30.3. What will be the motion of the conductor of the previous problem, if a resistor of resistance R is connected into the circuit instead of the capacitor? Neglect the resistance of the conductors.

30.4. A rod of length l is perpendicular to the lines of induction of a uniform magnetic field of induction B. The rod revolves at an angular speed ω about an axis passing through the rod's end parallel to the lines of induction. Find the voltage across the rod's ends.

30.5. The length of the conductor in, the diagram shown in Fig. 30.5 is $l = 20$ cm, its speed is $v = 1$ m/s and the resistance of the bulb is $R = 1$ ohm. A magnetic field with induction $B = 0.5$ T is set up perpendicular to the plane of the diagram. What force should be applied to the conductor to make it move at the speed specified?

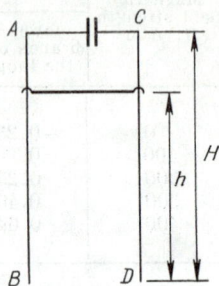

Fig. 30.2.

30.6. A horizontal flat coil of radius a made of w turns of wire carrying a current i sets up a magnetic field. A horizontal conducting ring of radius r is placed at a distance x_0 from the centre of the coil (Fig. 30.6). The ring is dropped. What e.m.f. will be established in it? Express the e.m.f. in terms of the speed.

30.7. A magnet was inserted into a wire ring connected to

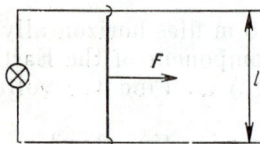

Fig. 30.5.

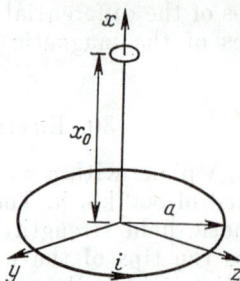

Fig. 30.6.

a ballistic galvanometer of 30 ohm resistance, this causing a 20 division deflection of the galvanometer's pointer. What magnetic flux passes through the pole piece of the magnet, if the galvanometer constant is 3×10^{-5} C/div? Neglect the resistance of the ring and of the leads.

30.8. To find the magnetic field induction in the gap between the pole pieces of an electromagnet, a coil of 3.2 cm² area made of 50 turns of thin wire connected to a ballistic galvanometer of 100 ohm resistance with a constant of 2×10^{-5} C/div is inserted into it. When the coil is withdrawn from the field, the galvanometer pointer moves 20 divisions. What is the field induction?

30.9. A ring is made from a dielectric with polar molecules. What will happen to the dielectric, if a magnet is inserted into it?

30.10. A flat circular coil of 10 cm radius has 200 turns of wire. The coil is connected to a capacitor of 20 μF and placed in a uniform magnetic field whose induction decreases at a constant rate of 10^{-2} T/s. Find the capacitor's charge. The plane of the coil is perpendicular to the lines of induction of the field.

30.11. An electric motor works from an accumulator battery with an e.m.f. of 12 V. With the rotor stalled the current in the circuit is 10 A. What is the motor's power at nominal load, if the respective current is 3 A?

30.12. 1200 turns of copper wire are wound onto a cardboard cylinder 60 cm long and 5 cm diameter. What is the inductance of the coil?

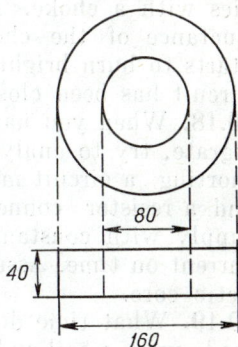

Fig. 30.14.

30.13. A current of 500 mA flows in the coil of the previous problem. When the current is switched off it vanishes after a time of 10^{-4} s. Supposing the current to decrease linearly, find the e.m.f. of self-induction.

30.14. A core with the shape and dimensions in millimeters shown in Fig. 30.14 has been manufactured of a ferromagnetic material whose magnetization curve is shown in Fig. 29.9a (p. 76). One layer of wire of 0.6 mm diameter (including insulation) was closely wound on the core. Find the inductance of the coil for a current of 200 mA flowing in it. Find the energy of the magnetic field and the energy density.

30.15. What would be the energy of the magnetic field of the coil of the previous problem, if its core were of a non-ferromagnetic material? What is the source of excess energy in the case of a ferromagnetic core?

30.16. The core and the armature of an electromagnet with dimensions in millimeters as shown in Fig. 30.16 have been manufactured from a ferromagnetic material whose properties have been described in Problem 29.10. What is the force with which the core attracts the armature, if the material has been magnetized to saturation? What force will remain active after the current is switched off?

30.17. A bulb with 1.2 ohm resistance is connected to an accumulator in series with a choke. Estimate the inductance of the choke, if the bulb starts to burn brightly 2.5 s after the circuit has been closed.

30.18. When you have learned to integrate, try to analyze the process of shorting a circuit made up of a coil and a resistor connected to a power

Fig. 30.16.

supply with constant e.m.f., i.e. the dependence of the current on time. Assume the coil to be without a ferromagnetic core.

30.19. What time does it take for the current in a circuit made up of a coil and a resistor to reach 0.9 of its stationary value?

30.20. According to the formula obtained in Problem 30.18 the stationary value of the current can be reached only after infinite time. How can this be made consistent with the fact that actually the stationary value is reached in a finite time? What are the limits in which the formula obtained in Problem 30.18 is applicable?

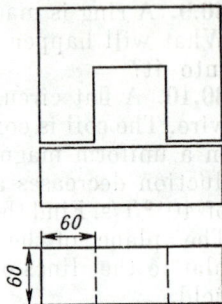

31. Classical Electron Theory

31.1. The coil employed in an experiment similar to that of Stewart and Tolman has a diameter $d = 500$ mm and $N = 400$ turns of copper wire. The moment the coil stops it is connected through a pair of sliding contacts to a ballistic galvanometer (Fig. 31.1). The total circuit resistance is $R = 50$ ohm. The coil is rotated at a constant speed of $n = 6000$ r.p.m. and quickly brought to a halt, the charge passing through the galvanometer being $Q = 1.1 \times 10^{-8}$ C. Find the specific charge of the charge carriers in copper.

31.2. A copper disk of $r_0 = 20$ cm radius revolves in a vertical plane at 3000 r.p.m. One contact from a sensitive galvanometer is connected to the disk's axis, the other by means of a mercury contact to the outer edge of the disk (Fig. 31.2a). Find the voltage.

Will the galvanometer pointer point in another direction, if the direction of rotation of the disk is changed?

The Earth's magnetic field is compensated.

31.3. The dimensions of a copper plate are as shown in the diagram (Fig. 31.3). When the longitudinal voltage is $\Delta\varphi$, a current i flows in the conductor. If a magnetic field with induction B perpendicular to the plate is established with the current still flowing, a Hall voltage of $\Delta\varphi_H$ appears between the upper and the lower faces of the plate. Find the concentration and the mobility of conduction electrons in copper, if $l =$

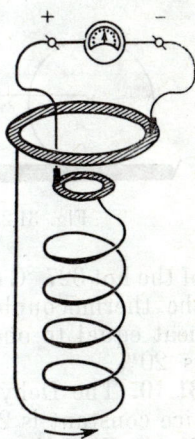

Fig. 31.1.

$= 60$ mm, $h = 20$ mm, $d = 1.0$ mm, $\Delta\varphi = 0.51$ mV, $\Delta\varphi_H = 55$ nV, $i = 10$ A, $B = 0.1$ T.

31.4. Calculate the Hall constant for silver knowing its density and atomic mass.

31.5. The resistivity of indium arsenide is 2.5×10^{-3} ohm·m, its Hall constant is 10^{-2} m^3/C. Assuming the conductivity to be due to carriers of one sign only, find the concentration and the mobility of the charge carriers. Compare with Problem 31.3.

31.6. The safe current in an insulated aluminium wire of 1 mm^2 cross section is 8 A. Find the average drift velocity of the conduction electrons.

31.7. Find the mean free transit time and the mean free path of the electrons in copper (at room temperature).

31.8. The constant of a constantan-copper thermocouple is 4.3×10^{-2} mV/K. The resistance of the thermocouple is 0.5 ohm, that of the galvanometer 100 ohm. One junction of the thermocouple is immersed in melting ice, the other in a hot liquid. What is its temperature if the current in the circuit is 56 μA?

31.9. The constant of a thermocouple is 7.6 μV/K, the temperature of its cold junction is −80 °C (dry ice), and that

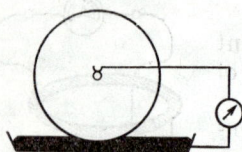

Fig. 31.2a.

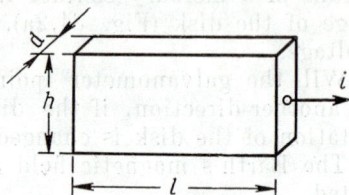

Fig. 31.3.

of the hot 327 °C (molten lead). What charge will flow through the thermocouple, if the hot junction absorbs quantity of heat equal to one joule? The efficiency of the thermocouple is 20%.

31.10. The Debye temperature for silver is 213 K, the lattice constant is 2 Å. Find the velocity of sound.

31.11. Find the heat flux through a copper plate 5 cm thick, if a temperature difference of 100 K is maintained between its ends.

31.12. The dimensions of a brick wall of a living room are: thickness 40 cm, width 5 m and height 2.8 m. A temperature of 20 °C is maintained inside the room, the temperature outside being −15 °C. How much heat is lost through this wall in 24 hours?

31.13. Find the mean free path of phonons in carbon tetrachloride.

31.14. Find the heat conductivity of silver and of mercury at room temperature (20 °C).

32. Electric Conductivity of Electrolytes

32.1. Find the dissociation coefficient of an aqueous potassium chloride solution with a concentration of 0.1 g/cm³, if the resistivity of this solution at 18 °C is $7.36 \times \times 10^{-2}$ ohm·m. The mobility of the potassium ions is

6.7×10^{-8} m²/(V·s), that of the chlorine ions $6.8 \times \times 10^{-8}$ m²/(V·s).

32.2. Find the thickness of a nickel layer deposited on an article with surface area of 1200 cm² in the course of a 6-hour electrolysis at a current of 10.5 A.

32.3. How much copper will be deposited from a vitriol solution in 3 minutes, if the current through the electrolyte changes in accordance with the law $i = 6 - 0.03t$? All quantities are expressed in the SI system.

32.4. An electrolytic bath containing a vitriol solution is connected to a d.c. power supply with an e.m.f. of 4 V and an internal resistance of 0.1 ohm. The resistance of the solution is 0.5 ohm, the polarization e.m.f. is 1.5 V. How much copper will be deposited in one hour?

32.5. Find the minimum e.m.f. of the power supply at which the electrolysis of acidified water can take place, if the combustion of 1 g of hydrogen liberates 1.45×10^2 kJ.

32.6. A 10 µF capacitor is charged to a voltage of 600 V. Suppose it is discharged through an electrolytic bath containing acidified water. How much hydrogen will be liberated? What energy can be gained by burning this hydrogen? How can it be made consistent with the energy conservation law?

32.7. What energy should be spent to fill a balloon with a lifting force of 3000 N with hydrogen under normal conditions? How much will it cost at the price of 4 copecks per kW·h? Ignore the heating of the solution in the course of electrolysis.

33. Electric Current in a Vacuum and in Gases

33.1. Find the saturation current in a diode with a tungsten cathode at cathode temperature of 2700 K, if the length of the cathode filament is 3 cm and its diameter is 0.1 mm. The constant $B = 6 \times 10^5$ A/(m²K²).

33.2. How will the saturation current in a diode with a caesium-coated tungsten cathode change, if the cathode temperature is raised from 1000 K to 1200 K?

33.3. In modern diodes the anode is often brought very close to the cathode so that their areas are approximately equal. Assuming the electrons to leave the cathode with zero velo-

city find the force with which they act on the anode. The
current in the tube is $i_{sat} = 500$ mA, the anode voltage is
$\varphi_a = 600$ V.

33.4. Compare the emissivities of a caesium-coated tungsten
cathode at 1000 K and that of a pure tungsten cathode at

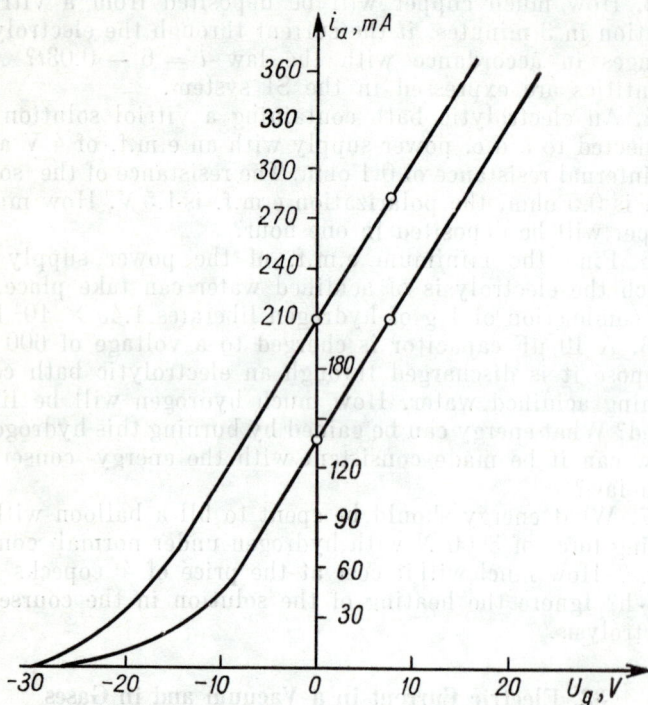

Fig. 33.5.

2700 K. Assume the constant B in the Richardson-Dushmann equation to be the same for both cathodes.

33.5. Figure 33.5 depicts the grid characteristics of a triode
plotted at anode voltages of 450 V and 600 V. Find the
triode's internal resistance R_i in the linear section of the
characteristic and its amplification factor μ, i.e. the ratio
of the change in the anode voltage to the change in the grid

voltage which causes a given change in the anode current.

33.6. Inside an ionization chamber there are two planar electrodes of 300 cm² area, 2 cm apart. The chamber is filled with air under normal conditions. At a voltage of 200 V the current is equal to 1.8 μA which is far below the saturation value.

Find the ion concentration and the ionization coefficient of air. The mobilities of the ions are: $b_+ = 1.37 \times 10^{-4}$ m²/(V·s), $b_- = 1.89 \times 10^{-4}$ m²/(V·s).

33.7. Oxygen is ionized by gamma-radiation, the ion concentration being 10^{15} m⁻³. Find the conductivity of the gas in these conditions. The ion mobilities are: $b_+ = 1.32 \times 10^{-4}$ m²/(V·s), $b_- = 1.81 \times 10^{-4}$ m²/(V·s).

33.8. What changes in the current in the range below saturation will take place, if the electrodes of an ionization chamber are brought closer? How will the saturation current change? Plot the current-voltage characteristics for some inter-electrode distance d_1 and for $d_2 < d_1$. Assume the other parameters to remain constant.

33.9. The saturation current in an ionization chamber of 0.5 l capacity is 0.02 μA. Find the ion generation rate per second.

33.10. The ionization energy of a hydrogen atom is $\varepsilon_{\mathrm{ion}} = 13.6$ eV. Yet the ionization of hydrogen atoms is observed at temperatures for which the average kinetic energy is much less. How can this fact be explained?

33.11. A high-temperature hydrogen plasma with a temperature of 10^5 K is placed in a magnetic field with induction of 0.1 T. Find the cyclotron radii of the ions and electrons (i.e. the radii of the orbits in which the positive ions and the electrons move).

33.12. Mercury flows at a speed of 20 cm/s in a pipe with conducting walls of 5 cm diameter. The pipe is in the gap between the pole pieces of an electromagnet, the magnetic field in the gap having induction of 0.6 T. Will the magnetic field affect the hydraulic friction coefficient? The conductivity of mercury is 10^6 ohm⁻¹·m⁻¹.

33.13. Estimate the effect of the magnetic field in the conditions of the previous problem, if a 30% solution of sulphuric acid flows in the pipe. The conductivity of the solution is 74 ohm⁻¹·m⁻¹.

33.14. Estimate the induction of the magnetic field of a pulsar taking into account that for ordinary stars the field induction is of the order of 10^{-5} to 10^{-4} T (see Problem 14.21).

33.15. Find the pressure of a pulsar's magnetic field and compare it with the pressure of gravitational forces (see Problem 16.9).

Part Six

VIBRATIONS AND WAVES

34. Harmonic Vibrations

34.1. Harmonic vibrations comply to the law

$$s = 0.20 \cos (300t + 2)$$

Find the amplitude, the frequency, the period and the
initial phase of the vibrations *.

34.2. A particle with a mass of 0.2 kg moves according to
the law

$$s = 0.08 \cos \left(20\pi t + \frac{\pi}{4} \right)$$

Find the velocity of the particle, its acceleration and the
acting force, as well as the amplitudes of the respective quantities.

34.3. In the conditions of the previous problem find the
kinetic, the potential and the total energy of the oscillator.

34.4. In conditions of the previous problem find the frequency and the period of the variation of kinetic energy.

34.5. A particle vibrates harmonically at a frequency of
0.5 Hz. At the initial moment it is in an equilibrium position moving at a speed of 20 cm/s. Write down the equation
of the vibrations.

34.6. At the initial moment a particle's displacement is
4.3 cm and its velocity is —3.2 m/s. The particle's mass
is 4 kg and its total energy 79.5 J. Write down the equation

---

* Here and below the units used are the SI units, i.e. the displacement amplitude is expressed in meters, the time in seconds, the
frequency in hertz, the phase in radians.

of the vibrations and find the distance travelled by the particle in 0.4 s.

34.7. Add up two vibratory motions analytically and using a vector diagram:

$$s_1 = 3 \sin \left(6t + \frac{\pi}{4} \right) \quad \text{and} \quad s_2 = 4 \sin \left(6t - \frac{\pi}{4} \right)$$

Find the amplitude of the velocity of the resulting vibrations.

34.8. Find the resulting amplitude and phase of the vibrations

$$s = A \cos \omega t + \frac{A}{2} \cos \left(\omega t + \frac{\pi}{2} \right) + \frac{A}{4} \cos (\omega t + \pi) +$$

$$+ \frac{A}{8} \cos \left(\omega t + \frac{3\pi}{2} \right)$$

34.9. Beats result from two vibratory motions:

$$s_1 = \cos 4999\pi t \quad \text{and} \quad s_2 = \cos 5001\pi t$$

Find the period of beat and the "conventional" period of the almost sinusoidal vibrations.

34.10. A particle oscillates according to the law

$$s = 4 (\cos^2 0.5t) (\sin 1000t)$$

Expand this motion into a harmonics series and plot its spectrum.

34.11. A particle vibrates according to the law

$$s = (1 + \cos^2 t + \sin^4 t) \sin 500t$$

Expand this motion into its harmonic components and plot its spectrum.

34.12. A particle oscillates according to the law

$$s = (1 + \cos^2 t + \cos^4 t) \sin 500t$$

Expand this motion into its harmonic components and plot its spectrum.

35. Free Vibrations

35.1. A weight of mass m is attached to a spring hanging vertically, which causes an extension l. Subsequently the weight is pulled down a little and let go. What is the natural frequency of the vibrations?

35.2. A spherical copper weight of 3.0 cm radius submerged in olive oil hangs from a spring whose elasticity coefficient (force constant) is 1.0×10^2 N/m (Fig. 35.2). Find the natural frequency of the oscillatory system, its Q-factor and the time the oscillations will take to practically damp out.

35.3. A weight of mass 1 kg attached to a spring with a force constant of 20 N/m is able to oscillate on a horizontal

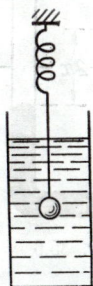 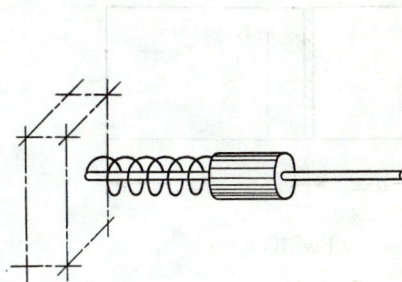

Fig. 35.2.   Fig. 35.3.

steel rod (Fig. 35.3). The initial displacement from the position of equilibrium is 30 cm. Find how many swings the weight will make before stopping completely. One swing is the movement from maximum displacement to the equilibrium position (or back). For numerical calculation put $g = 10$ m/s² and coefficient of friction $\mu = 0.05$.

35.4. A piston of mass m divides a cylinder containing gas into two equal parts. Suppose the piston is displaced to the left to a distance x and let go (Fig. 35.4). Assuming the process to take place at a constant temperature, find the frequency of the piston's oscillations.

35.5. Solve Problem 35.4 assuming that the process is adiabatic.

35.6. Mercury fills a glass tube (Fig. 35.6) so that the total column is 20 cm long. The tube is then rocked, so that the mercury begins to oscillate. Find the frequency and the period of the vibrations.

35.7. A block of solid oak with dimensions 10 cm × 20 cm × 20 cm floats in water (Fig. 35.7). The block is submerged a little and let go. Find the frequency and the period of vibrations.

35.8. A pendulum clock is accurate on the Earth's surface. How slow will it be, if it is lifted to the hundredth floor of a sky-scraper? The height of a storey is 3 m.

35.9. The period of a pendulum whose suspension is stationary relative to the Earth's surface is 1.50 s. What will

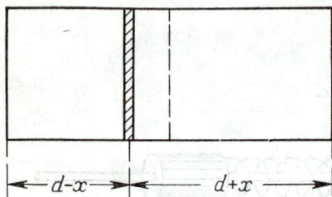

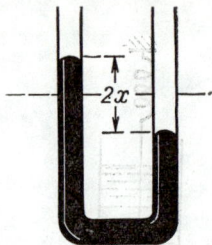

Fig. 35.4.   Fig. 35.6.

its period be, if it is placed in a car moving horizontally with an acceleration of 4.9 m/s²? What will be the change in the pendulum's angle of equilibrium?

35.10. A mathematical pendulum 1 m long is deflected from the vertical by an angle of 40° and let go. Find the period of oscillations using numerical methods.

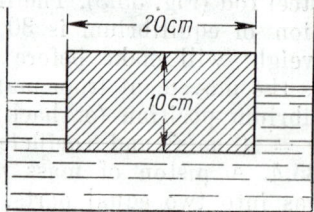

Fig. 35.7.

What will be the error, if in this case we use the formula for small oscillations?

35.11. The period of a simple pendulum for large deflection angles may be determined from the approximate formula

$$T = 2\pi \sqrt{\frac{l}{g}} \left(1 + \frac{1}{4} \sin^2 \frac{\alpha_0}{2}\right)$$

Compare with the result of numerical calculations for the previous problem.

35.12. A uniform rod of length l oscillates about an axis passing through its end. Find the oscillation period and the reduced length of this pendulum.

35.13. A physical pendulum shown in Fig. 35.13 is made up of a rod 60 cm long with mass 0.50 kg and a disk of 3.0 cm radius with mass 0.60 kg. Find the period of this pendulum.

35.14. An oscillatory circuit is made up of a 100 $\mu\mu$F capacitor and a 64 μH coil with resistance of 1.0 ohm. Find the natural frequency, the period of oscillations and the Q-factor of the circuit.

36. Forced Vibrations. Alternating Current

36.1. An iron ball of 0.8 kg mass hangs on a spring with a force constant of 10^3 N/m. An alternating magnetic field acts on the ball with a sinusoidal force whose amplitude is 2.0 N. The Q-factor of the system is 30. Find the amplitude of forced vibrations for $\omega = \omega_0/2$, $\omega = \omega_0$, $\omega = 2\omega_0$.

Fig. 35. 13.

36.2. Plot the resonance curve for the amplitude of the velocity in the previous problem.

36.3. A weight of 0.5 kg mass is suspended from a spring, causing it to extend by 5 mm. When the system is dis-

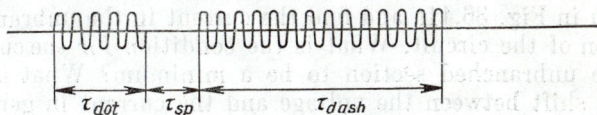

Fig. 36.4.

placed from its equilibrium position and then set free, its natural vibrations continue for 3.5 s. Find the amplitude of the system at resonance. What will happen in the case of resonance?

36.4. A radio receiver receives radio telegraph signals in Morse code in the form of sinusoidal wave packets (Fig. 36.4). The inductance of the circuit is 100 μH, the capacitance is 250 μμF and the resistance is 0.2 ohm. Find the interval between the impulses τ_{sp} needed to prevent two adjacent signals from merging.

Assuming the duration of the "dot" signal to be $\tau_{dot} = 1.5\tau_{sp}$ and that of the "dash" $\tau_{dash} = 4.5\tau_{sp}$ find the maximum amount of information that can be transmitted per unit time.

36.5. Derive the expression for the inductive reactance and for the phase shift in an a.c. circuit containing a coil of zero resistance.

36.6. Derive the expression for the capacitive reactance and for the phase shift in an a.c. circuit containing a capacitor.

36.7. Plot a vector diagram for a circuit containing a coil and a resistor connected in series, and find the impedence of this circuit. Find the phase shift.

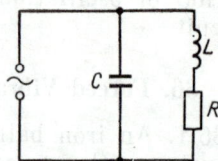

Fig. 36.11a.

36.8. Do the same for a capacitor connected in series with a resistor.

36.9. Do the same for a capacitor connected in parallel with a resistor.

36.10. Express the inductance of a series connected circuit made up of a resistor, a coil and a capacitor in terms of its Q-factor and the frequency ratio $\gamma = \omega/\omega_0$.

36.11. Plot the vector diagram for currents in the circuit shown in Fig. 36.11a and find the current in the unbranched section of the circuit. What is the condition for the current in the unbranched section to be a minimum? What is the phase shift between the voltage and the current in general, and at resonance?

36.12. The capacitance in the circuit shown in Fig. 36.11a is 20 μF, the inductance is 0.2 H and the resistance is 5 ohm. What power is consumed in this circuit, if the voltage at its terminals is $u = 312 \cos 314t$?

36.13. What is the frequency in the circuit with parameters as specified in the previous problem when the current in the unbranched section of the circuit is a minimum? What power will be consumed, if the voltage amplitude remains the same?

36.14. Prove that an electrodynamic wattmeter measures active power $P = IU \cos \varphi$ in an a.c. circuit.

36.15. The reading of the wattmeter on a panel is power 12 kW. The reading of the voltmeter is voltage 380 V, of the ammeter, current 36 A. What is the phase shift in the circuit? What are the impedance and the ohmic resistance of the load?

36.16. The starting voltage of a neon glow lamp is 80 V, the quenching potential is 70 V. A voltmeter in an a.c. circuit measures a voltage of 60 V. Will the lamp glow in this circuit?

36.17. The breakdown voltage indicated on a capacitor is 300 V. Can it be used in a 220 V a.c. circuit?

36.18. A two-wire power line transmits 100 MW power. Its power factor is 0.87 and its resistance 8 ohm. What is the transmission voltage, if the power loss is 2%?

36.19. The primary of an arc welding transformer has 120 turns of wire of 20 mm^2 cross section; its resistance is 8×10^{-2} ohm. The current at nominal load is 40 A.

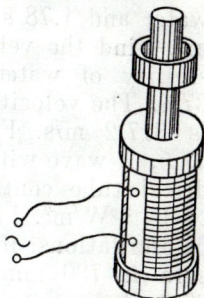

Fig. 36.21.

How many turns are there in the secondary and what is the cross section of the wire in the secondary, if the transformation ratio is $k = 220/60$?

Assuming the windings to be of a single-layer type, find the resistance of the secondary.

Neglecting losses due to magnetic reversal and Foucault currents (i.e. losses in the steel core), find the power loss due to the heating of the windings and the efficiency of the transformer. The transformer power rating is 8 kW.

36.20. Show that the "losses in the steel core" are practically equal to the open-circuit power consumption of the transformer.

36.21. Explain, why a copper ring "floats" in air when an a.c. current is supplied to the winding (Fig. 36.21).

36.22. The primary of a transformer is at a voltage of 220 V drawing a current of 1.5 A. The secondary feeds an incandescent lamp with a current of 20 A at a voltage of 12 V. The transformer's efficiency is 91%. Find the power factor at this load.

37. Elastic Waves

37.1. Compare the velocity of sound in a gas with the root-mean-square velocity of its molecules. Do the calculations for a diatomic gas.

37.2. The sound velocity in a duralumin rod is 5.1×10^3 m/s while the density of the material is 2.7×10^3 kg/m^3. Find the Young modulus.

37.3. An observer at a distance of 800 m from a sound source heard first the sound signal which travelled through water and 1.78 s later—the signal which travelled through air. Find the velocity of sound in water and the compressibility of water. The air temperature is 17 °C.

37.4. The velocity of sound in oxygen in normal conditions is 317.2 m/s. Find the Poisson ratio.

37.5. A wave with a frequency of 440 Hz travels in a cylindrical tube containing air. The wave intensity is 1.2×10^{-2} W/m^2. Find the energy density and the amplitude of oscillations, if the air temperature is 27 °C and its pressure is 780 mmHg.

37.6. A sound source of small dimensions radiates waves at frequency of 500 Hz. The power of the source is 5 W, the air temperature is 0 °C, the pressure is 1.01×10^5 Pa. What are the amplitudes of the sound wave 10 m and 15 m away from the source? Neglect attenuation.

37.7. Compare the intensity levels of the sound wave in the previous problem.

37.8. The intensity of a sound wave 20 m away from the sound source is 3.0 nW/m^2. Find the intensity of the wave 32 m away from the source, if the half-thickness for sound of this frequency is 120 m.

Compare the intensity levels.

37.9. Find the relation between the linear absorption coefficient of sound wave μ, and the half-thickness L.

37.10. Sound travels in a cylindrical tube 80 cm long. The linear absorption coefficient is 1.2×10^{-2} m^{-1}. Compare the sound intensity levels at the entrance and the exit of the tube.

37.11. Two tuning forks with natural frequencies of 340 Hz move relative to a stationary observer. One fork moves away from the observer, while the other moves towards him at the same speed. The observer hears beats of frequency 3 Hz. Find the speed of the tuning forks assuming the velocity of sound in air to be 340 m/s.

37.12. Two trains move towards each other at a speed of 80 km/h relative to the Earth's surface. One radiates a 520 Hz signal. What frequency will the observer on the other train hear?

How will this frequency change when the trains pass one another?

37.13. The equation of a plane sound wave is

$$s = 6.0 \times 10^{-6} \cos{(1900t + 5.72x)}$$

Find the frequency, the wavelength and the velocity of the wave. Compare the wavelength with the amplitude of the oscillations and the wave velocity with the amplitude of the velocity of the oscillations.

37.14. Under the conditions of the previous problem, find the distance between any two nearest points of the wave oscillating in opposite phase. What is the phase shift between the oscillations of two points 37 cm apart in the direction of the sound ray?

37.15. Find the minimum and the maximum wavelengths of sound in air that a man is able to hear (see § 58.1). How will this range change, if the sound travels in water?

37.16. A ceramic ultrasonic transducer is immersed in castor oil. What fraction of the energy is transmitted to the oil? The density of ceramic material is 2.8×10^3 kg/m³, the velocity of sound in it is 6.2×10^3 m/s.

37.17. Solve Problem 37.16 for a magnetostrictive nickel transducer working in water.

37.18. Why when operating in ultrasonic defectoscope is care always taken to see that there is a film of oil between the transducer and the part under inspection?

37.19. An ultrasonic defectoscope operates at a frequency of 1.2 MHz and radiates pulses of the order of 60 periods of oscillations. What is the resolution of the instrument? We shall define resolution as the minimum distance of the defect from the part's surface which may be determined with the aid of the instrument.

38. Interference and Diffraction

38.1. Prove that when a wave is reflected by a medium of higher characteristic acoustic impedance, a standing wave displacement node is formed at the boundary, and that when it is reflected by a medium of lower characteristic acoustic impedance, an antinode is formed.

38.2. A quartz plate (the X-cut) 7 mm thick serves as the radiating element of an ultrasonic transducer (see § 58.3, Fig. 58.4). What is the fundamental operating frequency of the ultrasonic generator?

Will the transducer's frequency change, if the air gap is filled with oil?

38.3. A magnetostrictive transducer operates at a frequency of 25 kHz. Find the thickness of the pack of nickel plates of the transducer.

38.4. An organ pipe 17 cm long open at one end radiates a tone of 1.5 kHz at an air temperature of 16 °C. What harmonic is this? What is the fundamental frequency of the oscillations?

38.5. Two organ pipes closed at both ends serve as sound sources, the resulting beat frequency being 2 Hz. The length

Fig. 38.6.

of both pipes is 24.0 cm, the temperature of air in one tube is 17 °C. What is the temperature of air in the other?

38.6. To measure the speed of sound in air the apparatus shown in Fig. 38.6 is used. A sound source with a frequency of 1.20 kHz is placed close to the upper end of a narrow tube. By moving the left-hand vessel we cause the level of the liquid in the narrow tube to change. Acoustic resonance is observed when the height of the air column is 6.8 cm, 20.6 cm and 34.8 cm. Find the velocity of sound and estimate the error of the value obtained.

38.7. The transducer of an ultrasonic defectoscope of 12 mm diameter operates on a frequency of 1.2 MHz. What is the angular width of the principal diffraction maximum, if the ultrasonic wave travels in castor oil?

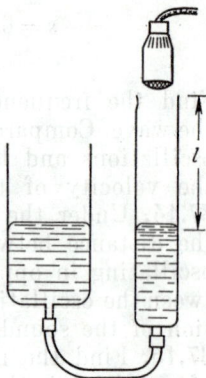

38.8. What is the diameter of the transducer of an echo-sounder operating on a frequency of 50 kHz in sea water, if the angular width of the principal maximum is about 60°?

39. Electromagnetic Waves

39.1. Find the wavelengths in air and in transformer oil, if the transmitter frequency is 60 MHz.

39.2. Find the fundamental frequency radiated by a half-wave antenna and the frequencies of the harmonics.

39.3. A half-wave antenna 0.5 m long is immersed in ethyl alcohol. What is the wavelength of the electromagnetic waves outside the vessel (in air)?

39.4. A plane electromagnetic wave

$$E_z = 200 \cos (6.28 \times 10^8 t + 4.55 x)$$

is completely absorbed by the surface of an object perpendicular to the x-axis. In what medium does the wave propagate? What pressure does it exert on the object? What energy is absorbed by 1 m² of the surface per second?

39.5. The current amplitude in a half-wave antenna is 0.5 A. What is the radiation power? What is the equivalent resistance of this vibrator? For simplicity of calculations assume the current to be the same in every point.

39.6. An electron bunch circulates in the storage ring of a colliding-beam accelerator. The current is 500 mA, the speed of the electrons is 0.99 of the speed of light. What is the power of synchrotron emission?

39.7. An oscillator radiating electromagnetic waves 25 m long is required to transmit with minimum distortion sound signals with frequencies up to 2 kHz. Find the parameters of the resonant circuit.

39.8. Derive the relation between the frequencies of a wave in two reference frames (the Doppler effect, see § 59.8) and the relation between the values of the cosines of the angles the ray makes with the direction of the source's motion (in both reference frames).

39.9. Try to derive the expression for the relativistic longitudinal Doppler effect from the principle of relativity and the classical Doppler effect, without using the Lorentz transformation.

39.10. Find the Doppler broadening of spectral lines in the spectrum of a "white dwarf" (surface temperature about 10 000 K). Compare with the gravitational red shift of the spectral lines, assuming the mass of the "white dwarf" to be equal to that of the Sun and its radius to be 0.01 of the Sun's radius.

39.11. The spectrum of excited singly ionized helium atoms includes a line of 410 nm wavelength. A beam of such ions leaves a cyclotron with an energy of 40.0 MeV. Find the Doppler shift of this line, if it is observed at an angle of 30° to the beam's direction.

39.12. The observations of the spectral line of hydrogen H_β with a wavelength of 4861.33 Å in the solar spectrum lead to the discovery of a difference in the wavelength of this line on the opposite fringes of the solar disk equal to 0.065 Å. Find the period of rotation of the Sun about its axis.

39.13. In astrophysics frequent use is made of the quantity $z = (\lambda - \lambda_0)/\lambda_0$, equal to the relative variation of a spectral line wavelength. Here λ_0 is the wavelength emitted by the source and λ is the wavelength observed. Express this quantity in terms of the radial velocity of the source in the reference frame of the observer.

39.14. The relative variations of spectral line wavelengths measured for an optical galaxy, for the radiogalaxy 3C295 and for a quasar (quasi-stellar radio source) 3C9 were $z_1 = 0.034$, $z_2 = 0.46$ and $z_3 = 2$. Find the ratios of the radial velocities of these sources to the velocity of light; find the velocities of the sources.

39.15. The Doppler effect made possible the discovery of the so-called spectroscopic binaries. The spectral lines of these stars are periodically doubled. This leads to the conclusion that the source is constituted of two stars revolving about a common centre of mass. The maximum distance between the components of a periodically splitting hydrogen line of 4340.47 Å wavelength in the spectrum of one such star is 0.53 Å. Find the projection of the orbital speeds of the two stars on the line of sight.

39.16. The maximum relative shift of spectral lines of a binary star is 2.08×10^{-3}, the period of line-splitting being 3 days 2 hours and 46 minutes. Both stars being identical find their masses and the distance between them.

40. Interference and Diffraction of Light

40.1. In Young's arrangement (see § 61.5, Fig. 61.5) the distance between the slits is 1.5 mm and the distance of the screen from the slits is 2 m. The slits are illuminated by a source provided with a red filter ($\lambda = 687$ nm). Find the distance between the interference fringes.

How will the distance between the fringes change, if the red filter is replaced by a green one ($\lambda = 527$ nm)?

40.2. How many interference maxima will be observed, if Young's arrangement described in the previous problem is illuminated with white light? The wavelength limits are $\lambda_r = 690$ nm, $\lambda_v = 420$ nm. What is the distance on the screen between the red and the violet maxima?

40.3. A thin wire of 0.05 mm diameter is placed between the

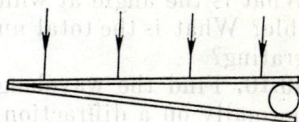

Fig. 40.3a.

edges of two well-polished planar plates; the opposite edges of the plates are tightly pressed together (Fig. 40.3a). Light falls perpendicularly onto the surface. An observer sees interference fringes on the 10 cm long plate, the distance between them being 0.6 mm. Find the wavelength.

40.4. When the mirror in the Michelson interferometer is displaced, the interference pattern is shifted by 100 bands. The light used in the experiment is of 5460 Å wavelength. What is the mirror's displacement?

40.5. Cylindrical tubes 10 cm long, each closed at both ends by transparent plane-parallel plates, were placed in the path of the two light rays in the Michelson interferometer. First the tubes were evacuated, then one was filled with hydrogen, and the interference pattern was observed to shift by 47.5 fringes. What is the refractive index of hydrogen? The light in the experiment was of wavelength 590 nm.

40.6. During the quality control of surface finish with the aid of the Linnik interference microscope, a scratch was observed on the surface which produced a curvature of 2.3 fringes in the pattern of interference fringes. Green light of 530 nm wavelength was used in the test. Find the depth of the scratch.

40.7. The yellow sodium line consists of two components with the wavelengths of 5890 Å and 5896 Å. When the Michelson interferometer is illuminated with this light and the mobile mirror is moved, the interference pattern periodically vanishes and then appears again. What is the cause of this phenomenon?

40.8. Green light of 500 nm wavelength falls on a slit 8 μm wide. Find the angles at which the first- and the second-order minima are observed.

40.9. A diffraction grating has 400 slits per 1 mm. A monochromatic red light of 650 nm wavelength falls on the grating. What is the angle at which the first-order maximum is visible? What is the total number of maxima produced by this grating?

40.10. Find the wavelength of monochromatic light falling normally on a diffraction grating with a grating constant of 2.20 μm, if the angle between the directions of the first- and the second-order maxima is 15.0°.

40.11. Light of 530 nm wavelength falls on a grating with a grating constant of 1.50 μm, and with a total length of 12.0 mm. Find the angular width of a principal maximum and the resolving power of the grating.

40.12. What should be the length of a diffraction grating with a density of ruling of 300 slits per 1 mm to resolve two spectral lines of 6000.00 Å and 6000.50 Å wavelength in the second-order spectrum? What should be the length in the spectrum of the highest order?

40.13. The grating constant of a diffraction grating is 0.01 mm, the total number of slits is 990. Are we able to see in the first-order spectrum the two components of the sodium yellow line doublet with wavelengths of 5890 Å and 5896 Å? What is the angular spacing between these maxima in the second-order spectrum?

40.14. A plane wave falls on a diffraction grating with a grating constant d_0 at a glancing angle α. Prove that the resulting diffraction will be the same as when the wave falls normally on a grating with a grating constant of $d = = d_0 \sin \alpha$.

40.15. A narrow beam of X-rays falls at a glancing angle of 20° on a diffraction grating with a constant of 2.0 μm. The first diffraction maximum is observed at an angle of

12′ to the direction of the beam. Find the wavelength of
the X-rays.

40.16. A parallel beam of X-rays with a wavelength of
1.47 Å falls at a glancing angle of 31°3′ on a face of a rocksalt
crystal. Find the spacing between the atomic planes of the
crystal, if the second-order diffraction maximum is observed
at this angle.

41. Dispersion and Absorption of Light

41.1. A proton beam with an energy of 10.0 GeV enters a Cerenkov counter made of rock salt. Find the deflection angle
of the threshold red (0.67 μm) and of the violet (0.40 μm)
rays from the cone axis.

41.2. A beam of relativistic electrons in a Cerenkov counter
filled with water radiates in the violet spectral range inside
a cone with an aperture of 82°20′. Find the kinetic energy
of the electrons.

41.3. Assuming the free electron concentration in a plasma
to be n_0, find the dependence of the plasma's dielectric
constant on the frequency of an electromagnetic wave, neglecting the interaction of the electromagnetic wave with
the positive ions.

41.4. Express the group velocity of light in terms of the
velocity of light in a vacuum, the refractive index and the
derivative of the refractive index with respect to frequency.

41.5. Prove that in the normal dispersion range the group
velocity is less than the velocity of light in a vacuum.

41.6. Find in the optical range the refractive index of a plasma and the phase and the group velocities of a wave in
a plasma.

41.7. The phase velocity of light in a plasma exceeds the
velocity of light in a vacuum. Is this not in contradiction
with the fundamental principle of the theory of relativity
that the velocity of light in a vacuum is the maximum possible velocity?

41.8. Can Cerenkov radiation be induced in a plasma?

41.9. Find the free electron concentration in the ionosphere,
if the refractive index of the ionosphere for radio waves
of 3.0 m wavelength is 0.90.

41.10. In discussing the action of X-rays of sufficient energy the bonding energy of the electrons in the lattice can be neglected, and the electrons may be considered free. Calculate in this approximation the refractive index of aluminium for X-rays of 0.50 Å wavelength.

41.11. Find the reflection coefficient for optical waves at the vacuum-plasma interface. (Take into account that in the optical range the approximate equality $n + 1 \approx 2$ is valid to a high degree of accuracy.)

41.12. Compare the reflection coefficients for red and for violet light at the air-molten quartz interface. The light is perpendicular to the interface.

41.13. The distance between the toothed wheel with 720 teeth and the mirror in the Fizeau experiment is 7.0 km. Two consecutive rotation speeds of the wheel for which the light disappeared were 283 r.p.s. and 313 r.p.s. Find the velocity of light.

41.14. Prove that in a plasma the relation $uU = c^2$ holds, where u is the phase and U the group velocity of an electromagnetic wave.

41.15. Find the group and the phase velocitiy of light in sylvite for the wavelength of 5086 Å in the 5461-4861 Å spectral interval.

41.16. Two plates, one 3.8 mm thick and the other 9.0 mm thick, were manufactured from the same material. The plates are placed in succession in a narrow beam of monochromatic light with the result that the first plate transmits 0.84 and the second 0.70 of the light flux. Find the absorption coefficient and the half-thickness of the material. Neglect secondary reflections.

41.17. A point light source is in the centre of a spherical layer of a substance, with an internal radius r_1 and an external radius r_2. The refractive index and the absorption coefficient of the substance are known. Find the transmittance of the layer of substance. Neglect secondary reflections.

41.18. A light filter 5 mm thick has a variable absorption coefficient which depends on the wavelength according to the law $\mu = \mu_0 + \alpha (\lambda_0 - \lambda)^2$, where $\alpha = 5.6 \times 10^{20}$ m^{-3}, $\lambda_0 = 5000$ Å, $\mu_0 = 4$ m^{-1}. Find the transmittance of the filter for the wavelength λ_0 and its transmission band width

The transmission band width includes all wavelengths for which the transparency of the filter is not less than half of the resonant transparency. Neglect the reflection of light from the surfaces.

41.19. How many half-thicknesses are there in a plate which reduces the intensity of a beam 60 times?

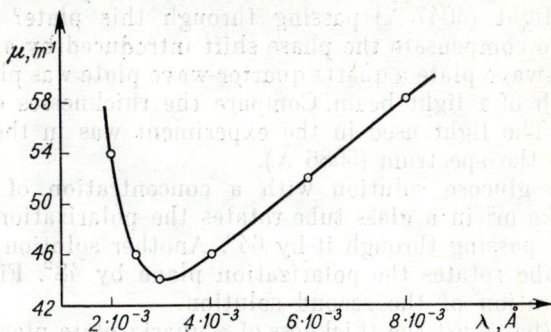

Fig. 41.20.

41.20. Figure 41.20 shows the dependence on the wavelength of the absorption coefficient of lead for gamma-rays from a radio-active source. What is the maximum half-thickness of lead for gamma-rays?

42. Polarization of Light

42.1. Natural light falls on a system of two polaroids the angle between whose optical axes is 45°. By how much will the intensity of the light be reduced? 10% of the light is lost in each polaroid. Neglect losses due to reflection.

42.2. If a third polaroid with its optical axis at an angle of α to the optical axis of the analyzer is placed between two crossed polaroids, the field of view brightens. Find the intensity of the transmitted light. Neglect losses due to reflection and absorption. What is the angle α of maximum brightness?

42.3. The ordinary and the extraordinary rays are obtained by decomposition of a given beam of natural light. Will there be an interference pattern of minima and maxima, if both rays are combined?

42.4. Find the thickness of a calcite plate which creates in yellow light a phase difference of $\pi/2$ between the ordinary and the extraordinary rays of light at a wavelength of 5893 Å (the quarter-wave plate). What will be the phase shift for violet light (4047 Å) passing through this plate?

42.5. To compensate the phase shift introduced by a calcite quarter-wave plate a quartz quarter-wave plate was placed in the path of a light beam. Compare the thicknesses of both plates. The light used in the experiment was in the green part of the spectrum (5086 Å).

42.6. A glucose solution with a concentration of $2.8 \times \times 10^2$ kg/m^3 in a glass tube rotates the polarization plane of light passing through it by 64°. Another solution in the same tube rotates the polarization plane by 48°. Find the concentration of the second solution.

42.7. What must the thickness of a quartz plate placed between crossed polaroids be to make the field of view turn red? blue? The polarizer is illuminated with white light.

43. Geometrical Optics

43.1. A plate of 4.0 cm thickness was cut out of calcite perpendicular to the optical axis. A narrow beam of natural yellow light with a wavelength of 5893 Å falls on the plate at an angle of 60°. Find the spacing between the ordinary and the extraordinary rays at the point of exit from the plate to the air.

43.2. A ray of white light falls on a prism of crown glass perpendicular to its face. Find the angle of refraction of the prism for which the red rays pass out of it into air while the violet rays experience total internal reflection.

43.3. The sides of an isosceles right prism are coated with a reflecting coating. A ray of light falls on the hypotenuse at an arbitrary angle. Prove that the ray leaving the prism is parallel to the incident ray.

43.4. A point source of light is placed on the bed of a pond 80 cm deep. Find the diameter of the illuminated circle on the surface of water.

43.5. A prism of flint glass with an angle of refraction of 30° is placed in water. At what angle should a ray of light fall on the face of the prism so that inside the prism the ray is perpendicular to the bisector of the angle of refraction? Through what angle will the ray turn after passing through both faces of the prism?

43.6. A lens made of crown glass has a focal power of 8 diopters in air. What will its focal power be in water? In hydrogen sulphide ($n = 1.63$)?

43.7. A system is made up of two thin converging lenses arranged perpendicularly to their common axis. Where is the image of the anterior focus of the left-hand lens? Trace the rays.

43.8. Prove that the lens focal power of a system made up of two tightly packed thin lenses is equal to the sum of the focal powers of each of them.

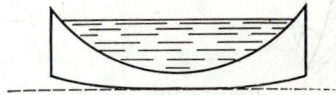

Fig. 43.10.

43.9. What is the experimental procedure to find the focal power of a diverging lens?

43.10. A convexo-concave lens of crown glass has the radii of curvature equal to 1 m and 12 cm. What is its focal power? The lens is placed horizontally and filled with water (Fig. 43.10). How will its focal power change?

43.11. Derive the formula for the focal power of a plano-convex lens by tracing the rays passing through it.

43.12. Two thin lenses with focal lengths of $f_1 = 7$ cm and $f_2 = 6$ cm are placed at a distance $d = 3$ cm apart. What is the distance of the focus of the system from the second lens? The system is a centred one.

43.13. Two thin converging lenses are placed on a common axis so that the centre of one of them coincides with the focus of the other. An object is placed at a distance twice the focal length from the left-hand lens. Where will its image be? What is the lateral magnification? The focal power of each lens is Φ.

43.14. A converging bundle of light rays in the shape of a cone with the vertex angle of 40° falls on a circular diaphragm of 20 cm diameter. A lens with a focal power of 5 diopters is fixed in the diaphragm. What will the new cone angle be?

43.15. Compare the longitudinal and the lateral magnifications of a thin lens. Consider the case of small longitudinal dimensions of the object.

43.16. A ball is placed at a distance double the focal length from the lens on its axis. What will be the shape of its image?

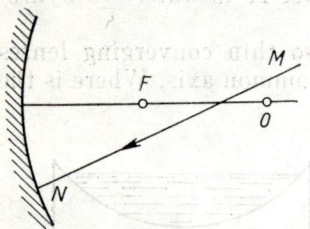

Fig. 43.19a.

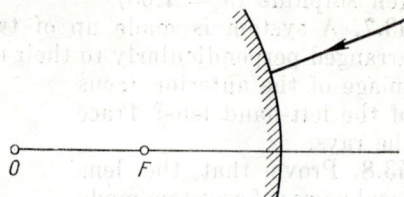

Fig. 43.20a.

43.17. Find the magnitude of the chromatic aberrations of a lens made of flint glass, if the radii of curvature of both its surfaces are 0.5 m. We define the chromatic aberration as the difference between the focal lengths for the red and

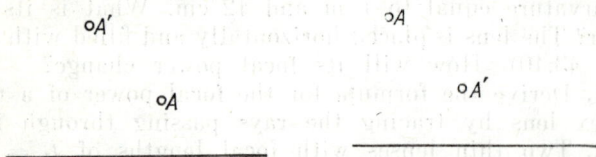

Fig. 43.22a.

the violet rays. Find the ratio of the chromatic aberration to the average focal length of the lens.

43.18. A concave spherical mirror with a radius of curvature of 0.2 m is filled with water. What is the focal power of this system?

43.19. A ray of light falls on a concave spherical mirror, as shown in Fig. 43.19a. Trace the path of the ray further.

43.20. A ray of light falls on a convex mirror, as shown in Fig. 43.20a. Trace the path of the ray further.

43.21. Figure 43.21a shows the optical axis of a lens, the point source of light A and its virtual image A'. Trace the rays to find the position of the lens and of its focuses. What type of lens is it?

43.22. Solve the problem similar to the previous one using Fig. 43.22a.

43.23. Prove that a parabolic mirror is free from spherical aberrations.

43.24. Can a strictly parallel bundle of light rays be obtained with a parabolic mirror?

44. Optical Instruments

44.1. A monochromatic light source of 555 nm wavelength radiates a total light flux of 1200 lm. What is the radiant power? What should be the radiant power in order to obtain the same light flux at a wavelength of 480 nm? 600 nm?

44.2. A monochromatic point source of 520 nm wavelength has a luminous intensity of 20 cd. What are the amplitudes of the electric field intensity and of magnetic field induction at a distance of 50 cm from the source?

44.3. A cylindrical hall of diameter D is illuminated by a lamp fixed at centre of the ceiling. Compare the minimum illuminance of the wall and of the floor. The height of each wall is h.

44.4. A round table of radius r is illuminated by a lamp of luminous intensity (candlepower) I hanging above its centre. What should be the height of the lamp above the table for the illuminance of the table fringe to be maximum? What is its value? What is the illuminance at the centre of the table in these conditions?

44.5. A point light source illuminates a screen, the maximum illuminance being E_0. How will the illuminance of this point change if a large plane ideally reflecting mirror is placed behind the source half way between the lamp and the screen?

44.6. Street lamps of 10 cm diameter and of 1.8×10^5 cd/m² brightness are suspended at a height of 12 m, the distance between them being 40 m. Find the illuminance under each lamp and midway between them.

44.7. A point light source of 10 cd luminous intensity is in the centre of a concave mirror with a radius of curvature of 40 cm and of 20 cm diameter. It illuminates a screen at a distance of 2 m from the source. What is the maximum illuminance of the screen? How will the illuminance change, if the mirror is withdrawn?

44.8. A lens of diameter D and a focal length f projects a small object placed at a great distance from the lens onto a screen. Show that the illuminance of the image on the screen will be proportional to the luminance and to the aperture ratio of the lens. (The aperture ratio is the square of the ratio of the lens' diameter to its focal length.)

44.9. A screen is 1 m away from a light source. A diverging lens of -5 diopters focal power is placed between the source and the screen so that the position of the light source coincides with that of the virtual focus. How will the illuminance of the screen on the optical axis of the system change?

44.10. The distance of maximum visual activity for a near-sighted eye is 9 cm. What glasses should be worn to correct the eyesight?

44.11. Show that the estimate of the resolving power of the eye based on diffraction from a single slit practically coincides with the minimum angle of view estimated on the basis of the minimum distance between nearest elements of the retina. The diameter of the pupil in conditions of good illuminance is 2-3 mm.

44.12. The length of a microscope tube is 16 cm, the focal power of the objective is 185 diopters and of the eyepiece 50 diopters. Find the angular magnification of the instrument.

44.13. The numerical aperture of a microscope in air is 0.46. What is the minimum distance this instrument can resolve?

44.14. A telescope objective of 2 diopters focal power and of 10 cm diameter is part of a Keplerian telescope whose magnification is 12. Find the focal power and the diameter of the eyepiece, as well as the minimum angle this telescope can resolve.

What are the dimensions of objects on the Sun this telescope can resolve?

44.15. Galileo's telescope is a telescopic system in which a long-focus convex lens serves as the objective, and a short-focus concave lens serves as the eyepiece. The posterior virtual focus of the eyepiece coincides with the posterior focus of the objective. Trace the path of rays in this system and find the angular magnification.

44.16. Compute the minimum distances between two points on the Moon and on Mars which can be resolved with the aid of a reflecting telescope having a mirror of 6 m diameter. The shortest distance between the Earth and Mars (the "great opposition") is 5.6×10^{10} m.

44.17. A radio telescope of about half a kilometer diameter operates in the centimeter wave range of the hydrogen spectrum (21 cm). Estimate its resolving power. Compare with the resolving power of an optical telescope with a three meter mirror.

44.18. At present the best sprinters run 100 m in 10 s. What is the appropriate exposure in making snapshots, if the blurring on the negative must not exceed $x = 0.5$ mm? The snapshots are made at a distance of $d = 6$ m, the focal power of the photographic objective is $\Phi = 20$ diopters.

44.19. Landscape shots are made with a camera having an objective of focal power 7.7 diopters. The camera is focused on objects 12 m away from it. It is desired to obtain a sufficiently clear image of objects within a distance of 3 m in front and behind—their blurring on the negative should not exceed 0.2 mm. What should be the setting (i.e. diameter) of the diaphragm? What will the aperture of the objective be at this setting?

44.20. A camera with an objective of 8 diopters focal power is used to take photographs of an object lying on the bottom of a pond 1.2 m deep. What is the distance of the film from the objective lens? The lens is placed close to the surface of the water.

Part Seven

FUNDAMENTALS OF QUANTUM PHYSICS

45. Photons

45.1. Solar radiation with an intensity of 1.36 kW/m² per second falls on the illuminated surface of the Earth. Assuming the Sun's radiation to be similar to that of an absolute black body, find the temperature of the photosphere.

45.2. The Sun radiates maximum energy at a wavelength of 470 nm. Assuming the Sun's radiation to be similar to that of an absolute black body, find the temperature of the photosphere.

45.3. The surface temperature of "white dwarfs" is of the order of 10^4 K. To what spectral band does the maximum value of their radiation belong?

45.4. The sensitivity of the human eye in darkness is high: at a wavelength of 555 nm it detects a light signal of no less than 60 photons per second. What is the wave intensity? What is the power of the light source, if its distance from the eye is 10 km? The diameter of the pupil in darkness is 8 mm.

45.5. Find the threshold frequency of the photoemissive effect for lithium, zinc, and tungsten.

45.6. Find the maximum kinetic energy and the velocity of photo-electrons emitted from a metal irradiated with γ-rays of 0.3 Å wavelength.

45.7. Find the cut-off voltage which stops the emission of electrons from a caesium cathode irradiated with light of 600 nm wavelength.

45.8. When a cathode was irradiated with light first of 440 nm wavelength and then of 680 nm, the cut-off voltage was changed by a factor of 3.3. Find the electron work function.

45.9. There are types of photographic paper which can be processed in red light of over 680 nm wavelength. Find the activation energy of the chemical reaction.

45.10. Find the energy, the mass and the momentum of a photon of ultraviolet radiation of 280 nm wavelength.

45.11. Find the wavelength of X-ray radiation for which the photon energy is equal to the intrinsic electron energy.

45.12. A moving source emits photons. Find the expressions for the energy and the momentum of a photon in the laboratory reference frame.

45.13. Making use of the photon concept compute the light pressure on a reflecting surface, if the angle of incidence is α.

45.14. A small ideally absorbing plate of 10 mg mass is suspended from a practically weightless quartz filament 20 mm long. A light flash from a laser falls on its surface perpendicularly to it, causing the filament with the plate to deflect from the vertical by an angle of 0.6°. Estimate the energy of the laser flash.

45.15. Estimate the dimensions of a particle, if the pressure of the light from the Sun on it compensates the gravitational force. Assume the particle to be an absolute black body, its density to be 2.0×10^3 kg/m^3, and the solar constant to be 1.36 kW/m^2.

45.16. What fraction of the photon's energy is transmitted to the recoil electron in the Compton effect? The energy of X-ray photons prior to scattering was $\mathscr{E}$. Do the calculations for a photon energy of 10 keV and for a scattering angle of 60°.

45.17. The photon scattering angle in the Compton effect is θ, the electron recoil angle is α. Find the energy of photons prior to scattering. Do the calculations for $\theta = 90°$, $\alpha = 30°$.

45.18. X-rays fall on a layer of substance placed in a Wilson chamber. The chamber is in a magnetic field of 0.02 T induction, and the Compton recoil electrons leave traces with a 2.4 cm radius of curvature. Find the minimum energy of the X-ray photons at which such recoil electrons may be formed, and the corresponding wavelength.

45.19. Prove that a free electron at rest in a vacuum cannot absorb a photon.

45.20. Prove that an electron moving uniformly in a straight line in a vacuum cannot emit a photon.

45.21. A photon of energy $\mathscr{E}$ flies through a slit in a nontransparent screen. Where may it be observed behind the screen? What is the corresponding probability of detecting it? The volume of the counter which registers the photon is V_0, the slit width is D, the counter is a long way from the screen.

45.22. Will the probability of a photon being detected behind a screen change, if a second parallel slit is cut in the screen? If a system of slits is cut?

45.23. A photon passes through a polaroid. What will happen to it? What are the corresponding probabilities?

45.24. An electron of 5 GeV energy collides head-on with a photon of visible light ($\mathscr{E}_{ph} = 1$ eV). Find the energy of the scattered photon.

46. Elementary Quantum Mechanics

46.1. Express the de Broglie wavelength in terms of the kinetic energy of a relativistic particle. What is the kinetic energy for which the nonrelativistic formula leads to an error of less than 1%?

46.2. Express the de Broglie wavelength in terms of the accelerating potential for the relativistic and the nonrelativistic cases.

46.3. The aperture of an electron microscope is 0.02, the accelerating potential is 10^4 V. Find the dimensions of details which may be resolved with the aid of this instrument.

46.4. Why is the resolving power of an ion projector by an order of magnitude higher than that of an electron microscope?

46.5. A parallel electron beam accelerated in an electric field with a potential difference of 15 V falls on a narrow rectangular diaphragm 0.08 mm wide. Find the width of the principal diffraction maximum on a screen placed 60 cm away from the diaphragm.

46.6. A narrow neutron beam falls on a natural face of an aluminium single-crystal at a glancing angle of 5°. The distance between crystallographic planes parallel to the single-crystal face is 0.20 nm. What is the velocity and the energy of neutrons for which a first-order maximum is observed in this direction? What is the temperature corresponding to this neutron velocity?

46.7. Find the de Broglie wavelength corresponding to the root-mean-square velocity of hydrogen molecules at room temperature (20° C).

46.8. An electron is accelerated by a potential difference of 10^2 V. Find the group and the phase velocities of the de Broglie waves. Do the same for a potential difference of 10^5 V.

46.9. A particle is in its ground state in a unidimensional potential well with infinitely high walls. Find the force with which the particle acts on the walls. Do the calculations for an electron in a well 10^{-10} m wide.

46.10. Find the first three energy levels, using the data of the previous problem.

46.11. The natural vibration frequency of a hydrogen molecule is 1.26×10^{14} Hz. Find the zero-point energy of the vibrations of the molecule. Can the vibrational degrees of freedom in the molecule be excited at 600 K?

46.12. Estimate the dimensions of a hydrogen atom in the nonexcited state, regarding it as an oscillator and assuming the zero-point energy of oscillations to be equal to the kinetic energy of the electron on the first orbit.

46.13. Find the probability of an electron tunneling through a 5 Å wide and 0.4 eV high potential barrier, if it is accelerated by a field of 0.3 V.

46.14. Estimate the probability of cold electron emission from a metal, if there is a uniform field of strength E close to the surface of the metal.

46.15. What is the probability of cold electron emission from tungsten, if the field strength at the point is 5×10^{10} V/m?

47. Atomic and Molecular Structure

47.1. What is the distance of closest approach of an alpha-particle to a silver nucleus if the kinetic energy of the alpha-particle is 0.40 MeV.

47.2. Applying Bohr's theory, find the orbital velocity of the electron on an arbitrary energy level. Compare the orbital velocity on the lowest energy level with that of light.

47.3. Calculate the photon energy corresponding to the first line of the ultraviolet hydrogen series (Lyman-α).

47.4. An electron in an unexcited hydrogen atom acquired an energy of 12.1 eV. To what energy level did it jump? How many spectral lines may be emitted in the course of its transition to lower energy levels? Calculate the corresponding wavelengths.

47.5. An electron of a stationary hydrogen atom passes from the fifth energy level to the fundamental state. What velocity did the atom acquire as the result of photon emission? What is the recoil energy?

47.6. Calculate the first Bohr radius of a singly ionized helium atom. Compare with the first Bohr radius a_0 of the hydrogen atom.

Write down the generalized Balmer formula for this ion. Find the first lines of the series corresponding to the Lyman and the Balmer series.

47.7. In his first work "On the Structure of Atoms and Molecules" (1913) Niels Bohr, as a proof of the validity of his theory, cited the fact that the number of spectral lines of the Balmer series observed in a gas-discharge tube never exceeds 12, while 33 lines are seen in the spectra of celestial bodies. Bohr's explanation was that the diameter of the hydrogen atom cannot exceed the average interatomic distance, which depends on the pressure. From these considerations, estimate the concentration of atoms, the pressure and the density of hydrogen in a gas-discharge tube and in a celestial body.

47.8. Find the ionization energy of a doubly ionized lithium atom.

47.9. Lines of 6877 Å, 4989 Å and 4548 Å are observed in the visible range of the spectrum of a certain galaxy. To what substance do they belong? What can you say about the motion of this galaxy?

47.10. A mesoatom of hydrogen is a hydrogen atom in which a negative muon with a mass 207 times that of an electron orbits the nucleus instead of an electron. Find the Bohr radii and the energy levels of a mesoatom.

47.11. Write down the Balmer formula for a mesoatom and find the leading lines corresponding to the leading lines of the first three series.

47.12. Positronium is the term for a system made up of an electron and a positron revolving about a common centre of mass. Find the interparticle distance and the energy of the positronium in the ground state.

47.13. What will be potential difference between the cathode and the grid voltage at which there will be a marked drop in the anode current in the Frank-Hertz experiment, if the tube is filled with atomic hydrogen?

47.14. Prove that not more than two electrons can occupy the s-state and not more than six can occupy the p-state.

47.15. Write down the values of all the four quantum numbers for each electron of the boron and sodium atoms.

47.16. The atoms of lithium, sodium and potassium each contain a different number of electrons. Why then are all these elements monovalent?

47.17. Solve Problem 46.9 assuming the potential well to contain three bosons. The energy of the system is at its minimum.

47.18. Solve a similar problem for three fermions.

47.19. An X-ray tube operates at a voltage of 40 kV. Find the continuous spectrum limit of the X-ray spectrum.

47.20. From what material is the anode of an X-ray tube made, if the K_α-line wavelength of the characteristic spectrum is 0.76 Å?

47.21. What is the minimum voltage applied to an X-ray tube with a vanadium cathode for which the lines of the K_α-series appear?

47.22. The difference between the nickel K_α-line wavelength and the continuous spectrum limit of the X-ray spectrum is 10%. Find the voltage applied to the X-ray tube.

47.23. Find the angular velocity of rotation of a hydrogen molecule on the first excited rotational level, if the distance between the centres of its atoms is 0.74 Å.

47.24. Suppose a hydrogen molecule passed to the first vibration-rotational energy level. What spectral line will be observed when it returns to the ground state?

47.25. The natural angular frequency of vibration of an HF molecule is 7.79×10^{14} rad/s. There are 13 rotational levels between the zero level and the first excitation level. Estimate the distance between the centres of the atoms in this molecule

47.26. Noticeable dissociation of hydrogen molecules into atoms starts at a temperature of the order of 10^3 K. The bond energy for hydrogen is 4.72 eV. Is there any contradiction?

47.27. Why do helium atom and the hydrogen molecule have such different spectra?

47.28. When Bohr's theory is used to compute the energy levels in a hydrogen atom, only the Coulomb interaction between the electron and the proton is taken into account, the magnetic moments of these particles being ignored. Assess the resulting error.

How will the energy level pattern change, if, in addition to the Coulomb interaction, the magnetic interaction between the electron and the proton is also taken into account?

47.29. A rigorous quantum-mechanical calculation shows that in a hydrogen atom a transition between two sublevels of the fundamental state (see the previous problem) results in the emission or absorption of photons corresponding to a wavelength of 21.1 cm. Experiment is in excellent agreement with this result (to 11 significant figures!).

Making use of classical concepts, try to find the wavelength corresponding to the transition between two sublevels of the ground state of a hydrogen atom, and compare the result with the actual wavelength.

47.30. A substance is illuminated with light from a mercury lamp. Two nearest companions with wavelengths of 4244 Å (red companions) and 3885 Å (violet companion) are observed in the combination scattering spectrum. Find the natural frequency of vibration of the molecules of this substance.

47.31. Is a laser which emits monochromatic fermions (electrons, neutrinos, etc.) possible?

47.32. The crystal rod of a ruby laser is of 4 mm diameter and 35 mm long. The laser radiates coherent light with wavelengths of 6943 Å and 6929 Å. Find the lowest angular divergence of its rays.

48. Quantum Properties of Metals and of Semiconductors

48.1. Find the energy and the momentum of an electron occupying the Fermi level in aluminium, in sodium and in copper.

48.2. Calculate the degeneracy temperature for the electron gas in aluminium, in sodium and in copper.

48.3. Assuming the average energy of electrons to be 3/5 of the Fermi energy estimate the pressure of the electron gas in a metal. Do the calculations for aluminium.

48.4. Prove that the pressure and the volume of a degenerate electron gas are related by an equation similar to the Poisson equation, and find the adiabatic index $\gamma = C_p/C_V$.

48.5. Matter inside a "white dwarf" is in a state of degeneracy, and the dependence of the pressure on the density is of the form $P = A\rho^{5/3}$, where P is the pressure and ρ is the density. Find the expression for the constant A and show that the pressure is due to the electron gas, the pressure due to the heavy particles being negligible.

48.6. Estimate the fraction of electrons in copper which will rise above the Fermi level when it is heated to 100 °C.

48.7. Estimate the specific heat of the electron gas in copper at 100 °C, and compare it with the lattice heat capacity.

48.8. Find the mean free path of electrons in copper and compare it with the interatomic distance.

48.9. A sustained current circulates in a ring-shaped superconductor. Assuming the superconductor to be a gigantic Bohr orbit show that the current and the magnetic flux are quantized. Take into account the pairing of electrons in a superconductor.

48.10. Experiments show the electrical conductivity of semiconductors to rise drastically with temperature. Assuming that it is possible to calculate the probability of electron transition from the valence to the conduction band using the barometric distribution, derive the formula for the temperature dependence of a semiconductor's conductivity.

48.11. Compare the electrical conductivity of pure germanium at −40 °C and +100 °C. The activation energy for germanium is 0.72 eV.

48.12. The intrinsic conductivity of germanium at 27 °C is 2.13 ohm^{-1}·m^{-1}, the mobilities of electrons and holes are

0.38 and 0.18 m^2/(V·s), respectively. Compute the carrier densities and the Hall coefficient.

48.13. Find the extrinsic conductivity of germanium doped with indium to a concentration of 2×10^{22} m^{-3}, with antimony to a concentration of 5×10^{21} m^{-3}.

48.14. Find the internal contact potential difference between aluminium and copper; between copper and zinc oxide.

Part Eight

NUCLEAR AND ELEMENTARY PARTICLE PHYSICS

49. Nuclear Structure

49.1. What is the difference between the structures of the light helium isotope nucleus and of the superheavy hydrogen (tritium) nucleus?

49.2. The atomic mass of natural boron is 10.811. It consists of two isotopes with masses of 10.013 and 11.009. Find their fractions.

49.3. Asses the radii of the deuterium and the polonium nuclei and the height of the Coulomb potential barrier of these nuclei.

49.4. Find the binding energy of the deuterium nucleus and the specific binding energy (binding energy per nucleon).

49.5. Compare the specific binding energies of tritium and of the light helium isotope.

49.6. An isotope of radium with mass number 226 undergoes radioactive transformation to a lead isotope with mass number 206. How many alpha- and beta-disintegrations were involved in the process?

49.7. A polonium nucleus transforms into one of lead. Find the kinetic energy of the alpha-particle and of the recoil nucleus.

49.8. Can the nuclear reaction $_4Be^7 \rightarrow {}_2He^4 + {}_2He^3$ take place? Why?

49.9. Can a silicon nucleus transform into an aluminium nucleus, emitting a proton in the process? Why?

49.10. Can a silicon nucleus transform into a phosphorus nucleus? What particles would be emitted in the process? What is their total energy?

49.11. What energy is required to extract a neutron from a carbon nucleus with mass number 13?

49.12. What is the probability of alpha-particles with kinetic energy 5 MeV tunnelling through the potential barrier of a polonium nucleus?

49.13. How will the radioactivity of a cobalt specimen change in two years? The half-life is 5.2 years.

49.14. In two days the radioactivity of a radon specimen decreased to $1/1.45$ of its original value. Find its half-life.

49.15. The radioactivity of a uranium specimen with mass number 238 is 2.5×10^4 s^{-1}, the specimen's mass is 2.0 g. Find the half-life.

49.16. Find the age of a wooden article, if it is known that its C^{14} isotope activity is one third of that of newly cut wood.

49.17. In the investigation of the alpha-decay of polonium, alpha-particles with energies of 5.30 and 4.50 MeV were detected. Find the energy of the gamma-rays emitted in the decay, taking account of the recoil of the nucleus.

49.18. A Fe^{57} nucleus emits gamma-rays with an energy of 14.4 keV. Find the relative variation of the energy of gamma-photon due to the recoil of the nucleus. Compare this quantity with the natural width of a spectral line, if the lifetime of a nucleus in the excited state is 1.4×10^{-7} s.

49.19. What should be the relative speed of approach of a source and an absorber consisting of free iron atoms for the resonance absorption of gamma-rays to take place? The energy of the photon is specified in the previous problem.

49.20. Derive the law of radioactive decay on the basis of the fact that the decay probability for a nucleus is independent of the number of nuclei and is proportional to the period of observation.

49.21. Making use of the uncertainty relation, calculate the energy of the localization of a neutron in a nucleus, i.e. the kinetic energy that a neutron must possess to enter a nucleus. The dimensions of the nucleus are of the order of 10^{-14} m.

Isn't there contradiction between this result and the experimental fact that even thermal neutrons with kinetic energies of the order of 10^{-2} eV are able to penetrate the nucleus?

50. Nuclear Reactions

50.1. A uranium U^{235} nucleus liberates an energy of 200 MeV in the process of fission. 1.5 kg of uranium take part in the reaction during the explosion of a uranium bomb. What is the mass of an equivalent TNT bomb, if the heating capacity of TNT is 4.1 MJ/kg?

50.2. Find the energy liberated in the course of the thermonuclear reaction

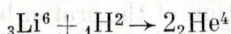

$$_3Li^6 + _1H^2 \rightarrow 2_2He^4$$

Do the calculations for one nucleus and for one nucleon. Compare with the energy liberated in the process of fission of uranium.

50.3. Can the thermonuclear reaction $_1H^2 + _1H^2 \rightarrow _2He^4$ be initiated in gaseous deuterium at a temperature of the order of 10^8 K?

50.4. A neutral pion decays into two gamma-photons:

$$\pi^0 \rightarrow \gamma + \gamma$$

Why cannot a single photon be born? What conservation law is in contradiction with it? What is the energy of the photon?

50.5. The lifetime of a neutral pion is 8.0×10^{-17} s. What is the accuracy with which its mass can be determined?

50.6. A high-energy gamma-photon may turn into an electron-positron pair in the field of heavy nuclei. What is the minimum energy of the gamma-photon?

50.7. Prove that a photon in a vacuum, no matter how high its energy is, cannot transform to an electron-positron pair.

50.8. A stationary pion decays into a muon and a neutrino:

$$\pi^+ \rightarrow \mu^+ + \nu_\mu$$

Find the ratio of the energy of the neutrino to the kinetic energy of the muon.

50.9. A neutron at rest decays. Assuming the resulting proton to remain at rest, too, find the kinetic energy of the electron and the energy of the antineutrino.

50.10. The observation of the tracks of secondary electrons showed that a neutral pion decayed into two identical photons. The angle of separation of the photons is 90°. Find the kinetic energy of the pion and the energy of each photon.

50.11. Protons accelerated by a potential difference of 6.8 MV bombard a stationary lithium target. The collision of a proton with a nucleus of Li^7 isotope results in the birth of two alpha-particles which separate symmetrically with respect to the direction of the proton beam. Find the kinetic energy and the separation angle of the alpha-particles.

50.12. An accelerated electron is absorbed by a proton at rest and a neutron is formed. Write the reaction equation. Assuming that the resulting neutron remains at rest, calculate the minimum kinetic energy of the electron at which the reaction is possible.

SOLUTIONS

1. Kinetics of a Particle

1.1. The graph is shown in Fig. 1.1. The law of motion is: $x_1 = -21 + 8t$; $x_2 = 7 + 4t$.

1.2. The graph is shown in Fig. 1.2. The law of motion is: $x_1 = 1.5t$; $x_2 = -300 + 3.5t$.

1.3. The graph is shown in Fig. 1.3. The law of motion is: $x_1 = 80t$; $x_2 = 120(t - 1.5)$.

1.4. For the swimmer not to drift with the stream, the condition $-v_x + u = 0$ must be satisfied (see Fig. 1.4). Hence the given answer. The problem has a solution for $v > u$.

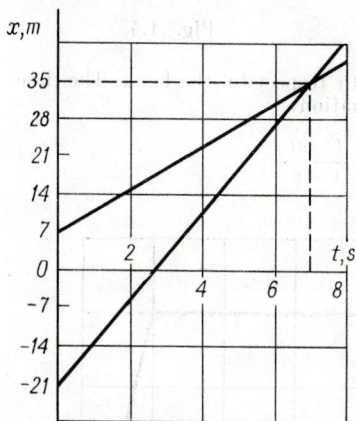

Fig. 1.1.

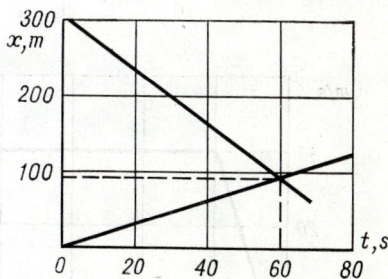

Fig. 1.2.

1.5. The swimmer swims at an angle α to the y-axis. His speed along the y-axis is $v_y = v \cos \alpha$, along the x-axis $v_x = v \sin \alpha + u$. Hence

$$\tan \beta = \frac{v_x}{v_y} = \frac{v \sin \alpha + u}{v \cos \alpha}$$

The given answer is obtained after some simple transforms.

The problem has a solution for $v \geqslant u \cos \beta$.

1.6. The speed of the swimmer in the direction of the y-axis is a maximum, if he swims perpendicularly to the stream. This is obvious, if we use a reference frame fixed relative to water.

1.7. *First solution.* Take a reference frame fixed relative to the bank. Moving up-stream at a speed $v - u$ the launch covered a distance l. Moving down-stream at a speed $v + u$ it covered a greater distance, namely $l + ut$, where ut is

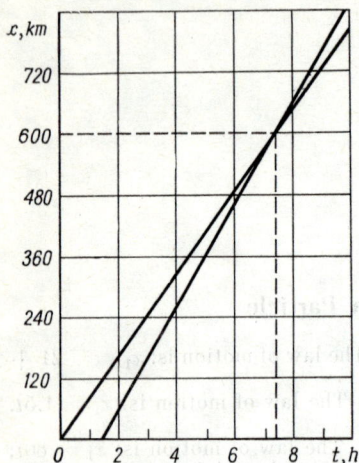

Fig. 1.3.

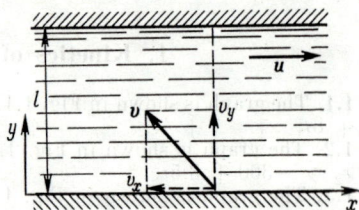

Fig. 1.4.

the distance covered by the float with respect to the bank. The time of motion may be found from the equation

$$t = \frac{l}{v - u} + \frac{l + ut}{v + u}$$

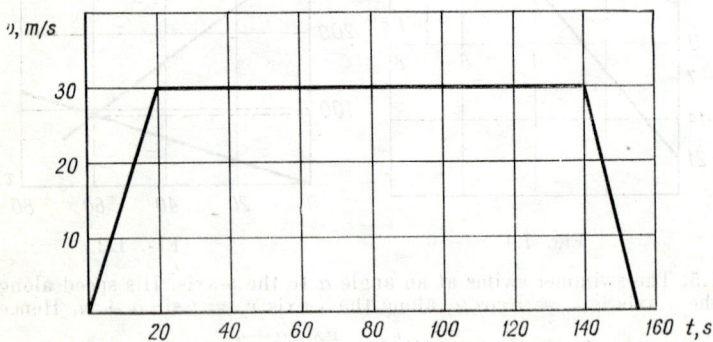

Fig. 1.8.

whence

$$t = 2l/(v-u)$$

Second solution. Take a reference frame fixed with respect to the water. The speed of the launch in this reference frame is v, the float is at rest. The time of motion of the launch is $t = 2l'/v$, where l' is the distance covered by the launch with respect to the water in one direction. It is obvious that

$$\frac{l}{v-u} = \frac{l'}{v} = \frac{t}{2}$$

Substituting into the previous equality we obtain the same answer. Evidently, the solution is simpler in a moving reference frame.

1.8. See Fig. 1.8.

2. Force

2.1. The force F causes the extension of the entire system $\Delta l = F/k$, the extensions of the first and the second springs being $\Delta l_1 = F/k_1$ and $\Delta l_2 = F/k_2$, respectively. Since $\Delta l = \Delta l_1 + \Delta l_2$, it follows that

$$\frac{1}{k} = \frac{1}{k_1} + \frac{1}{k_2}$$

2.2. Apply to the body two forces $\mathbf{T}_1$ and $\mathbf{T}_2$ equal in magnitude and opposite in direction (Fig. 2.2).

Adding up the forces $\mathbf{F}_1$ and $\mathbf{T}_1$ and $\mathbf{F}_2$ and $\mathbf{T}_2$, respectively, we obtain two forces $\mathbf{R}_1$ and $\mathbf{R}_2$ intersecting in point B. Translate the forces $\mathbf{R}_1$ and $\mathbf{R}_2$ to this point and resolve them again into the former components. The forces $\mathbf{T}_1$ and $\mathbf{T}_2$ are in equilibrium, but the forces $\mathbf{F}_1' = \mathbf{F}_1$, and $\mathbf{F}_2' = \mathbf{F}_2$ act in the same direction and their resultant force $R = F_1' + F_2' = F_1 + F_2$.

The position of point O, the centre of parallel forces, may be found from the similarity of triangles. From the condition $\Delta A_1 OB \sim \Delta F_1' R_1' B$ and $\Delta A_2 OB \sim \Delta F_2' R_2' B$ we obtain

$$\frac{l_1}{T} = \frac{OB}{F_1} \quad \text{and} \quad \frac{l_2}{T} = \frac{OB}{F_2}$$

from which $l_1 F_1 = l_2 F_2$, which was required to prove.

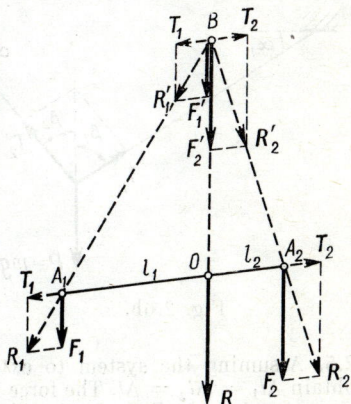

Fig. 2.2.

2.3. Let the x-axis pass through the points of application of the forces, A_1 and A_2, with the coordinates x_1 and x_2, the coordinate of the centre O being x_0. Then $l_1 = x_0 - x_1$, $l_2 = x_2 - x_0$. Substituting this into **the result of the previous problem,** we obtain: $F_1 (x_0 - x_1) =$

$= F_2 (x_2 - x_0)$, whence

$$x_0 = \frac{F_1 x_1 + F_2 x_2}{F_1 + F_2}$$

The position of the centre of several parallel forces may be found by using the method of complete induction.

2.4. Resolve the greater force $\mathbf{F}_1$ into two parallel components (Fig. 2.4), applying the force $\mathbf{T}_2 = -\mathbf{F}_2$ at the point A_2 and the second force $\mathbf{T}_1$ of magnitude $T_1 = F_1 - F_2$ at the point C at a distance

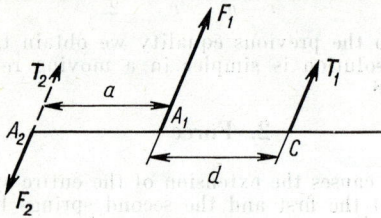

Fig. 2.4.

$d = a T_2 / T_1$ from point A_1. Since the forces $\mathbf{F}_2$ and $\mathbf{T}_2$ are in equilibrium, the resultant $\mathbf{R} = \mathbf{T}_1$; its magnitude is $R = T_1 = F_1 - F_2$.

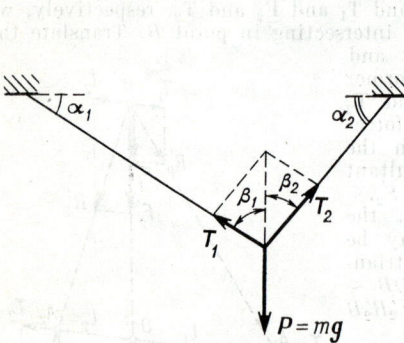

Fig. 2.6b.

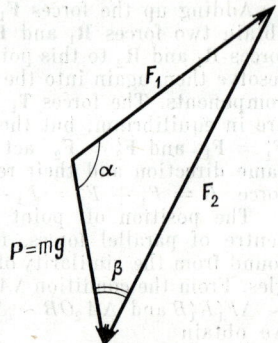

Fig. 2.7b.

2.5. Assuming the system to extend without angular deflection we obtain $\Delta l_1 = \Delta l_2 = \Delta l$. The force $F = k \Delta l$ is resolved into two forces: $F_1 = k_1 \Delta l$ and $F_2 = k_2 \Delta l$. Since $F = F_1 + F_2$, it follows that $k = k_1 + k_2$.

2.6. Using the sine rule, we obtain from Fig. 2.6b

$$\frac{T_1}{\sin \beta_2} = \frac{T_2}{\sin \beta_1} = \frac{P}{\sin [\pi - (\beta_1 + \beta_2)]}$$

Noting that $\beta_1 = \dfrac{\pi}{2} - \alpha_1$, $\beta_2 = \dfrac{\pi}{2} - \alpha_2$, we obtain the given answer.

2.7. The triangle of forces is similar to the bracket's triangle (Fig.2.7b). Using the sine theorem, we obtain

$$\frac{F_1}{\sin \beta} = \frac{F_2}{\sin \alpha} = \frac{mg}{\sin [\pi - (\alpha + \beta)]}$$

2.8. Since $DC = a\sqrt{3/2}$ and $DE = a/2$ it follows that $\angle CDE = 90°$. Resolve the force $\mathbf{P} = m\mathbf{g}$ into two components in the directions CD and CE (Fig. 2.8b). We obtain $N = 2P$, $F = P\sqrt{3}$. Now resolve

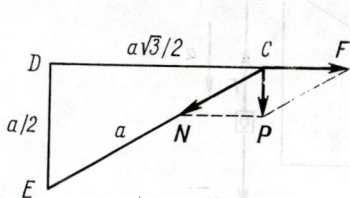

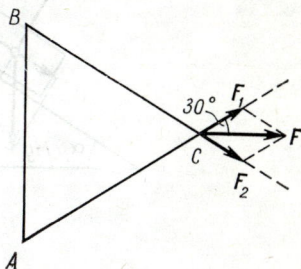

Fig. 2.8b.   Fig. 2.8c.

the force $\mathbf{F}$ into components directed along the rods BC and AC (Fig. 2.8c). Since in this case the parallelogram of forces is a rhombus with an apex angle of 60°, it follows that

$$F_1 = F_2 = \frac{F}{2 \cos 30°} = \frac{P\sqrt{3}}{2\sqrt{3/2}} = P$$

3. Particle Dynamics

3.2. Let's direct the y-axis vertically downwards. The equation of motion may be written as follows:

$$-F + m_1 g = -m_1 a, \qquad -F + m_2 g = m_2 a$$

where F is the tension of the string. Solving the system, we obtain the acceleration and the tension.

3.3. The equations of motions for the case shown in Fig. 3.3 are of the form

$$Q - F_1 = m_2 a, \qquad F_1 = m_1 a$$

from which we get

$$F_1 = Q m_1 / (m_1 + m_2)$$

If the force is applied to the smaller body, the string tension would become

$$F_2 = Q m_2 / (m_1 + m_2) > F_1$$

3.4. (1) If the monkey is at rest on the rope, the acceleration of both bodies will be the same, equal to a_1. The equations of motion are

$$F_1 = Ma_1, \qquad mg - F_1 = ma_1$$

where F_1 is the tension of the rope.

(2) If the monkey moves upwards with respect to the rope with an acceleration b, the motion of both bodies will be different: the

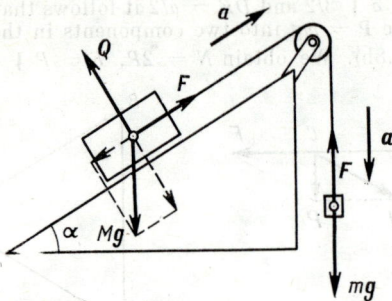

Fig. 3.5b.

weight will move with an acceleration a_2 and the monkey with an acceleration $a_2' = a_2 - b$. The equation of motions will assume the form

$$F_2 = Ma_2, \qquad mg - F_2 = ma_2'.$$

(3) The downward motion of the monkey with respect to the rope with acceleration b is described by the same equations; one has only to change the sign of b.

The downward acceleration of the monkey with respect to the rope cannot exceed the acceleration due to gravity. (Why?) Therefore $a_3 \geqslant 0$ and $F_3 \geqslant 0$.

3.5. The forces acting on the weight are the gravitational force mg and the tension of the thread F (Fig. 3.5b). The equation of motion is

$$mg - F = ma$$

Three forces act on the block: the gravitational force Mg, the reaction of the inclined plane Q and the tension of the thread F. The equation of motion is

$$F - Mg \sin \alpha = Ma$$

Hence the answer given follows.

It may be seen that for $m > M \sin \alpha$ the system will be accelerated in the direction shown in Fig. 3.5b. For $m < M \sin \alpha$ the acceleration will be reversed, and for $m = M \sin \alpha$ the system will move at the constant speed imparted to it initially, or remain at rest.

Note that Problems 3.2 and 3.4 are particular cases of Problem 3.5. By setting $\alpha = \pi/2$ we obtain the solution of Problem 3.2, and by setting $\alpha = 0$ the first case of Problem 3.4 is obtained.

3.6. Three forces act on the rod: the reaction of the wedge Q, the reaction of the guides F and the gravitational force $m_2 g$ (Fig. 3.6b). The equation of motion (in the y-direction) is

$$-m_2 g + Q \cos \alpha = m_2 a_2$$

Correspondingly, three forces also act on the wedge: the reaction of the table N, the gravitational force $m_1 g$, and the reaction of the rod Q

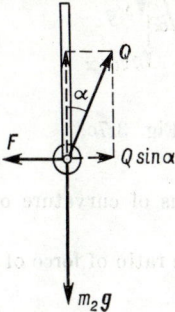

Fig. 3.6b.

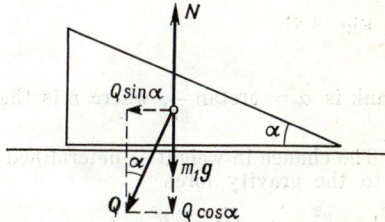

Fig. 3.6c.

(Fig. 3.6c). The equation of motion (in the x-direction) is

$$-Q \sin \alpha = m_1 a_1$$

To obtain the third equation, we compare the displacements of the rod $\Delta y = 1/2 a_2 t^2$ with that of the wedge $\Delta x = 1/2 a_1 t^2$. Since $\Delta y = \Delta x \tan \alpha$ it follows that

$$a_2 = a_1 \tan \alpha$$

Then we solve the system of three equations with three unknowns.

3.7. The problem reduces to the solution of a system of four equations:

$$-Q \sin \alpha = M b_x, \qquad -mg + Q \cos \alpha = m a_y$$
$$Q \sin \alpha = m a_x, \qquad a_y = (-a_x + b_x) \tan \alpha$$

The case of a fixed wedge may be considered separately, but it may also be obtained from the general case, if we put $m \ll M$. We obtain

$$a_x = g \sin \alpha \cos \alpha, \qquad a_y = -g \sin^2 \alpha$$
$$a = \sqrt{a_x^2 + a_y^2} = g \sin \alpha, \qquad Q = mg \cos \alpha$$

3.9. The elastic force $F_{el} = k (l - l_0)$ imparts a centripetal acceleration to the weight.

3.10. The forces acting on the plane are the force of gravity P and the lift F perpendicular to the wing's plane. Their resultant R imparts a centripetal acceleration to the plane (Fig. 3.10). The angle

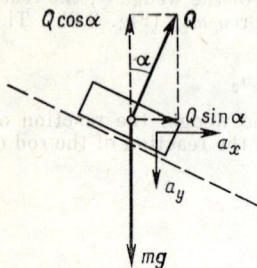

Fig. 3.7b.

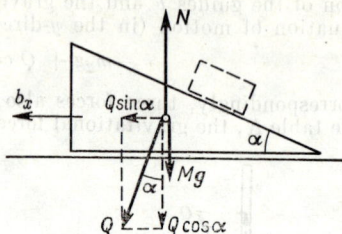

Fig. 3.7c.

of bank is $\alpha = \arctan \dfrac{v^2}{gr}$, where r is the radius of curvature of the path.

3.11. The change in weight is determined as the ratio of force of pressure to the gravity force

$$\frac{N_1}{mg} = \frac{v^2}{gr} + 1, \quad \frac{N_2}{mg} = \frac{v^2}{gr} - 1$$

3.12 The speed at the uppermost point of the path is $v = v_x = v_0 \cos \alpha$, the normal acceleration is equal to the acceleration due to gravity. We have

$$r = \frac{v^2}{a_n} = \frac{v_0^2 \cos^2 \alpha}{g}$$

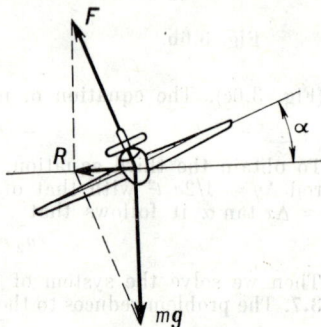

Fig. 3.10

3.13. Suppose that an object is thrown in the direction of the x-axis at an initial speed v_0 and that the force of gravity imparts an acceleration g in the positive direction of the y-axis to the object (Fig. 3.13). Then the law of motion will assume the form

$$x = v_0 t, \quad y = 1/2\, g t^2$$

The equation for the path is obtained by eliminating the time: $x^2 = \dfrac{2v_0^2}{g}\, y$, i.e. the parameter $p = v_0^2/g$. It may be seen from the figure that

$$v = \sqrt{v_0^2 + g^2 t^2} = v_0 \sqrt{1 + x^2/p^2}, \quad a_n = g \cos \alpha = g v_0 / v$$

Substituting the results into the expression for the radius of curvature, we obtain

$$r = \frac{v^2}{a_n} = \frac{v^3}{g v_0} = p \left(1 + \frac{x^2}{p^2} \right)^{3/2}$$

3.14. The direction of the speed of a particle is just the direction of the tangent to its path. It may be seen from Fig. 3.13 that $\tan \alpha = gt/v_0$. But since $t = x/v_0$, it follows that

$$\tan \alpha = gx/v_0^2 = x/p$$

When you have learned to differentiate, you will be able to solve the problem using the derivative in the following way*:

$$\tan \alpha = \frac{dy}{dx} = \frac{d}{dx} \left(\frac{x^2}{2p} \right) =$$

$$= \frac{2x}{2p} = \frac{x}{p}$$

3.15. The law of motion of the stone is

$$y = h + v_0 t \cos \beta -$$
$$- \frac{1}{2} g t^2, \qquad x = v_0 t \sin \beta$$

When the stone strikes the hill,

$$x_B = b \cos \alpha, \qquad y_B = h - b \sin \alpha$$

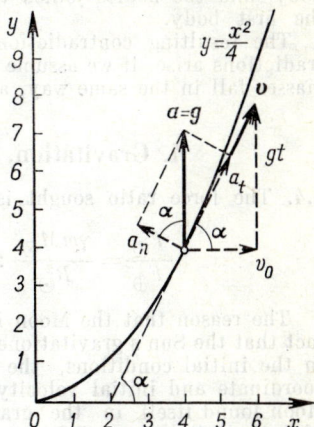

Fig. 3.13

Substituting this into the law of motion we obtain the result sought.
3.16. The laws of motion of the first and of the second objects are

$$x_1 = l, \qquad y_1 = H - \frac{1}{2} g t^2$$

$$x_2 = v_0 t \cos \alpha, \qquad y_2 = v_0 t \sin \alpha - \frac{1}{2} g t^2$$

When they meet, $x = l$, $y = H/2$. It follows that

$$l = v_0 t \cos \alpha, \qquad \frac{H}{2} = v_0 t \sin \alpha - \frac{1}{2} g t^2, \qquad \frac{H}{2} = H - \frac{1}{2} g t^2$$

After some transforms we obtain the given answer.

---

* In school mathematics courses the derivative is usually denoted by a stroke, for instance, $a = v'$. However, this is not always convenient, since it is often not clear with respect to which variable the derivative is taken. For this reason, if $y = f(x)$, we shall denote the derivative by $\frac{dy}{dx}$.

3.17. Suppose we assume the contrary, namely, that the body with greater mass falls at a greater speed. Suppose we have two bodies of different masses. Then the body with the greater mass falls more quickly than the body with the smaller mass. Join both bodies. Since the mass of the composite body is equal to the sum of the masses being added, the composite body should fall more quickly than the first. On the other hand, since the lighter body supposedly has the property of falling slowly, it should slow down the motion of the composite body, and the bodies joined together should fall more slowly than the first body.

The resulting contradiction disproves our assumption. No contradictions arise, if we assume that all bodies independently of their masses fall in the same way, and experiment shows this to be true.

4. Gravitation. Electrical Forces

4.4. The force ratio sought is

$$\frac{F_\odot}{F_\oplus} = \frac{\gamma m M_\odot}{R_\odot^2} : \frac{\gamma m M_\oplus}{R_\oplus^2} = \frac{M_\odot R_\oplus^2}{M_\oplus R_\odot^2} \approx 2$$

The reason that the Moon is a satellite of the Earth despite the fact that the Sun's gravitational attraction is twice as strong is found in the initial conditions, the Moon's initial coordinate and initial velocity at the time the Moon found itself in the gravitational fields of both bodies (see § 8.2).

4.9. Equilibrium will be established, if the resultant of the electric force **F**, the force of gravity $\mathbf{P} = mg$ and the tension of the thread **T** is zero (Fig. 4.9). Hence $F = P \tan \alpha$. Substituting the value of the electric force, we obtain after some transformations:

$$Q = 2q = 2 \sqrt{4\pi\varepsilon_0 mg \tan \alpha \, l^2 \sin^2 \alpha}$$

4.10. If the charges are placed as in Fig. 4.10a, the field intensity in the centre of the square will be zero.

If the charges are placed as in Fig. 4.10b, we find the field intensities due to the individual charges and then add up the field intensity vectors.

Fig. 4.9.

4.11. Divide the conductor into segments of such small length that they may be considered to be points (Fig. 4.11). Then the projection of the field intensity set up by a small segment on the axis of symmetry of the conductor will be

$$\Delta E_x = \frac{\Delta q \cos \alpha}{4\pi\varepsilon_0 r^2} = \frac{\Delta q \cdot x}{4\pi\varepsilon_0 r^3} = \frac{\Delta q \cdot x}{4\pi\varepsilon_0 \, (a^2 + x^2)^{3/2}}$$

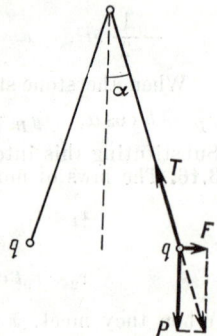

From considerations of symmetry it is evident that the field is directed along the axis and that the field intensity is the sum of the projections of the field intensities set up by the individual segments of the conductor.

4.12. First find the intermolecular distance. The mass of one cubic meter of water is 10^3 kg, a kilomole of water (18 kg) contains 6.0×10^{26} molecules. Therefore one cubic meter of water contains $N =$

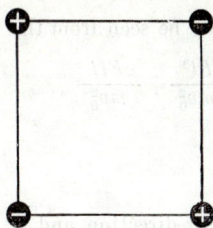

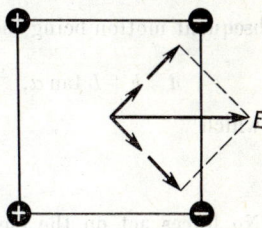

Fig. 4.10a.   Fig. 4.10b.

$= 6.0 \times 10^{26} \times 10^3/18 = 3.3 \times 10^{28}$ molecules. Then the distance between the water molecules is

$$d = 1/\sqrt[3]{N} = \sqrt[3]{3.0 \times 10^{-29}} = 3.1 \times 10^{-10}\ \text{m}$$

The force of interaction is

$$F \approx \frac{6p_e^2}{4\pi\varepsilon_0 d^3} = 6.7 \times 10^{-20}\ \text{N}$$

4.13. Since there are no forces in the direction of the x-axis acting on the electron (we neglect the force of gravity), $v_x = \text{const}$, and the electron transit time in the field is $t = L/v_x$. The force acting on the electron in the direction of the y-axis is $F_y = -eE$. This force imparts to the electron an acceleration $a_y = -eE/m$. The projection of the velocity on the y-axis varies with time according to the equation $v_y = v_{0y} + a_y t$. At the point of the electron's exit from the field we have

$$v_x \tan \beta = v_x \tan \alpha - \frac{eEL}{mv_x}, \quad \text{from which} \quad v_x^2 (\tan \alpha - \tan \beta) = \frac{eEL}{m}$$

Since $v_x = v_0 \cos \alpha$, we obtain

$$v_0^2 \cos^2 \alpha\, (\tan \alpha - \tan \beta) = eEL/m$$

4.14. No forces act on the electron in the direction of the x-axis (Fig. 4.14), and the projection of its velocity on this axis does not change with time: $v_x = v_0 = \text{const}$. While the electron moves in the field, a force $F_y = -eE$ acts on it in the direction of the y-axis. This causes a displacement of the electron

$$h = \frac{at^2}{2} = \frac{eEl^2}{2mv_0^2}$$

its speed in the y-direction being

$$v_y = at = eElt/mv_0$$

The electron leaves the field at an angle determined from the condition

$$\tan \alpha = \frac{v_y}{v_x} = \frac{eEl}{mv_0^2}$$

its subsequent motion being inertial. As may be seen from the figure,

$$d = h + L \tan \alpha, \quad \text{or} \quad d = \frac{eEl^2}{2mv_0^2} + \frac{eElL}{mv_0^2}$$

from which

$$E = \frac{mv_0^2 d}{el\,(L + l/2)}$$

4.15. No forces act on the electron in the x-direction and it moves along this axis at a constant speed $v_x = v_0 \cos \alpha$. In the y-direction a force $F_y = -eE$ acts on the electron, and it moves with an accelera-
tion $a_y = -eE/m$; its instantaneous velocity is

$$v_y = v_0 \sin \alpha + a_y t = v_0 \sin \alpha - \frac{eEt}{m}$$

To prevent the electron moving upwards from striking the upper plate, a field has to be established that would in time t_1 reduce the vertical velocity component to zero and would guarantee the condition $h_1 < h$. But $2a_y h_1 = -v_{0y}^2$ (see Problem 1.9); therefore

$$|a_y| = \frac{v_{0y}^2}{2h_1} > \frac{v_0^2 \sin^2 \alpha}{2h}$$

Hence, the first condition may be written in the form

$$E > \frac{mv_0^2 \sin^2 \alpha}{2eh}$$

Fig. 4.11.

The time the electron moves upwards is $t_1 = \dfrac{-v_0 \sin \alpha}{a_y}$. The time it moves downwards will be the same (prove this!). To prevent it from striking the lower plate it must be made to travel during this time a distance in the x-direction exceeding the length of the plate, i.e. $x = 2v_x t_1 > l$. Hence

$$\frac{-2v_0^2 \sin \alpha \cos \alpha}{a_y} > l$$

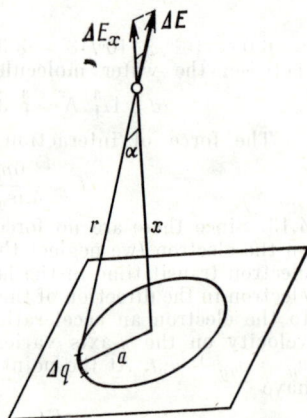

and the second condition assumes the form

$$E < \frac{2mv_0^2 \sin \alpha \cos \alpha}{el}$$

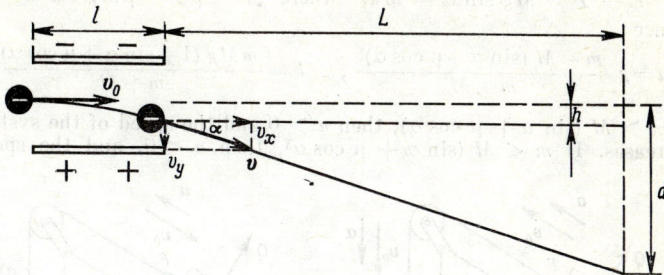

Fig. 4.14.

Combining both solutions we obtain the result sought.

5. Friction

5.1. Let us go over to the reference frame connected with the platform. Here the initial speed of the body is $-v_0$ and the final is zero. We have

$$a = \frac{T}{m} = \frac{\mu mg}{m} = \mu g, \qquad \tau = \frac{0-(-v_0)}{a} = \frac{v_0}{\mu g}$$

$$x = -v_0\tau + \frac{a\tau^2}{2} = -\frac{v_0^2}{2\mu g}$$

5.2. (1) If the monkey is at rest with respect to the rope, the equations of motion are of the form

$$F_1 - \mu Mg = Ma_1, \qquad mg - F_1 = ma_1$$

whence the answer sought. The solution is meaningful if $m > \mu M$. When $m \leqslant \mu M$, $a_1 = 0$ and $F_1 = mg$.

(2) If the monkey moves upwards with respect to the rope with an acceleration b, the equations of motion assume the form

$$F_2 - \mu Mg = Ma_2, \qquad mg - F_2 = m(a_2 - b)$$

The solution is meaningful if $\mu Mg < m(g + b)$. In the contrary case $a_2 = 0$, $a_2' = -b$, $F_2 = m(g + b)$.

(3) If the monkey moves downwards with respect to the rope with an acceleration b, the sign of b in the equations of motion for the previous case should be reversed.

5.3. Since the force of sliding friction T is opposite in direction to that of the block's motion, the result will be essentially dependent on the initial direction of the block velocity. Consider all the possible cases.

(1) Let the initial velocity of the weight be directed downwards (Fig. 5.3a). The equations of motion will be of the form

$$mg - F = ma$$

$$F - T - Mg \sin \alpha = Ma, \quad \text{where} \quad T = \mu Q = \mu Mg \cos \alpha$$

Hence

$$a = g \frac{m - M (\sin \alpha + \mu \cos \alpha)}{m + M}, \qquad F = \frac{m Mg (1 + \sin \alpha + \mu \cos \alpha)}{m + M}$$

If $m > M (\sin \alpha + \mu \cos \alpha)$, then $a > 0$ and the speed of the system increases. If $m < M (\sin \alpha + \mu \cos \alpha)$, then $a < 0$, and the speed

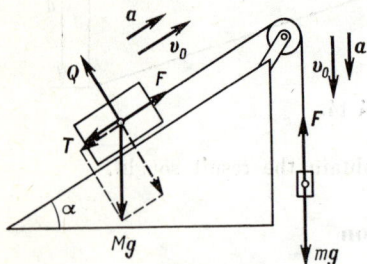
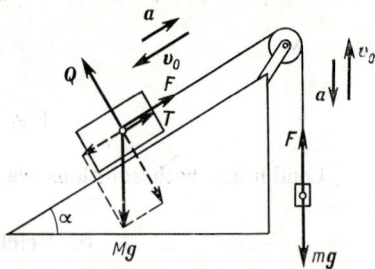

Fig. 5.3a.   Fig. 5.3b.

of the system decreases. Lastly, when $m = M (\sin \alpha + \mu \cos \alpha)$, we have $a = 0$, and the system moves at a constant speed.

(2) Let the initial velocity of the weight be directed upwards (Fig. 5.3b). Then, as may easily be inferred,

$$a = g \frac{m - M (\sin \alpha - \mu \cos \alpha)}{m + M}, \qquad F = \frac{m Mg (1 + \sin \alpha - \mu \cos \alpha)}{m + M}$$

If $m > M (\sin \alpha - \mu \cos \alpha)$, then $a > 0$, and the speed of the system decreases. If $m < M (\sin \alpha - \mu \cos \alpha)$, then $a < 0$, and the speed of the system increases. Lastly, if $m = M (\sin \alpha - \mu \cos \alpha)$, then $a = 0$, and the system moves at a constant speed.

(3) Finally, let the system be at rest. Then a force of static friction will act between the block and the inclined plane, its direction being dependent on the direction in which the system would move in the absence of friction. If $m > M \sin \alpha$, the block in the absence of friction moves upwards. Therefore the force of static friction is directed downwards, as in Fig. 5.3a. If $m < M \sin \alpha$, the block in the absence of friction moves downwards, and for this reason the force of static friction is directed upwards, as in Fig. 5.3b.

If one analyses the two preceding cases, one can easily see that for $m > M (\sin \alpha + \mu \cos \alpha)$ the block will move up the inclined plane with an acceleration; for $m < M (\sin \alpha - \mu \cos \alpha)$ it will move down the inclined plane with an acceleration; while for

$$M (\sin \alpha - \mu \cos \alpha) \leqslant m \leqslant M (\sin \alpha + \mu \cos \alpha)$$

the system will remain at rest.

5.4. The equation of motion of the rod will remain unaltered; in the equation of motion of the wedge one should take into account the presence of the force of kinetic friction $T = \mu (Q \cos \alpha + m_1 g)$,

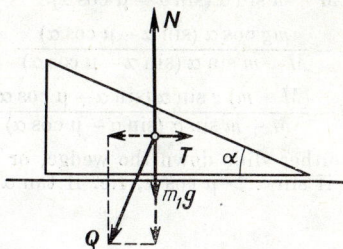

Fig. 5.4.

directed opposite to the acceleration (Fig. 5.4). Thus

$$-m_2 g + Q \cos \alpha = m_2 a_y, \quad -Q \sin \alpha + \mu (Q \cos \alpha + m_1 g) = m_1 a_x$$

After some transformations, noting that $a_y = a_x \tan \alpha$, we obtain

$$Q = \frac{m_1 m_2 g (\cos \alpha + \mu \sin \alpha)}{m_1 \cos^2 \alpha + m_2 \sin^2 \alpha - \mu m_2 \sin \alpha \cos \alpha}$$

$$a_x = \frac{-m_2 g + \mu g \cot \alpha (m_2 + m_1)}{m_1 \cot \alpha + m_2 \tan \alpha - \mu m_2} < 0$$

$$a_y = \frac{-m_2 g \tan \alpha + \mu g (m_2 + m_1)}{m_1 \cot \alpha + m_2 \tan \alpha - \mu m_2} < 0$$

The solution makes sense when

$$m_1 \cot \alpha + m_2 \tan \alpha > \mu m_2, \quad m_2 \tan \alpha > \mu (m_2 + m_1)$$

It follows from the second inequality that

$$\tan \alpha > \frac{\mu (m_2 + m_1)}{m_2}$$

If, on the other hand, $\tan \alpha \leqslant \dfrac{\mu (m_2 + m_1)}{m_2}$, then $a_x = 0$, $a_y = 0$

and $Q = \dfrac{m_2 g}{\cos \alpha}$.

5.5. The equations of motion will assume the form (see Fig. 5.5a and 5.5b)

$$-Q \sin \alpha + T \cos \alpha = M b_x$$

$$Q \sin \alpha - T \cos \alpha = m a_x, \quad -mg + Q \cos \alpha + T \sin \alpha = m a_y$$

$$a_y = (-a_x + b_x)\tan\alpha, \qquad T = \mu Q$$

Hence

$$Q = \frac{mMg\cos\alpha}{M + m\sin\alpha\,(\sin\alpha - \mu\cos\alpha)}$$

$$a_x = \frac{Mg\cos\alpha\,(\sin\alpha - \mu\cos\alpha)}{M + m\sin\alpha\,(\sin\alpha - \mu\cos\alpha)}$$

$$b_x = -\frac{mg\cos\alpha\,(\sin\alpha - \mu\cos\alpha)}{M + m\sin\alpha\,(\sin\alpha - \mu\cos\alpha)}$$

$$a_y = -\frac{(M + m)\,g\sin\alpha\,(\sin\alpha - \mu\cos\alpha)}{M + m\sin\alpha\,(\sin\alpha - \mu\cos\alpha)}$$

The block can either slide down the wedge, or remain stationary. It can slide down if $\sin\alpha > \mu\cos\alpha$, i.e. if $\tan\alpha > \mu$. In this case

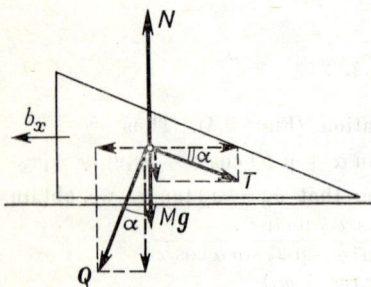

Fig. 5.5a.

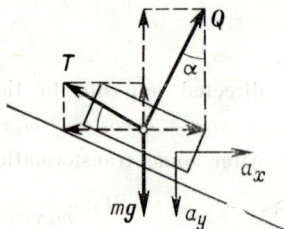

Fig. 5.5b.

$a_x > 0$, $a_y < 0$ and $b_x < 0$. If, on the other hand, $\tan\alpha \leqslant \mu$, the block and the wedge will remain stationary.

Note that the solution of Problem 3.7 is obtained automatically from the solution of this problem, if one puts $\mu = 0$.

5.6. If the wedge moves to the left, the equations of motion assume the following form:

$$Q\sin\alpha = ma_x, \quad -mg + Q\cos\alpha = ma_y, \quad -Q\sin\alpha + T = Mb_x$$

$$a_y = (-a_x + b_x)\tan\alpha, \qquad T = \mu\,(Q\cos\alpha + Mg)$$

from which

$$Q = \frac{Mmg\,(\cos\alpha + \mu\sin\alpha)}{M + m\sin\alpha\,(\sin\alpha - \mu\cos\alpha)}$$

$$a_x = \frac{Mg\sin\alpha\,(\cos\alpha + \mu\sin\alpha)}{M + m\sin\alpha\,(\sin\alpha - \mu\cos\alpha)}$$

$$a_y = -\frac{(M+m)\,g\sin\alpha\,(\sin\alpha - \mu\cos\alpha)}{M + m\sin\alpha\,(\sin\alpha - \mu\cos\alpha)}$$

$$b_x = \mu g - \frac{mg\,(\cos\alpha + \mu\sin\alpha)\,(\sin\alpha - \mu\cos\alpha)}{M + m\sin\alpha\,(\sin\alpha - \mu\cos\alpha)}$$

Since $b_x \leqslant 0$ (explain why), it follows that

$$\mu g \leqslant \frac{mg\,(\cos\alpha + \mu\sin\alpha)\,(\sin\alpha - \mu\cos\alpha)}{M + m\sin\alpha\,(\sin\alpha - \mu\cos\alpha)}$$

Hence after some simple transformations we obtain that our solution is meaningful in conditions when

$$\mu < \frac{m\sin\alpha\cos\alpha}{M + m\cos^2\alpha}$$

In this case the expression

$$\sin\alpha - \mu\cos\alpha > \frac{M\sin\alpha}{M + m\cos^2\alpha}$$

and consequently $a_y < 0$, which agrees with the problem's idea.

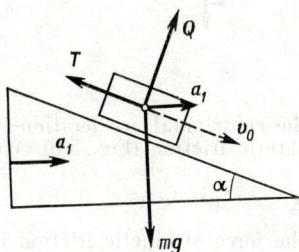

Fig. 5.7a.

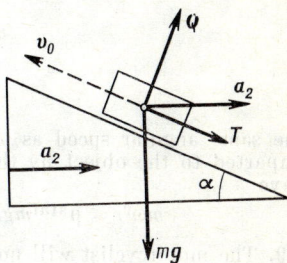

Fig. 5.7b.

If it turns out that $\mu = \dfrac{m\sin\alpha\cos\alpha}{M + m\cos^2\alpha}$, then $b_x = 0$, i.e. the wedge will move on the table at the initial speed v_0 (or remain stationary, if $v_0 = 0$). In this case

$$\sin\alpha - \mu\cos\alpha = \frac{M\sin\alpha}{M + m\cos^2\alpha}, \qquad \cos\alpha + \mu\sin\alpha = \frac{(M+m)\cos\alpha}{M + m\cos^2\alpha}$$

from which

$$Q = mg\cos\alpha$$

$$a_x = g\sin\alpha\cos\alpha, \qquad a_y = -g\sin^2\alpha, \qquad a = \sqrt{a_x^2 + a_y^2} = g\sin\alpha$$

5.7. Since the block does not slide on the wedge, the direction of the force of kinetic friction is not known. Evidently, if the acceleration of the wedge is small, the block will slide downwards and the friction force will be directed as shown in Fig. 5.7a. When the acceleration of the block is large, the wedge slides upwards and the direction of the force of friction changes sign (see Fig. 5.7b).

Write down the equations of motion along the coordinate axes for both cases:

y-axis: $Q \cos \alpha + T \sin \alpha - mg = 0$, $\quad Q \cos \alpha - T \sin \alpha - mg = 0$

x-axis: $Q \sin \alpha - T \cos \alpha = ma_1$, $\quad Q \sin \alpha + T \cos \alpha = ma_2$

Noting that $T = \mu Q$, we obtain after some transformations:

$$a_1 = g \frac{\tan \alpha - \mu}{1 + \mu \tan \alpha}, \qquad a_2 = g \frac{\tan \alpha + \mu}{1 - \mu \tan \alpha}$$

Writing $\mu = \tan \varphi$, we obtain $g \tan (\alpha - \varphi) \leqslant a \leqslant g \tan (\alpha + \varphi)$.

5.8. In the case the object doesn't slide off the disk, it will rotate with

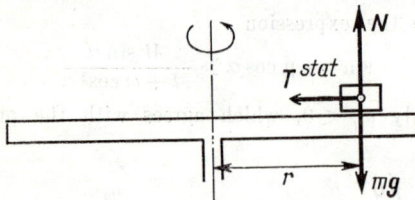

Fig. 5.8.

the same angular speed as the disk. The centripetal acceleration is imparted to the object by the force of static friction (Fig. 5.8). We have

$$m\omega^2 r \leqslant \mu^{\text{stat}} mg, \qquad \text{whence} \qquad r \leqslant \mu^{\text{stat}} g/\omega^2$$

5.9. The motorcyclist will not slip, if the force of kinetic friction is equal to the force of gravity acting on him. As the motorcyclist moves on a round surface, the motorcycle presses against it, and the reaction imparts to him the centripetal acceleration. The equation of motion is of the form

$$T - mg = 0$$

where the force of friction $T = \mu N$ and the reaction $N = mv^2/r$. Hence

$$v \geqslant \sqrt{gr/\mu}$$

5.10. Since the object is at rest, the direction of the force of friction is not known. For this reason we shall imagine the angular velocity to be decreased until the object starts sliding downwards. The force of friction will then be directed as shown in Fig. 5.10b. The equations of motion are of the form

$$N \sin \alpha - T \cos \alpha = m\omega^2 R \sin \alpha$$
$$N \cos \alpha + T \sin \alpha - mg = 0$$

where $T = \mu^{\text{stat}} N$. Hence putting $\mu^{\text{stat}} = \tan \varphi$ we obtain after some simple transformations

$$\omega_1 = \sqrt{\frac{g \tan (\alpha - \varphi)}{R \sin \alpha}}$$

Suppose we imagine the angular velocity to be increased, so that the object starts sliding upwards. Then the direction of the force of

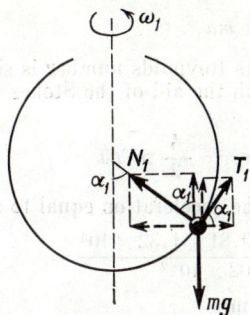

Fig. 5.10b.

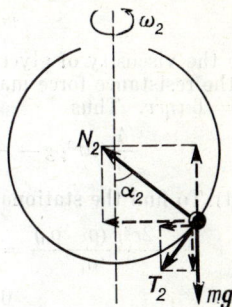

Fig. 5.10c.

friction will change sign (Fig. 5.10c), and the equations of motion will assume the form

$$N \sin \alpha + T \cos \alpha = m\omega^2 R \sin \alpha$$
$$N \cos \alpha - T \sin \alpha - mg = 0$$
$$T = \mu^{\text{stat}} N = N \tan \varphi$$

from which we get

$$\omega_2 = \sqrt{\frac{g \tan (\alpha + \varphi)}{R \sin \alpha}}$$

Thus the body will be in equilibrium if

$$\sqrt{\frac{g \tan (\alpha - \varphi)}{R \sin \alpha}} \leqslant \omega \leqslant \sqrt{\frac{g \tan (\alpha + \varphi)}{R \sin \alpha}}$$

Obviously, if $\alpha \leqslant \varphi$, i.e. if $\tan \alpha \leqslant \mu^{\text{stat}}$, the object will not slide down, even when the bowl stops rotating.

As a particular case of the solution when static friction is absent ($\mu^{\text{stat}} = \tan \varphi = 0$) equilibrium will be established when the bowl rotates at an angular velocity of

$$\omega_0 = \sqrt{g/R \cos \alpha}$$

5.11. The centripetal acceleration of the motorcyclist is due to the force of friction, therefore $\mu mg = mv^2/r$. Hence

$$r \geqslant v^2/\mu g$$

The motorcyclist's angle with the horizontal should be such that the resultant of the reaction and the force of friction is directed along his body. Hence, $\tan \alpha = N/T = 1/\mu$.

5.12. The equation of motion of a ball falling in a liquid is of the form

$$mg - F_A - F_{res} = ma$$

Since the viscosity of glycerine is high, its Reynolds number is small and the resistance force may be found with the aid of the Stokes law: $F_{res} = 6\pi\eta rv$. Thus

$$\frac{4}{3}\pi r^3 \rho g - \frac{4}{3}\pi r^3 \rho_0 g - 6\pi\eta rv = \frac{4}{3}\pi r^3 \rho a$$

(1) To find the stationary speed put the acceleration equal to zero

$$v = \frac{2r^2 g\,(\rho - \rho_0)}{9\eta} = \frac{2 \times 4 \times 10^{-6} \times 9.81 \times 1.32 \times 10^3}{9 \times 5.02 \times 10^{-2}} =$$

$$= 0.227 \text{ m/s} = 23 \text{ cm/s}$$

The Reynolds number is

$$\mathrm{Re} = \frac{\rho_0 vr}{\eta} = \frac{1.21 \times 10^3 \times 2.3 \times 10^{-1} \times 2 \times 10^{-3}}{5.02 \times 10^{-2}} = 0.11$$

For such small Reynolds number the Stokes law may be applied.

(2) The initial acceleration may be obtained from the equation of motion by putting the speed equal to zero:

$$a_0 = \frac{(\rho - \rho_0)\,g}{\rho} = \frac{(2.53 - 1.21) \times 9.81}{2.53} = 5.1 \text{ m/s}^2$$

(3) Making the approximation that the average acceleration is equal to one half of the sum of the initial and final accelerations, we obtain the time in which a stationary speed is established:

$$\tau = \frac{v}{a_{av}} \approx \frac{2v}{a_0} = \frac{0.23 \times 2}{5.1} = 9 \times 10^{-2} \text{ s}$$

The displacement corresponding to this time is

$$s = \frac{a_{av}\tau^2}{2} \approx \frac{a_0\tau^2}{4} = \frac{5.1 \times 81 \times 10^{-4}}{4} = 10^{-2} \text{ m} = 1 \text{ cm}$$

5.13. From the law of motion (see the previous problem) we obtain the law of the variation of acceleration with speed:

$$a = 5.10 - 22.5v$$

For small time intervals ($\Delta t = 0.02$ s)

$$v_n = v_{n-1} + a_{n-1}\Delta t$$

We can now compute Table 5.13 and draw the graph (Fig. 5.13). From them it may be seen that the stationary speed is $v = 0.227$ m/s, the transient period is $\tau = 0.22$ s (compare with the answer to Prob-

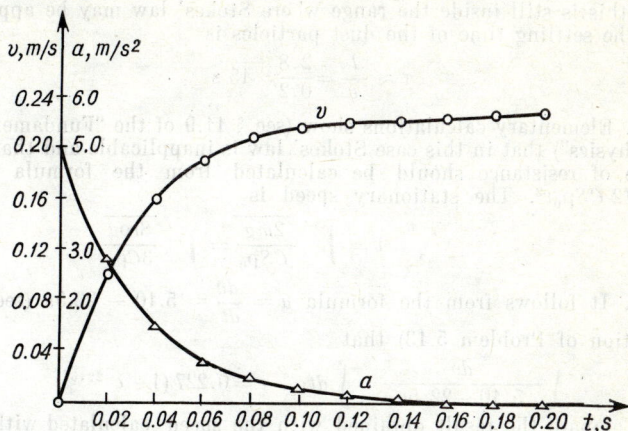

Fig. 5.13.

lem 5.12, where an approximate solution based on the assumption of uniformly accelerated motion was discussed).

Table 5.13

n	t, s	v, m/s	a, m/s^2	n	t, s	v, m/s	a, m/s^2
0	0.00	0.000	5.10	6	0.12	0.220	0.15
1	0.02	0.102	2.80	7	0.14	0.223	0.08
2	0.04	0.158	1.54	8	0.16	0.225	0.04
3	0.06	0.189	0.84	9	0.18	0.226	0.01
4	0.08	0.206	0.47	10	0.20	0.226	0.01
5	0.10	0.215	0.26	11	0.22	0.227	0.00

5.14. The density of the dust particles ρ is much greater than that of air ρ_0, therefore the Archimedes force may be neglected. Since the rate of settling of the dust particles is small, it may be calculated on the basis of Stokes' law. We have for the case of stationary speed

$$v = \frac{2r^2 \rho g}{9\eta} = \frac{2 \times 9 \times 10^{-10} \times 2 \times 10^3 \times 9.81}{9 \times 1.8 \times 10^{-5}} = 0.2 \text{ m/s}$$

The Reynolds number is

$$\mathrm{Re} = \frac{\rho_0 v r}{\eta} = \frac{1.3 \times 0.2 \times 3 \times 10^{-5}}{1.8 \times 10^{-5}} \approx 0.4$$

and this is still inside the range where Stokes' law may be applied. The settling time of the dust particles is

$$\tau \approx \frac{l}{v} = \frac{2.8}{0.2} = 15 \text{ s}$$

5.15. Elementary calculations show (see § 11.9 of the "Fundamentals of Physics") that in this case Stokes' law is inapplicable and that the force of resistance should be calculated from the formula $R = \frac{1}{2} CS\rho_0 v^2$. The stationary speed is

$$v = \sqrt{\frac{2mg}{CS\rho_0}} = \sqrt{\frac{8r\rho g}{3C\rho_0}}$$

5.16. It follows from the formula $a = \dfrac{dv}{dt} = 5.10 - 22.5v$ (see the solution of Problem 5.13) that

$$\int \frac{dv}{5.10 - 22.5v} = \int dt, \quad v = 0.227\,(1 - e^{-22.5t})$$

Compare the result obtained with the speed calculated with the aid of numerical methods.

6. Theory of Relativity

6.1. Suppose that in the course of motion with respect to some frame of reference the lateral dimensions of a body change, for instance, become smaller. Let there be a close fit of the rod and the hole in

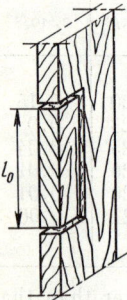 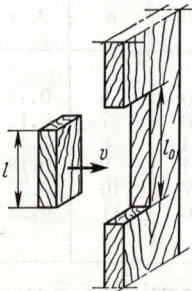 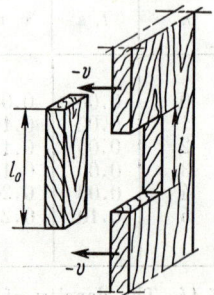

Fig. 6.1a.   Fig. 6.1b.   Fig. 6.1c.

the board in some reference frame (Fig. 6.1a). Now fix the reference frame to the board and let the rod move in it (Fig. 6.1b). Then, according to our assumption about the decrease in the lateral dimensions, the rod will pass freely through the hole. If we fix the reference frame to the rod, the dimensions of the hole will, according to our assumption, decrease, and the rod will be unable to pass through it (Fig. 6.1c). The resulting contradiction proves the assumption about the decrease in the lateral dimensions to be wrong. The result follows from the Lorentz transformations.

6.2. The relative error is

$$\varepsilon = \frac{u_{c1} - u_{rel}}{u_{rel}} = \frac{(u+v)(1+uv/c^2)}{u+v} - 1 = \frac{uv}{c^2}$$

6.3.
$$u = \frac{0.99000c + 0.99000c}{1 + 0.99000^2} = \frac{1.98000c}{1.98010}$$

$$= \left(1 - \frac{10 \times 10^{-5}}{1.98010}\right) c = (1 - 5.05 \times 10^{-5})c = 0.99995c$$

6.4. The discussion is free from errors, and the value obtained for the speed of approach u is correct. But this does not disprove the relativistic formula for the addition of velocities. The crux of the matter is that when talking of velocities being added we do not mean the addition of these velocities in the *given reference frame*, but the calculation of the velocity of the same object in another reference frame. For example, the velocity with which the right-hand object moves away from the left-hand object in the reference frame fixed to the left-hand object is of interest to us. To find it let's use the reference frame fixed to the left-hand object. We have $u' = \Delta l'/\Delta t'$, since in the new frame of reference both the distance and the course of the time experience changes. It follows from the Lorentz transformations that

$$\Delta l' = -x_2' + x_1' = \frac{-x_2 - v_2\Delta t + x_1 + v_2\Delta t}{\sqrt{1 - v_2^2/c^2}} =$$

$$= \frac{-x_2 + x_1}{\sqrt{1 - \beta^2}} = \frac{\Delta l}{\sqrt{1 - \beta^2}}$$

$$\Delta t' = \frac{\Delta t + v_2 x_1/c^2}{\sqrt{1 - v_2^2/c^2}} = \frac{\Delta t}{\sqrt{1 - \beta^2}}\left(1 + \frac{v_2 x_1}{\Delta t \cdot c^2}\right) =$$

$$= \frac{\Delta t}{\sqrt{1 - \beta^2}}\left(1 + \frac{v_1 v_2}{c^2}\right)$$

Hence

$$u' = \frac{\Delta l'}{\Delta t'} = \frac{\Delta l}{\Delta t} \cdot \frac{1}{1 + v_1 v_2/c^2} = \frac{u}{1 + v_1 v_2/c^2} = \frac{v_1 + v_2}{1 + v_1 v_2/c^2}$$

We have thus obtained the relativistic formula for the addition of velocities, as was to be expected.

6.5. Suppose a substance approaches the light source with a velocity v. Then, according to the formula for the addition of velocities, we obtain

$$u' = \frac{u + v}{1 + uv/c^2} = \frac{c/n + v}{1 + v/cn}$$

If the substance moves away from the light source, then

$$u'' = \frac{c/n - v}{1 - v/cn}$$

6.6. The time the light takes to travel with the fluid stream is

$$t_1 = \frac{2l}{u''} = \frac{2l\,(1-v/cn)}{c/n-v}$$

The time light travels against the stream is

$$t_2 = \frac{2l}{u'} = \frac{2l\,(1+v/cn)}{c/n+v}$$

The time difference is

$$\tau = t_1 - t_2 = \frac{2l}{(c/n)^2 - v^2}\left[\left(1-\frac{v}{cn}\right)\left(\frac{c}{n}+v\right)-\right.$$

$$\left.-\left(1+\frac{v}{cn}\right)\left(\frac{c}{n}-v\right)\right] = \frac{4lv\,(1-1/n^2)}{(c/n)^2 - v^2}$$

Noting that $c/n \gg v$ we obtain $\tau = \dfrac{4lv}{c^2}\,(n^2 - 1)$.

6.7.
$$l = v\tau = \frac{v\tau_0}{\sqrt{1-v^2/c^2}} = \frac{0.99 \times 3.0 \times 10^8 \times 2.6 \times 10^{-8}}{\sqrt{1-0.99^2}}$$

$$= \frac{0.99 \times 3.0 \times 2.6}{\sqrt{0.01 \times 1.99}} = \frac{0.99 \times 3.0 \times 2.6}{0.1 \times 1.41} = 55 \text{ m.}$$

$$l_0 = v\tau_0 = 0.99 \times 3.0 \times 10^8 \times 2.6 \times 10^{-8} = 7.7 \text{ m}$$

6.8.
$$\tau_0 = \tau\,\sqrt{1-v^2/c^2} = \frac{l\,\sqrt{1-v^2/c^2}}{v}$$

$$= \frac{3 \times 10^5\,\sqrt{1-0.998^2}}{0.998 \times 3 \times 10^8} = \frac{10^{-3}\,\sqrt{0.002 \times 1.998}}{0.998} = 6.3 \times 10^{-5} \text{ s.}$$

6.10. In the intrinsic reference frame $\rho_0 = m_0/V_0$, in all others $\rho = m/V$. The mass $m = \dfrac{m_0}{\sqrt{1-v^2/c^2}}$, the volume

$$V = \Delta z \cdot \Delta y \cdot \Delta x = \Delta z_0 \cdot \Delta y_0 \cdot \Delta x_0\,\sqrt{1-v^2/c^2} = V_0\,\sqrt{1-v^2/c^2}$$

The density

$$\rho = \frac{\rho_0}{1-v^2/c^2}$$

6.11. $t_2 - t_1 = 0$, for in the given reference frame both events take place simultaneously. In an arbitrary inertial reference frame

$$\tau = t_2' - t_1' = \frac{t_2 + x_2 v/c^2 - t_1 - x_1 v/c^2}{\sqrt{1-v^2/c^2}} = \frac{lv}{c^2\,\sqrt{1-v^2/c^2}}$$

where v is the velocity of the new reference frame. The sign of the time interval depends on the sign of the velocity v, i.e. on the direction of motion of the reference frame.

6.12. The electron velocity may be found from the formula (§13-2)

$$u = \frac{bt}{\sqrt{1 + b^2 t^2/c^2}}$$

Here $b = F/m_0 = eE/m_0$. For an electron $e = 1.6 \times 10^{-19}$ C, $m_0 = 9.1 \times 10^{-31}$ kg. We have

$$b = \frac{1.6 \times 10^{-19} \times 3.0 \times 10^6}{9.1 \times 10^{-31}} = 5.3 \times 10^{17} \text{ m/s}^2,$$

$$\frac{bt}{c} = \frac{5.3 \times 10^{17} \times 10^{-9}}{3.0 \times 10^8} = 1.76$$

$$u = \frac{bt}{\sqrt{1 + b^2 t^2/c^2}} = \frac{5.3 \times 10^{17} \times 10^{-9}}{\sqrt{1 + 1.76^2}} = \frac{5.3 \times 10^8}{2.0} = 2.6 \times 10^8 \text{ m/s}$$

If there is no relativistic mass increase, the electron velocity reaches the value

$$u = \frac{eEt}{m_0} = \frac{1.6 \times 10^{-19} \times 3.0 \times 10^6 \times 10^{-9}}{9.1 \times 10^{-31}} = 5.3 \times 10^8 \text{ m/s}$$

i.e. the velocity computed with the aid of the formulas of Newtonian mechanics exceeds the maximum velocity.

6.13. Since the force is perpendicular to the path, the magnitude of the momentum does not change (Fig. 6.13), $|\mathbf{p}_1| = |\mathbf{p}_2| = p$ (see §§ 16.4 and 18.1). The magnitude of the momentum's variation is $|\Delta\mathbf{p}| = p |\Delta\varphi|$. The normal force is

$$F_n = \frac{|\Delta\mathbf{p}|}{\Delta t} = p \frac{|\Delta\varphi|}{\Delta t} = p\omega =$$

$$= m\omega^2 r = \frac{mv^2}{r}$$

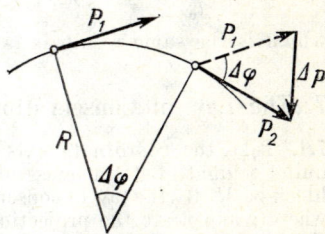

Fig. 6.13.

Formally, we have obtained the same result as in the case of the nonrelativistic motion of a particle in a circular path (see § 7.2). However, in the relativistic case the expression for the force contains the relativistic mass. Thus, in the particular case (the force is perpendicular to the path) the relativistic approach produces formally the same result as the classical approach, although in general the second law of Newton in the form $F = ma$ is not valid for relativistic motion.

6.14. Consider the case of a constant force acting on the object. In this case the expression

$$F = ma = \frac{m_0}{\sqrt{1 - v^2/c^2}} \frac{dv}{dt}$$

reduces to the expression

$$a = \frac{dv}{dt} = b \sqrt{1 - v^2/c^2}$$

where $\frac{dv}{dt}$ is the time derivative of the velocity, $b = F/m_0$ is a constant. It may easily be seen that the equation for the derivative becomes an identity, if one puts $v = c \sin \frac{lt}{c}$. Indeed, in this case $\frac{dv}{dt} = b \cos \frac{bt}{c}$, $\sqrt{1 - v^2/c^2} = \cos \frac{bt}{c}$; consequently $\frac{dv}{dt} = b \sqrt{1 - v^2/c^2}$.

But the result obtained for the velocity is meaningless since after a finite time interval

$$t = \frac{\pi c}{2b} = \frac{\pi c m_0}{2F}$$

the velocity of the object will be equal to the velocity of light in a vacuum, and this is in contradiction with the theory of relativity.

6.15. The length of a rod moving with respect to the reference frame is $l = v\tau_0$, where τ_0 is the time interval between the instants the front and the tail ends of the rod pass the clock at rest in the reference frame. On the other hand, the length of a stationary rod is measured with the aid of moving clocks: $l_0 = v\tau$.

Hence, $\frac{l}{l_0} = \frac{\tau_0}{\tau} = \sqrt{1 - v^2/c^2}$, therefore $l = l_0 \sqrt{1 - v^2/c^2}$,

which is the same result as is given by the Lorentz transformation.

7. The Law of Conservation of Momentum. Centre of Mass

7.1. Take the coordinate axis to coincide with the direction of the bullet's flight. Let the mass of the bullet be m and the mass of the block be M. By the law of conservation of momentum $mv = (M + m) u$, where v and u are the projections of the velocity of the bullet and of the block after it is hit by the bullet. A force of friction acts on the sliding block in the opposite direction to the velocity vector: $T = -\mu g (M + m)$. The acceleration of the block is $a = T/(M + m) = -\mu g$. The block comes to rest after travelling a distance l, therefore $0 - u^2 = 2al$ (see Problem 1.9), or $u = \sqrt{2\mu g l}$. Hence

$$v = \frac{M + m}{m} \sqrt{2\mu g l}$$

Substituting numerical values and noting that $m \ll M$, we obtain the value of the velocity cited in the answer.

7.2. We shall solve the problem in the reference frame of the Earth. The x-projection of the projectile's velocity in this frame, by the classical formula for the addition of velocities, is $u + v \cos \alpha$. From the law of conservation of momentum it follows

$$(M + m) V = Mu + m (u + v \cos \alpha)$$

from which

$$u = \frac{(M + m) V - mv \cos \alpha}{M + m}$$

The flatcar will stop after it fired the round, if its speed prior to the firing is $V = \frac{mv \cos \alpha}{M + m}$.

7.3. Using the fact that the centre of mass remains at rest, we obtain

$$m (l - x) = Mx$$

Hence the displacement of the boat cited in the answer.

7.5. (a) Using the Tsiolkovsky formula, we obtain the final speed of the first stage:

$$v_1 = 2.3u \log (M_0/M_1) = 2.3 \times 4 \times \log (160/70)$$

Hence $v_1 = 3.3$ km/s.

The mass of the second stage is $M_{02} = 160 - 90 - 30 = 40$ tons, 28 tons of which is the mass of the fuel. Note that the Tsiolkovsky formula includes the increase in speed. Since the initial velocity of the second stage coincides with the final velocity of the first stage, the Tsiolkovsky formula for the second stage of the rocket will assume the form

$$\frac{v_2 - v_1}{u} = 2.3 \log \frac{M_{02}}{M_2} , \quad \text{or} \quad v_2 = v_1 + 2.3 \times 4 \times \log (40/12)$$

Hence $v_2 = 8.1$ km/s.

(b) If the rocket is a single-stage rocket, and the amount of fuel consumed is $90 + 28 = 118$ tons, its final mass will be $160 - 118 = 42$ tons and its final speed, according to the Tsiolkovsky formula,

$$v = 2.3 \times 4 \times \log (160/42) = 5.3 \text{ km/s}$$

Evidently, the two-stage rocket is more efficient—for the same mass of fuel burnt it accelerates the spacecraft to a much greater speed.

7.6. The equation (15.7) from § 15.5 in differential form is

$$-m \, dv = u \, dm$$

Integrating, we obtain

$$-\int_{M_0}^{M} \frac{dm}{m} = \frac{1}{u} \int_{v_0}^{v} dv, \quad \text{from which} \quad \frac{v - v_0}{u} = \ln \frac{M_0}{M}$$

7.7. As long as the fuel consumption remains constant, the thrust $F = -\mu u$ remains constant too. At the same time as the mass of fuel decreases due to its consumption, the rocket's acceleration increases. Because of that the overload

$$\frac{N}{P} = \frac{a + g}{g}$$

increases, too.

7.8. Yes, they can, for instance, by running periodically from one end of the car to the other and back.

7.9. Imagine the triangle cut into a large number of strips parallel to its base (Fig. 7.9). The centre of mass of each strip is at its centre, all the centres of all the strips lie on the median, and so the centre of mass of the triangle also lies on the median. The same conclusion is valid for the other two medians as well. Therefore the point of intersection of the medians is the centre of mass.

7.10. Since the plate is uniform, the mass of any part of it is proportional to its area. Moreover, noting that the x-axis, directed as shown in the figures, is the axis of symmetry of the plate, we may conclude that the centre of mass lies on this axis, i.e. that $y_c = z_c = 0$. Then the solution may be obtained by two methods.

First method. Imagine the plate cut in two—into a triangle and a symmetrical remaining piece (Fig. 7.10b). The centre of mass of the triangle lies at a distance of one third

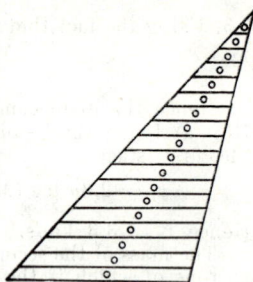

Fig. 7.9.

of a median from the origin, i.e. $x_1 = 1$, the centre of mass of the second body lies at its centre of symmetry, i.e. at a distance $x_2 = 5$

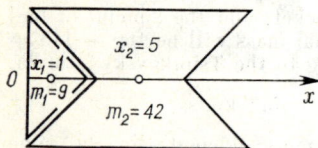

Fig. 7.10b.

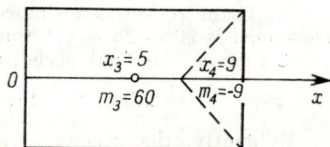

Fig. 7.10c.

from the origin. The masses of those bodies are $m_1 = 6 \times 3/2 = 9$ and $m_2 = 6 \times 10 - 2 \times 9 = 42$ conventional units. The coordinate of the centre of mass is

$$x_c = \frac{m_1 x_1 + m_2 x_2}{m_1 + m_2} = \frac{9 \times 1 + 42 \times 5}{51} = 4.3$$

Second method. Consider the plate as a sum of two bodies, a rectangle of mass $m_3 = 60$ units and a triangle of *negative* mass $m_4 = -9$ units (Fig. 7.10c). The coordinates of their centres of mass are $x_3 = 5$ and $x_4 = 9$. We have according to the definition

$$x_c = \frac{m_3 x_3 + m_4 x_4}{m_3 + m_4} = \frac{60 \times 5 - 9 \times 9}{60 - 9} = 4.3$$

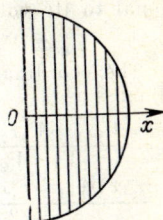

Naturally, both methods produce the same result.

7.12. Divide the radius into 10 equal parts and find the coordinates of the centres of mass of the strips (see Fig. 7.12). All of them lie on the x-axis, their coordinates being shown in the second column of Table 7.12. Since we assume the plate to be uniform, the mass of each strip is proportional to its area, i.e.

Fig. 7.12.

$$m_n \propto S_n = 2\Delta x r_n$$

Table 7.12

n	x_n	x_n^2	r_n^2	r_n	$x_n r_n$	$x_n r_n^2$
1	0.05	0.0025	0.9975	0.999	0.050	0.050
2	0.15	0.0225	0.9775	0.989	0.148	0.147
3	0.25	0.0625	0.9375	0.968	0.242	0.234
4	0.35	0.1225	0.8775	0.936	0.328	0.307
5	0.45	0.2025	0.7975	0.893	0.402	0.359
6	0.55	0.3025	0.6975	0.835	0.459	0.384
7	0.65	0.4225	0.5775	0.760	0.494	0.376
8	0.75	0.5625	0.4375	0.661	0.496	0.328
9	0.85	0.7225	0.2775	0.526	0.448	0.236
10	0.95	0.9025	0.0975	0.312	0.296	0.093
				Total	3.363	2.514

where $\Delta x = 0.1$. Now the product of the segments of a chord is equal to the product of the segments of the diameter, i.e.

$$r_n^2 = (1 - x_n)(1 + x_n) = 1 - x_n^2$$

To determine the position of the centre of mass compute

$$x_c = \frac{S_1 x_1 + S_2 x_2 + \ldots + S_{10} x_{10}}{S_1 + S_2 + \ldots + S_{10}}$$

$$= \frac{2\Delta x (r_1 x_1 + r_2 x_2 + \ldots + r_{10} x_{10})}{\pi/2} = \frac{0.4 \times 3.363}{\pi} = 0.428$$

Hence, the coordinate of the centre of inertia of a semicircle is $x_c =$
$= 0.428R$.

7.13. Divide the hemisphere into 10 "slices" $\Delta x = 0.1$ thick each.
The mass of a "slice" is propor-
tional to its volume:

$$m_n \propto V_n = \pi r_n^2 \Delta x$$

The coordinate of the centre
of mass is

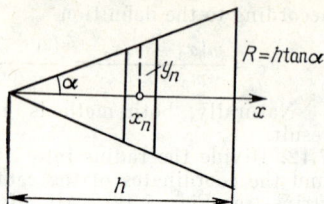

$$x_c = \frac{V_1 x_1 + V_2 x_2 + \ldots + V_{10} x_{10}}{V_1 + V_2 + \ldots + V_{10}} =$$
$$= \frac{\pi \Delta x \left(r_1^2 x_1 + r_2^2 x_2 + \ldots + r_{10}^2 x_{10} \right)}{2\pi/3} =$$
$$= 0.150 \left(r_1^2 x_1 + r_2^2 x_2 + \ldots + r_{10}^2 x_{10} \right)$$

Fig. 7.14.

Substituting the data contained
in the last column of Table 7.12, we obtain

$$x_c = 0.150 \times 2.514R = 0.376R$$

7.14. Divide the cone into 10 "slices" $\Delta x = 0.1$ thick, as was done in
the preceding case. The mass of each slice is

$$m_n \propto V_n = \pi \Delta x \cdot r_n^2 = \pi x_n^2 \tan^2 \alpha \cdot \Delta x$$

The coordinate of the centre of mass is

$$x_c = \frac{V_1 x_1 + V_2 x_2 + \ldots + V_{10} x_{10}}{V_1 + V_2 + \ldots + V_{10}} = \frac{\pi \tan^2 \alpha \cdot \Delta x \left(x_1^3 + x_2^3 + \ldots + x_{10}^3 \right)}{1/3 \pi \tan^2 \alpha}$$

$$= 0.300 \left(x_1^3 + x_2^3 + \ldots + x_{10}^3 \right)$$

The results of the computation are combined in Table 7.14. The
coordinate of the centre of inertia is $x_c = 0.3 \times 2.5h = 0.75h$.

Table 7.14

n	x_n	x_n^3
1	0.05	0.125×10^{-3}
2	0.15	3.375×10^{-3}
3	0.25	15.625×10^{-3}
4	0.35	42.875×10^{-3}
5	0.45	91.125×10^{-3}
6	0.55	166.375×10^{-3}
7	0.65	274.625×10^{-3}
8	0.75	421.875×10^{-3}
9	0.85	614.125×10^{-3}
10	0.95	857.375×10^{-3}
	Total	$2487.500 \times 10^{-3} = 2.5$

7.15. (a) For a semicircle

$$x_c = \frac{2}{\pi R^2} \int\limits_0^R 2yx \, dx$$

But from the equation for a circumference $x^2 + y^2 = R^2$ it follows that $x \, dx = -y \, dy$. We have

$$x_c = \frac{2}{\pi R^2} \int\limits_R^0 (-2y^2 \, dy) = \frac{4}{\pi R^2} \int\limits_0^R y^2 \, dy = \frac{4}{\pi R^2} \left[\frac{y^3}{3} \right]_0^R = \frac{4R}{3\pi} = 0.424R$$

The numerical computation produced an error of $\varepsilon = (0.428 - 0.424)/0.424 = 0.94\% < 1\%$
  (b) For a hemisphere

$$x_c = \frac{3}{2\pi R^3} \int\limits_0^R \pi y^2 x \, dx = \frac{3}{2R^3} \int\limits_0^R y^3 \, dy = \frac{3}{2R^3} \left[\frac{y^4}{4} \right]_0^R = \frac{3R}{8} = 0.375R.$$

The numerical computation produced an error of $\varepsilon = (0.376 - 0.375)/0.375 < 0.3\%$
  (c) For a cone

$$x_c = \frac{3}{\pi h^3 \tan^2 \alpha} \int\limits_0^h \pi x^2 \tan^2 \alpha \cdot x \, dx = \frac{3}{h^3} \int\limits_0^h x^3 \, dx = \frac{3}{h^3} \frac{h^4}{4} = 0.75h$$

The numerical computation gave the same result.
7.16. The position of the centre of mass (Fig. 7.16) is determined rom the condition $m_1 r_1 = m_2 r_2$.
Denoting $r_1 + r_2 = R$ we obtain from the fundamental equation of dynamics:

$$\frac{m_1 v_1^2}{r_1} = \frac{\gamma m_1 m_2}{R^2}, \qquad \frac{m_2 v_2^2}{r_2} = \frac{\gamma m_1 m_2}{R^2}$$

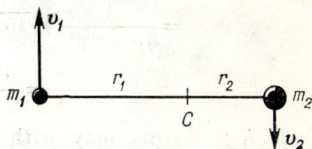

Fig. 7.16.

  Dividing the equality $m_1 v_1^2/r_1 = m_2 v_2^2/r_2$ by $m_1 r_1 = m_2 r_2$ we obtain
$\frac{v_1^2}{r_1^2} = \frac{v_2^2}{r_2^2}$, from which it follows that both objects revolve about the centre of mass with the same period

$$T = \frac{2\pi r_1}{v_1} = \frac{2\pi r_2}{v_2}$$

Reduce the fundamental equation of dynamics to the form

$$\frac{v_1^2}{r_1^2} = \frac{4\pi^2}{T^2} = \frac{\gamma m_2}{R^2 r_1}, \qquad \frac{v_2^2}{r_2^2} = \frac{4\pi^2}{T^2} = \frac{\gamma m_1}{R^2 r_2}$$

whence

$$R^2 r_1 = \gamma m_2 T^2 / 4\pi^2, \qquad R^2 r_2 = \gamma m_1 T^2 / 4\pi^2$$

Adding both equalities, we obtain

$$R^3 = \frac{\gamma (m_1 + m_2)}{4\pi^2} \, T^2$$

This is the desired expression for the generalized third Kepler law.

8. Total and Kinetic Energy

8.2. It follows from $K = \mathscr{E}_0$ that $\mathscr{E} = 2\mathscr{E}_0$, or $\sqrt{1 - v^2/c^2} = 1/2$. Hence

$$v = c \, \sqrt{3}/2 = 2.6 \times 10^8 \text{ m/s}$$

8.3. The electron mass is

$$m = \frac{m_0}{\sqrt{1 - 0.92^2}} = \frac{m_0}{\sqrt{1.92 \times 0.08}} = \frac{10 m_0}{\sqrt{15.3}} = 2.56 m_0$$

Therefore the total energy is $\mathscr{E} = 2.56 \mathscr{E}_0$, and the kinetic energy

$$K = \mathscr{E} - \mathscr{E}_0 = 1.56 \mathscr{E}_0$$

The momentum is

$$p = mu = 2.56 \times 9.1 \times 10^{-31} \times 0.92 \times 3.0 \times 10^8 = 6.4 \times 10^{-22} \text{ kg·m/s}$$

8.4. The total energy is $\mathscr{E} = K + \mathscr{E}_0 = 10.94$ GeV. The momentum may be found from the relation

$$p = \frac{1}{c} \sqrt{\mathscr{E}^2 - \mathscr{E}_0^2} = \frac{1}{c} \sqrt{K(2\mathscr{E}_0 + K)} =$$

$$= \frac{1}{3.0 \times 10^8} \sqrt{10 \times 11.88 \times 1.6^2 \times 10^{-20}} =$$

$$= \frac{10.9 \times 1.6 \times 10^{-10}}{3.0 \times 10^8} = 5.8 \times 10^{-18} \text{ kg·m/s}$$

If $K \gg \mathscr{E}_0$ one may with sufficient accuracy assume that

$$p = \frac{K}{c} = \frac{10 \times 1.6 \times 10^{-10}}{3.0 \times 10^8} = 5.3 \times 10^{-18} \text{ kg·m/s}$$

The error will be

$$\varepsilon = (5.8 - 5.3)/5.8 \approx 5\%$$

The velocity may be found from the relation

$$\beta = \frac{u}{c} = \frac{muc}{mc^2} = \frac{pc}{\mathscr{E}} \approx \frac{K}{\mathscr{E}} = \frac{10.0}{10.9} = 0.92$$

8.6. The relative error is

$$\varepsilon = \frac{K_{\text{rel}} - K_{\text{cl}}}{K_{\text{rel}}} = 1 - \frac{m_0 u^2}{2 (mc^2 - m_0 c^2)}$$

Denoting $\beta = u/c$ and noting that $m_0/m = \sqrt{1-\beta^2}$, we obtain

$$\varepsilon = 1 - \frac{\beta^2 \sqrt{1-\beta^2}}{2(1-\sqrt{1-\beta^2})} = 1 - \frac{\beta^2 \sqrt{1-\beta^2}(1+\sqrt{1-\beta^2})}{2(1-1+\beta^2)} =$$

$$= \frac{1}{2}(1+\beta^2 - \sqrt{1-\beta^2})$$

8.7. $v = \sqrt[3]{2P\eta/CS\rho}$.

8.8. As the weight moves along an inclined plane at constant speed, the power is

$$P = (F+T)v = mgv(\sin\alpha + \mu\cos\alpha) = mgv(\sin\alpha + \tan\varphi\cos\alpha) =$$

$$= \frac{mgv\sin(\alpha+\varphi)}{\cos\varphi}$$

where $\tan\varphi = \mu$. The speed

$$v = \frac{P\cos\varphi}{mg\sin(\alpha+\varphi)}$$

will be at its minimum if $\sin(\alpha+\varphi) = 1$, i.e. if $\alpha + \varphi = \dfrac{\pi}{2}$. Hence

$$\alpha = \frac{\pi}{2} - \arctan\mu = \arctan\frac{1}{\mu}$$

8.10. Noting that $K_0 = 0$ we see that the work of the electrical forces is equal to the ultimate kinetic energy:

$$K = A = eEl$$

(1) The nonrelativistic case: $1/2 m_0 u^2 = eEl$, hence

$$u = \sqrt{2eEl/m_0}$$

(2) The relativistic case: $\sqrt{\mathscr{E}_0^2 + p^2c^2} - \mathscr{E}_0 = eEl$. Hence

$$p^2c^2 = eEl(2\mathscr{E}_0 + eEl), \quad \text{or} \quad \frac{m_0^2u^2c^2}{1-u^2/c^2} = eEl(2\mathscr{E}_0 + eEl).$$

After some simple transformations we obtain

$$u = \frac{c\sqrt{eEl(2\mathscr{E}_0 + eEl)}}{\mathscr{E}_0 + eEl}$$

(3) If $eEl \ll \mathscr{E}_0$, then

$$u = \frac{c\sqrt{2\mathscr{E}_0 eEl}}{\mathscr{E}_0} = \sqrt{\frac{2m_0c^2eEl}{m_0^2c^2}} = \sqrt{\frac{2eEl}{m_0}}$$

i.e. the nonrelativistic formula is valid.

8.11. The absolute error is

$$\Delta = \mathscr{E} - pc = \frac{\mathscr{E}^2 - p^2c^2}{\mathscr{E} + pc} < \frac{\mathscr{E}_0^2}{2pc}.$$

9. Uncertainty Relation

9.1. Assuming the electron moves in a circular orbit about the nucleus (proton), we can write the equation of motion in the form

$$\frac{e^2}{4\pi\varepsilon_0 r^2} = \frac{mv^2}{r}$$

Hence the kinetic energy of the electron is

$$K = \frac{mv^2}{2} = \frac{e^2}{8\pi\varepsilon_0 r}$$

But if the electron is localized in a region of characteristic dimension *r*, its kinetic energy

$$K \geqslant \hbar^2/2mr^2$$

Comparing the two expressions, we obtain $r \gg \dfrac{4\pi\varepsilon_0 \hbar^2}{me^2}$.

The quantity $a_0 = \dfrac{4\pi\varepsilon_0 \hbar^2}{me^2} = 5.24 \times 10^{-11}$ m is called the *first*

Bohr radius (see § 7.15).

9.2. Let's first estimate the momentum and the velocity of the electron. We have

$$p \gg \hbar/a \approx 10^{-19} \ \text{kg·m/s}$$

From the formula $p = \dfrac{m_0 \beta c}{\sqrt{1-\beta^2}}$, where $\beta = u/c$, we obtain

$$\frac{\beta}{\sqrt{1-\beta^2}} = \frac{p}{m_0 c} = 360$$

Hence $\beta \approx 1$, i.e. the electron is an ultra-relativistic one. Its kinetic energy is

$$K = pc = 3 \times 10^{-11} \ \text{J} = 200 \ \text{MeV}$$

9.3. Estimate first the region of localization of the electron, its momentum and its velocity. We have

$$a = n^{-1/3} = \sqrt[3]{10^{-29}} \approx 2 \times 10^{-10} \ \text{m}, \quad p \gg \hbar/a = 5 \times 10^{-25} \ \text{kg·m/s}$$

The velocity may be found in the same way, as was done in the previous problem:

$$\frac{\beta}{\sqrt{1-\beta^2}} = \frac{p}{m_0 c} = 2 \times 10^{-3}$$

Since $\beta \approx 2 \times 10^{-3}$, the velocity of the electron is much lower than the velocity of light, i.e. the conduction electrons in a metal are nonrelativistic particles. Their kinetic energy is

$$K \approx \frac{\hbar^2 n^{2/3}}{2m} \approx 1.3 \times 10^{-19} \text{ J} \approx 1 \text{ eV}$$

9.4. First find the number of neutrons and their concentration:

$$N = \frac{2 \times 10^{30}}{1.67 \times 10^{-27}} = 1.2 \times 10^{57}, \quad n = \frac{N}{4/3 \pi r^3} = 3 \times 10^{44} \text{ m}^{-3}$$

The region of localization of a neutron is $a = n^{-1/3} = 1.5 \times 10^{-15}$ m. The momentum of a neutron is $p \geqslant \hbar/a \approx 7 \times 10^{-20}$ kg·m/s; the relativistic factor is

$$\frac{\beta}{\sqrt{1-\beta^2}} = \frac{p}{m_0 c} = \frac{7 \times 10^{-20}}{1.67 \times 10^{-27} \times 30 \times 10^8} = 0.14$$

from which it follows that $\beta \approx 0.14$, i.e. the neutron is a nonrelativistic particle. Its kinetic energy is

$$K \approx \frac{\hbar^2 n^{2/3}}{2m} \approx 1.3 \times 10^{-12} \text{ J} \approx 9 \text{ MeV}$$

10. Elementary Theory of Collisions

10.1. The result is not in contradiction with the law of conservation of momentum: the vertical component of the momentum is transmitted to the Earth.

10.3. Direct the x-axis along the wall and the y-axis normal to it (see Fig. 10.3). Since the

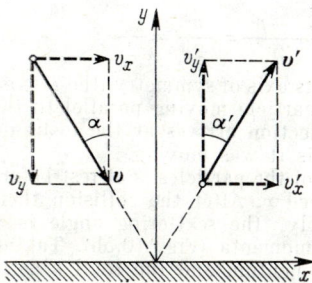

Fig. 10.3.

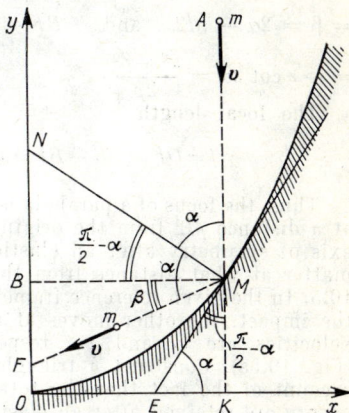

Fig. 10.4.

wall is smooth, the momentum component along the x-axis will not change. Assuming the mass of the wall to be infinitely greater than that of the ball, we find that the momentum component along the y-axis changes sign while its magnitude remains constant (see

§ 17.3). Thus

$$p'_x = p_x, \quad p'_y = -p_y$$

Hence $\alpha' = \alpha$ (we are not interested in the sign of the angle).
10.4. The ball, after striking the surface of the parabolic mirror at point M (Fig. 10.4), will be reflected to point F called the focus. The angle of incidence α is the angle between the direction of the velocity of the ball and the normal MN; it is equal to the angle be-

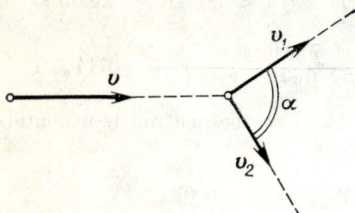
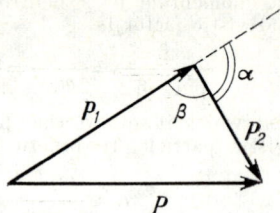

Fig. 10.5a.   Fig. 10.5b.

tween the tangent ME and the x-axis. According to Problem 3.14, we have $\tan \alpha = x/p$, where $x = OK = MB$ is the x-coordinate of the ball before impact. As may be seen from the figure, $\angle BMF =$

$$= \beta = 2\alpha - \pi/2 \quad \text{and} \quad BF = BM \tan \beta = x \tan \left(2\alpha - \frac{\pi}{2} \right) =$$

$$= -x \cot 2\alpha = \frac{x^2 - p^2}{2p}.$$

The focal length

$$f = OF = OB - BF = y - \frac{x^2 - p^2}{2p} = \frac{p^2}{2p} = \frac{p}{2}.$$

Thus, the focus of a parabola is on its axis of symmetry (the y-axis) at a distance $p/2$ from the origin. A particle moving parallel to the axis of symmetry after an elastic reflection arrives at the focus no matter at what distance from the axis it was moving.
10.5. In the given reference frame one of the particles is at rest before the impact, the other moves at a speed v. After the collision their velocities are v_1 and v_2, respectively, the scattering angle is α (Fig. 10.5a). Construct a triangle of momenta (Fig. 10.5b). Taking account of the fact that the total momentum and the total kinetic energy are retained after an elastic collision, we obtain

$$p^2 = p_1^2 + p_2^2 - 2p_1p_2 \cos \beta, \quad \frac{p^2}{2m} = \frac{p_1^2}{2m} + \frac{p_2^2}{2m}$$

Hence $\cos \beta = 0$ and $\alpha = \beta = 90°$.
10.6. Since the energy is equipartitioned between the particles, the same will happen to the momenta. Consequently, after the collisions the protons scatter at equal angles to the original direction of the

proton projectile (see Fig. 10.6). From the laws of conservation of total momentum and of total kinetic energy we obtain

$$2p_1 \cos \frac{\alpha}{2} = p, \qquad 2K_1 = K$$

From the relation between the energy and the momentum $\mathscr{E}^2 =$

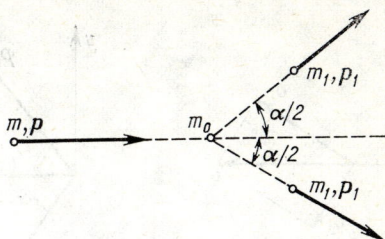

Fig. 10.6.

$= \mathscr{E}_0^2 + p^2 c^2$ we obtain, noting that $\mathscr{E} = \mathscr{E}_0 + K$,

$$K^2 + 2K\mathscr{E}_0 = p^2 c^2, \qquad K_1^2 + 2K_1\mathscr{E}_0 = p_1^2 c^2$$

Eliminating the momenta and the proton's kinetic energy after collision, K_1, from these equations, we obtain

$$\cos^2 \frac{\alpha}{2} = \frac{2\mathscr{E}_0 + K}{4\mathscr{E}_0 + K}$$

whence

$$\cos \alpha = 2 \cos^2 \frac{\alpha}{2} - 1 = \frac{K}{4\mathscr{E}_0 + K}$$

Note that in the nonrelativistic case, when $K \ll \mathscr{E}_0$, we shall have $\cos \alpha \approx 0$ and $\alpha \approx \pi/2$ (compare with Problem 10.5).

For $K = 500$ MeV we obtain, noting that $\mathscr{E}_0 = 938$ MeV, (see Problem 7.1) $\cos \alpha = 0.117$, $\alpha = 0.46\pi$.

For $K = 10$ GeV we obtain $\cos \alpha = 0.728$, $\alpha = 0.24\pi$. We see that as the kinetic energy of the projectile particle rises, the scattering angle decreases, approaching zero for ultra-relativistic particles ($K \gg \mathscr{E}_0$).

10.7. One of the disks is at rest before the impact; after the impact its velocity will be in the direction of the centre line at the moment of contact (Fig. 10.7b) for this is the direction in which the force acted on it. Thus, $\sin \alpha_2 = d/2r$, $\alpha_1 + \alpha_2 = \pi/2$ (see Problem 10.5).

Since the masses of both disks are equal, the triangle of momenta turns into the triangle of velocities (see figure). We have

$$v_1 = v \cos \alpha_1 = v \sin \alpha_2 = vd/2r$$

$$v_2 = v \cos \alpha_2 = v \sqrt{1 - d^2/4r^2}$$

10.8. Direct the coordinate axes as shown in Fig. 10.8b. The direction of velocity of the larger disk may be found, as in the previous problem, from the condition

$$\sin \alpha_2 = d/(r_1 + r_2)$$

The remaining three unknowns, the velocities v_1 and v_2 and the angle α_1, will be found if we write down the equations for the conser-

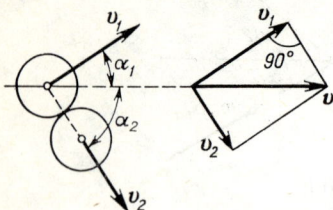

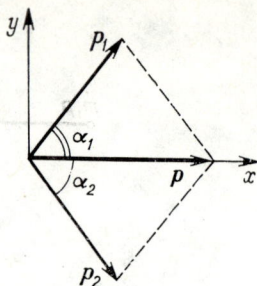

Fig. 10.7b.   Fig. 10.8b.

vation of the x- and y-components of the momenta and the equation for the conservation of kinetic energy

$$p_{1y} - p_{2y} = 0, \qquad p_{1x} + p_{2x} = p, \qquad K_1 + K_2 = K$$

or in the form

$$p_1 \sin \alpha_1 - p_2 \sin \alpha_2 = 0, \qquad p_1 \cos \alpha_1 + p_2 \cos \alpha_2 = p,$$

$$\frac{p_1^2}{2m_1} + \frac{p_2^2}{2m_2} = \frac{p^2}{2m_1}$$

After some transformations we obtain

$$p_2 = \frac{2m_2 p \cos \alpha_2}{m_1 + m_2}, \qquad p_1 = \frac{p}{m_1 + m_2} \sqrt{(m_1 + m_2)^2 - 4m_1 m_2 \cos^2 \alpha_2}$$

$$\sin \alpha_1 = (p_2 \sin \alpha_2)/p_1.$$

Note that for $m_1 = m_2$ and $r_1 = r_2$ we shall arrive at the results of the previous problem.

10.9. The number of particles striking the wall during the time Δt (Fig. 10.9) is

$$N = nvS_\perp \, \Delta t = nvS \, \Delta t \cos \alpha$$

(see § 17.5). Since only the normal component of the velocity changes after impact, the force is

$$f = \frac{\Delta (mv_\perp)}{\Delta t} = \frac{2mv \cos \alpha}{\Delta t}$$

The force of pressure is

$$F = Nf = 2nSmv^2 \cos^2 \alpha$$

and the pressure

$$p = 2nmv^2 \cos^2 \alpha$$

10.10. The problem stipulates that the boat moves over water at a constant speed, and this means that the drag and the force acting on the sails are equal in magnitude.

To find the formula for the drag of the water compute the Reynolds number $\mathrm{Re} = \rho_0 v_0 l_0 / \eta_0$. It is given that $v_0 = 3$ m/s and that

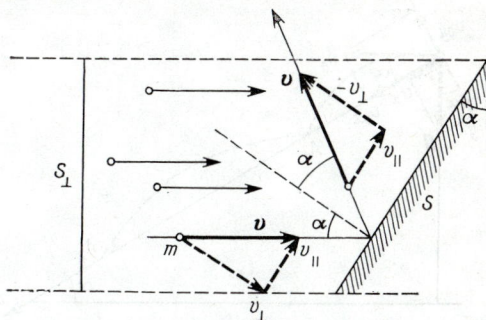

Fig. 10.9.

the characteristic dimension is $l_0 \approx 1$ m. Thus, $\mathrm{Re} = 3 \times 10^6$, and so the pressure drag $R = CS_0 \rho_0 v_0^2 / 2$ plays a basic role.

To be definite let us assume that the interaction of the air with the sails is elastic. Noting also that $nm = \rho$ is the density of air, we obtain $\frac{1}{2} CS_0 \rho_0 v_0^2 = 2\rho S v^2$. The area of the sails is

$$S = \frac{CS_0 \rho_0 v_0^2}{4\rho v^2} = \frac{0.1 \times 1.0 \times 10^3 \times 9.0}{4 \times 1.3 \times 36.0} = 5 \text{ m}^2$$

10.11. Arrange the coordinate axes as shown in Fig. 10.11. Then components of the initial velocity along the axes will be $v_{0x} = v_0 \cos \alpha$, $v_{0y} = v_0 \sin \alpha$ and the acceleration components will be $a_x = g \sin \alpha$, $a_y = -g \cos \alpha$. The equation of motion for the first part of the trajectory should be written thus:

$$v_x = v_{0x} + a_x t = v_0 \cos \alpha + gt \sin \alpha$$

$$v_y = v_{0y} + a_y t = v_0 \sin \alpha - gt \cos \alpha$$

$$x = x_0 + v_{0x} t + \frac{a_x t^2}{2} = v_0 t \cos \alpha + \frac{gt^2 \sin \alpha}{2}$$

$$y = y_0 + v_{0y} t + \frac{a_y t^2}{2} = v_0 t \sin \alpha - \frac{gt^2 \cos \alpha}{2}$$

Since at the point A_1, the ordinate $y_1 = 0$, it follows that

$$t_1 = \frac{2v_0 \tan \alpha}{g}, \qquad x_1 = \frac{2v_0^2 \sin \alpha}{g \cos^2 \alpha},$$

$$v_{1x} = \frac{v_0}{\cos \alpha} (1 + \sin^2 \alpha), \qquad v_{1y} = -v_0 \sin \alpha$$

The longitudinal velocity component does not change after an elastic impact, but the lateral component changes sign. Therefore

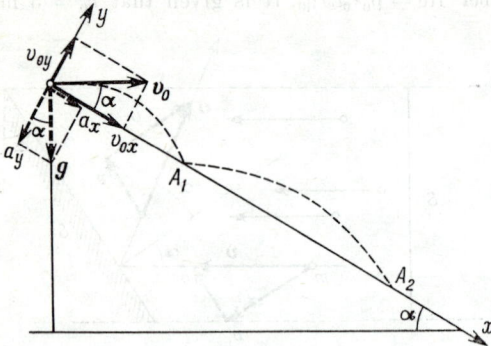

Fig. 10.11.

for the second part of the trajectory

$$v_{0x} = v_{1x} = \frac{v_0}{\cos \alpha} (1 + \sin^2 \alpha), \qquad v_{0y} = -v_{1y} = v_0 \sin \alpha$$

The equation of motion, by analogy with the first case, will be

$$x = x_1 + v_{0x}t + \frac{a_x t^2}{2} = \frac{2v_0^2 \sin \alpha}{g \cos^2 \alpha} + \frac{v_0 t (1 + \sin^2 \alpha)}{\cos \alpha} + \frac{gt^2 \sin \alpha}{2}$$

$$y = y_1 + v_{0y}t + \frac{a_y t^2}{2} = v_0 t \sin \alpha - \frac{gt^2 \cos \alpha}{2}$$

At the point A_2 the ordinate is again zero, i.e. $y_2 = 0$, therefore the x-coordinate of the point A_2 is

$$x_2 = \frac{4v_0^2 \sin^2 \alpha}{g \cos^2 \alpha} (1 + \sin^2 \alpha)$$

The ratio of displacements is

$$\frac{l_2}{l_1} = \frac{x_2 - x_1}{x_1} = 1 + 2 \sin^2 \alpha$$

11. Potential Energy. Potential

11.1. Let the object move in the field from point M to point N (Fig. 11.1) first along the rectilinear segment $MN = l$, and then along the broken line $MKN = l_1 + l_2$. In the first case the work done is

$$A = Fl \cos \alpha = Fd$$

In the second case the work done is

$$A = A_1 + A_2 = Fl_1 \cos \alpha_1 + Fl_2 \cos \alpha_2 = F(l_1 \cos \alpha_1 + l_2 \cos \alpha_2) = Fd$$

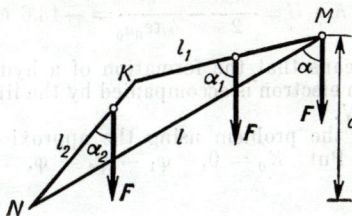

Fig. 11.1

We see that the work done is independent of the path.

11.2. (a) $\quad F = -kx, \quad A = \int\limits_{x_1}^{x_2} F\,dx = -k \int\limits_{x_1}^{x_2} x\,dx = -\dfrac{kx^2}{2} \Big|_{x_1}^{x_2} =$

$$= \frac{kx_1^2}{2} - \frac{kx_2^2}{2};$$

(b) $\quad F = \dfrac{qQ}{4\pi\varepsilon_0 r^2}, \quad A = \int\limits_{r_1}^{r_2} F\,dr = \dfrac{qQ}{4\pi\varepsilon_0} \int\limits_{r_1}^{r_2} \dfrac{dr}{r^2} = -\dfrac{qQ}{4\pi\varepsilon_0 r} \Big|_{r_1}^{r_2} =$

$$= \frac{qQ}{4\pi\varepsilon_0 r_1} - \frac{qQ}{4\pi\varepsilon_0 r_2};$$

(c) $\quad F = -\dfrac{\gamma mM}{r^2}, \quad A = \int\limits_{r_1}^{r_2} F\,dr = -\gamma mM \int\limits_{r_1}^{r_2} \dfrac{dr}{r} = \dfrac{\gamma mM}{r} \Big|_{r_1}^{r_2} =$

$$= \frac{\gamma mM}{r_2} - \frac{\gamma mM}{r_1}.$$

11.5. In a dipole one point charge is in the field of the other point charge, therefore

$$U = q_1 \varphi_2 = \frac{q_1 q_2}{4\pi\varepsilon_0 d} = -\frac{q^2}{4\pi\varepsilon_0 d} = -\frac{p_e^2}{4\pi\varepsilon_0 d^3}$$

where $p_e = qd$ is the dipole moment, d being the separation of the dipole. The minus sign shows that the formation of a dipole from two charges equal in magnitude but opposite in sign, initially an infinite distance apart, results in the liberation of energy.

11.6. The energy liberated as the result of the formation of one hydrogen chloride molecule is about $U = 10.3 \times 10^{-20}$ J $= 0.65$ eV. Per 1 kg we obtain $\Delta \mathcal{E} = NU = 1.65 \times 10^6$ J. (Actually, the energy liberated in the process of formation of 1 kg of hydrogen chloride is 2.5 MJ; this means that our rough estimate gave the right order of magnitude.)

11.8. $$\mathcal{E} = K + U = \frac{mv^2}{2} - \frac{e^2}{4\pi\varepsilon_0 a_0} = -13.6 \text{ eV}.$$

The minus sign means that the formation of a hydrogen atom from a free proton and an electron is accompanied by the liberation of energy equal to 13.6 eV.

11.9. (a) Consider the problem using the approximation of Newtonian mechanics. Put $K_0 = 0$, $\varphi_1 - \varphi_2 = \varphi$, $A = K - K_0 = q(\varphi_1 - \varphi_2)$.

We have

$$q\varphi = \frac{1}{2} mu^2, \quad u = \sqrt{2q\varphi/m}, \quad p = mu = \sqrt{2mq\varphi}$$

(b) In the relativistic case

$$K = q\varphi = \sqrt{p^2 c^2 - \mathcal{E}_0^2} - \mathcal{E}_0$$

We obtain

$$p = \frac{1}{c} \sqrt{q\varphi(2\mathcal{E}_0 + q\varphi)}, \quad u = \frac{muc^2}{mc^2} = \frac{pc^2}{\mathcal{E}} = \frac{c\sqrt{q\varphi(2\mathcal{E}_0 + q\varphi)}}{\mathcal{E}_0 + q\varphi}$$

In the Newtonian approximation $\mathcal{E}_0 \gg q\varphi$, and the formulas assume the form

$$p \approx \frac{1}{c} \sqrt{2\mathcal{E}_0 q\varphi} = \sqrt{2m_0 q\varphi}, \quad u = \frac{c\sqrt{2\mathcal{E}_0 q\varphi}}{\mathcal{E}_0} = \sqrt{\frac{2q\varphi}{m_0}}$$

We have of course obtained the same expressions as in (a), for in that case $m = m_0$.

11.10. The relative error is

$$\varepsilon = \frac{p_{rel} - p_{cl}}{p_{rel}} = 1 - \frac{c\sqrt{2q\varphi m_0}}{\sqrt{q\varphi(2\mathcal{E}_0 + q\varphi)}} = 1 - \sqrt{\frac{2\mathcal{E}_0}{2\mathcal{E}_0 + q\varphi}}$$

Hence

$$\varphi = \frac{2\mathcal{E}_0}{q} \cdot \frac{2\varepsilon - \varepsilon^2}{(1 - \varepsilon)^2}$$

Since $\varepsilon \ll 1$, we have $\varphi = \dfrac{4\varepsilon \mathcal{E}_0}{q}$.

1.11. The relative error is

$$\varepsilon = \frac{p_{rel} - e\varphi/c}{p_{rel}} = 1 - \sqrt{\frac{e\varphi}{2\mathscr{E}_0 + e\varphi}}$$

Hence

$$\varphi = \frac{2\mathscr{E}_0}{e} \cdot \frac{(1-\varepsilon)^2}{2\varepsilon - \varepsilon^2} = \frac{\mathscr{E}_0}{\varepsilon e}$$

12. The Law of Conservation of Energy in Newtonian Mechanics

12.1. According to the law of conservation of momentum $mv = (M + m) u$, according to the law of conservation of energy $1/2 \, (M + m) \, u^2 = (M + m) \, gh$. Hence

$$v = \frac{M+m}{m} \sqrt{2gh} = \frac{M+m}{m} \sqrt{2gl\,(1 - \cos\alpha)}$$

12.2. (a) According to Newton's second law

$$a = \frac{F}{m} - g, \quad v = \sqrt{2ah} = \sqrt{2h\left(\frac{F}{m} - g\right)}$$

(b) According to the law of conservation of energy the work performed by a force is equal to the change in energy

$$A = \Delta U + K, \quad \text{or} \quad Fh = mgh + \frac{mv^2}{2}$$

Hence

$$v = \sqrt{2h\left(\frac{F}{m} - g\right)}$$

12.3. Here the work of the force of friction T is equal to the decrease in kinetic energy. In the reference frame of the platform

$$Tl = K_0 \quad \text{or} \quad \mu mgl = \frac{mv_0^2}{2}, \quad \text{whence} \quad l = \frac{v_0^2}{2\mu g}$$

The braking time is

$$\tau = \frac{l}{v_{av}} = \frac{2l}{v_0} = \frac{v_0}{\mu g}$$

12.4. The speed of the weight at the uppermost point should be such that the tension of the thread T and the force of gravity impart to it the necessary centripetal acceleration (see Fig. 12.4):

$$mg + T = mv^2/l$$

To find the minimum speed at the uppermost point, put $T = 0$. We have

$$mg = mv^2_{min}/l \quad \text{or} \quad v^2_{min} = 2gl$$

Taking the potential energy to be zero at point O (the axis of rotation) we obtain according to the law of conservation of energy

$$\frac{mv_0^2}{2} - mgl = \frac{mv_{min}^2}{2} + mgl$$

Hence $v_0 \geqslant \sqrt{5gl}$.

12.5. If the weight rotates on a rod, its speed in the uppermost point may be zero. We obtain according to the law of conservation of energy

$$mgl = \frac{mv_0^2}{2} - mgl, \quad \text{whence } v_0 \geqslant \sqrt{4gl}$$

12.6. In the direction normal to the velocity the forces acting on the weight are the tension of the thread T and the component of the force of gravity, $F_2 = mg \cos \alpha$ (Fig. 12.6). According to Newton's second law

$$T - F_2 = mv^2/l$$

To find the velocity apply the law of conservation of energy

$$mgh_0 = mgh + mv^2/2$$

Hence

$$T = mg \cos \alpha + \frac{2mg}{l} (h_0 - h)$$

However, $h_0 = l \ (1 - \cos \ \alpha_0)$, $h = l \ (1 - \cos \alpha)$, therefore $h_0 - h = l \ (\cos \alpha - \cos \alpha_0)$. Substituting into the expression for the tension of the thread we obtain

Fig. 12.4.

$$T = mg \ (3 \cos \alpha - 2 \cos \alpha_0)$$

12.7. According to Newton's third law, the pressure of the washer against the sphere is equal in magnitude to the reaction. The forces acting on the object in the direction normal to the velocity vector are the reaction N and the component of the force of gravity $F_2 = mg \cos \alpha$ (see Fig. 12.7). According to Newton's second law

$$F_2 - N = mv^2/R$$

To find the velocity apply the law of conservation of energy $mgh = mv^2/2$. Since $h = R \ (1 - \cos \alpha)$, we obtain after some simple transformations

$$N = mg \ (3 \cos \alpha - 2)$$

When the washer leaves the sphere it ceases to press against it, and the reaction becomes zero. The condition for the loss of contact is $\cos \alpha = 2/3$; $\alpha = 48°$; $h = R/3$.

12.8. According to Fig. 12.8, we have

$$N - mg \cos \alpha = mv^2/R$$

To find speed apply the law of conservation of energy:

$$mgH = mgR \ (1 - \cos \alpha) + mv^2/2$$

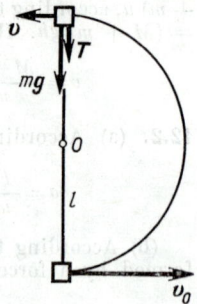

Hence

$$N = mg \left(3\cos\alpha - 2 + \frac{2H}{R} \right)$$

In the highest point of the loop $\alpha = \pi$, so

$$N_{\text{top}} = mg \left(-5 + \frac{2H}{R} \right)$$

The minimum height is found from the condition $N_{\text{top}} = 0$, therefore $H_{\min} = \frac{5}{2} R$. In this case

$$N = 3mg (1 + \cos\alpha) = 6mg \cos^2 \frac{\alpha}{2}$$

12.9. The object thrown at an initial speed v_0 at an angle α to the horizontal must fly through the air a distance $AB = L = 2R\sin\alpha$. We know (see § 8.2) that

$$L = \frac{2v_0^2 \sin\alpha \cos\alpha}{g},$$

$$\text{so} \quad v_0^2 = \frac{gR}{\cos\alpha}$$

To find the speed v_0 apply the law of conservation of energy

$$mgH = mgR (1 + \cos\alpha) + \frac{1}{2} mv_0^2$$

from which $k = \dfrac{H}{R} = 1 + \cos\alpha +$

$$+ \frac{1}{2\cos\alpha}.$$

For the computation of $\cos\alpha$ we obtain an equation

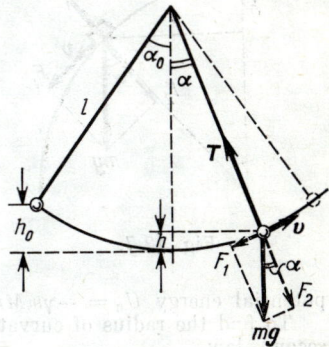

Fig. 12.6.

$$2\cos^2\alpha - 2(k-1)\cos\alpha + 1 = 0$$

Hence

$$\cos\alpha = \frac{1}{2} \left(k - 1 \pm \sqrt{(k-1)^2 - 2} \right)$$

Since the number under the root sign must be non-negative, we obtain $k - 1 \geqslant \sqrt{2}$, i.e. $k \geqslant 1 + \sqrt{2}$.

On the other hand, $0 < \cos\alpha \leqslant 1$, i.e. $k - 1 + \sqrt{(k-1)^2 - 2} \leqslant \leqslant 2$ and $k \leqslant 2.5$. Thus

$$1 + \sqrt{2} \leqslant k \leqslant 2.5, \quad \text{i.e.} \quad (1 + \sqrt{2}) R \leqslant H \leqslant 2.5R$$

For the limiting values of the cosines we have

$$\cos\alpha = \frac{\sqrt{2}}{2}, \quad \text{i.e.} \quad \alpha_1 = 45°$$

$$\cos\alpha = (1.5 \pm 0.5)/2, \quad \cos\alpha_2 = 0.5, \quad \cos\alpha_3 = 1$$

Obviously the solution $\cos \alpha_3 = 1$ does not satisfy the condition of the problem, since for $\alpha_3 = 0$ there will be no cut. So the remaining solution is $\cos \alpha_2 = 0.5$, $\alpha_2 = 60°$.

Accordingly, for the heights in the range $(1 + \sqrt{2}) R \leqslant H \leqslant 2.5R$, corresponding suitable cuts are those with angles of $45° \leqslant \alpha \leqslant 60°$ chosen so as to satisfy the condition

$$\cos \alpha = \frac{1}{2} (k - 1 - \sqrt{k^2 - 2k - 1})$$

12.10. Denote the radius of curvature in the perihelion by R_0, the kinetic energy of the planet in perihelion by $K_0 = mv_0^2/2$, and its

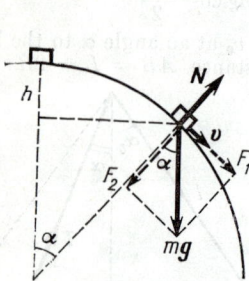

Fig. 12.7.

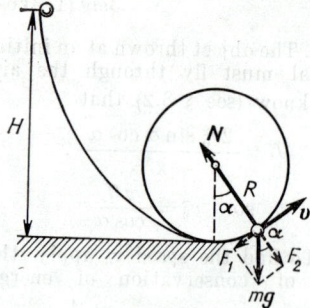

Fig. 12.8.

potential energy $U_0 = -\gamma mM/r_0$.

To find the radius of curvature in the perihelion apply Newton's second law

$$\frac{mv_0^2}{R_0} = \frac{\gamma m M}{r_0^2}, \quad \text{from which} \quad R_0 = \frac{mv_0^2 r_0^2}{\gamma M m} = -\frac{2r_0 K_0}{U_0}$$

The radius of curvature at the aphelion is the same as in the perihelion since the ellipse is a symmetrical figure. We have, according to Newton's second law,

$$\frac{mv_a^2}{R_0} = \frac{\gamma m M}{r_a^2}$$

The total mechanical energy of the planet, according to the law of conservation of energy is

$$W = \frac{mv_0^2}{2} - \frac{\gamma m M}{r_0} = \frac{mv_a^2}{2} - \frac{\gamma m M}{r_a}$$

Eliminating the velocity we obtain

$$\frac{\gamma m M R_0}{2r_0^2} - \frac{\gamma m M}{r_0} = \frac{\gamma m M R_0}{2r_a^2} - \frac{\gamma m M}{r_a}$$

Cancelling out γm, we obtain a quadratic equation

$$r_a^2 (2r_0 - R_0) - 2r_a r_0^2 + R_0 r_0^2 = 0$$

The first root of the equation is $r_a = r_0$. This means that in this case the ellipse reduces to a circle of radius r_0. In this case the radius of curvature is also $R_0 = r_0$, and, consequently, the orbital velocity is $v = v_0 = \sqrt{\gamma M / r_0}$.

The second root of the equation is

$$r_a = \frac{r_0 R_0}{2r_0 - R_0} = -\frac{r_0 K_0}{W}$$

Since the distance from the aphelion to the Sun is a positive quantity we must have $W < 0$. This means that a planet can move in an elliptical orbit only if the sum of its kinetic and potential energies (i.e. its total mechanical energy) is negative. In particular in the case of a circular orbit, $W = -\dfrac{\gamma m M}{2r_0}$.

12.11. Calculate first the total energy of the spacecraft at the perigee (i.e. at the apex of the parabola): $W = \dfrac{mv_0^2}{2} - \dfrac{\gamma m M}{r_0}$. According to Newton's second law $\dfrac{\gamma m M}{r_0^2} = \dfrac{mv_0^2}{R_0}$, where R_0 is the radius of curvature at this point. Hence $\dfrac{\gamma m M}{r_0} = \dfrac{mv_0^2 r_0}{R_0}$ and the total energy is $W = mv_0^2 \left(\dfrac{1}{2} - \dfrac{r_0}{R_0} \right)$.

But the distance from the focus to the apex is $r_0 = f = p/2$ (see Problem 10.4), and the radius of curvature at this point is $R_0 = p$ (see Problem 3.13). Substituting these values we see that the total energy is zero. In compliance with the law of conservation of energy it will be zero at any other point of the path as well.

12.12. Let the rod sink by a distance Δy. Then the wedge will shift a distance Δx to the left. Evidently $\Delta y = \Delta x \tan \alpha$. Since the motion takes place with zero initial velocity, it follows that

$$\Delta x = a_x t^2/2, \quad v_x = a_x t, \quad \Delta y = a_y t^2/2, \quad v_y = a_y t$$

According to the law of conservation of energy, the decrease in the potential energy of the rod as it sinks is equal to the increase in the kinetic energies of the rod and of the wedge:

$$m_2 g \Delta y = \frac{m_2 v_y^2}{2} + \frac{m_1 v_x^2}{2}$$

Substituting the values of the displacements and the velocities we obtain

$$m_2 g a_y = m_2 a_y^2 + m_1 a_x^2, \quad a_y = a_x \tan \alpha$$

from which we get

$$a_x = \frac{m_2 g \tan \alpha}{m_1 + m_2 \tan^2 \alpha}, \quad a_y = \frac{m_2 g \tan^2 \alpha}{m_1 + m_2 \tan^2 \alpha}$$

The reaction is

$$Q = \frac{m_1 a_x}{\sin \alpha} = \frac{m_1 m_2 g \cos \alpha}{m_1 \cos^2 \alpha + m_2 \sin^2 \alpha}$$

12.13. Applying laws of conservation of energy and momentum, we obtain

$$mg\Delta y = \frac{mv_x^2}{2} + \frac{mv_y^2}{2} + \frac{MV^2}{2}, \quad -MV = mv_x$$

Noting that $\Delta y = a_y t^2/2$, $\Delta x = a_x t^2/2$, $\Delta X = bt^2/2$, $v_x = a_x t$, $v_y = a_y t$ and $V = bt$, and that $\Delta y = (\Delta x - \Delta X)\tan\alpha$ we obtain after some simple transformations

$$a_x = \frac{Mg\sin\alpha\cos\alpha}{M + m\sin^2\alpha}$$

i.e. the same result as in Problem 3.7. The value of a_y is obtained from these equations in a similar way. The reaction is obtained from the condition

$$Q = ma = m\sqrt{a_x^2 + a_y^2}$$

12.14. The escape velocity for the Moon is $v = \sqrt{2\gamma M_{\mathbb{C}}/R_{\mathbb{C}}} = 2.4$ km/s. Assuming the exhaust velocity of the gases to be 4 km/s, we obtain with the aid of the Tsiolkovsky formula $M_{\text{fuel}} = 0.83$ ton. For the Earth the escape velocity is 11.2 km/s, and the mass of fuel is $M_{\text{fuel}} = 15.6$ tons.

12.15. The star retains material particles and light in its gravitational field, if its escape velocity is equal to the velocity of light in a vacuum. This idea was suggested by Laplace as far back as 1796. We have

$$c^2 = 2\gamma M/R, \quad R = 2\gamma M/c^2 \approx 9 \text{ km}$$

13. The Law of Conservation of Energy

13.1. The increase of the internal energy of the system is at the expense of the decrease of its kinetic energy. For an inelastic collision of two identical objects flying head on at equal speeds, $\Delta K = 2K_0 = mv^2$. The change in the internal energy is

$$\Delta \mathscr{E}_0 = 2m(c_1 \Delta t_1 + \lambda + c_2 \Delta t_2 + L)$$

where c_1 and c_2 are the specific heats of ice and water, respectively, and

$$\Delta t_1 = 0° - (-30°) = 30 \text{ °C}, \quad \Delta t_2 = 100° - 0° = 100 \text{ °C}$$

Hence

$$v = \sqrt{2(c_1 \Delta t_1 + \lambda + c_2 \Delta t_2 + L)}$$

13.3. Multiplying the solar constant by the area of a sphere of radius equal to the astronomical unit, we obtain the total power of solar radiation $P = 4\pi J R^2$. The loss of mass per second is $\mu = P/c^2$. The

Sun will lose ten percent of its mass in the time

$$\tau = \frac{0.1 M_{\odot}}{\mu} = \frac{M_{\odot} c^2}{40 \pi J R^2}$$

13.5. Before decaying the particle is at rest and its energy is $\mathscr{E}_0 = = M_0 c^2$. Since it decays into two identical fragments their total energy must be $\mathscr{E} = 2mc^2 = \dfrac{2m_0 c^2}{\sqrt{1-\beta^2}}$, where m_0 is the rest mass of a fragment and $u = \beta c$ is its velocity. It follows from the law of conservation of energy that $\dfrac{2m_0 c^2}{\sqrt{1-\beta^2}} = M_0 c^2$, whence the rest mass of a fragment is

$$m_0 = \frac{1}{2} M_0 \sqrt{1-\beta^2}$$

Substituting the speed we obtain the rest mass of the fragment.

13.6. Applying the laws of conservation of momentum and of the total energy, we obtain

$$p' = p, \quad \mathscr{E}' = \mathscr{E} + \mathscr{E}_0$$

where $\mathscr{E} = \mathscr{E}_0 + K = \mathscr{E}_0 + e\varphi$ is the total energy of the particle before the impact, p is its momentum, and $\mathscr{E}'$ and p' are the total energy and momentum of the object formed after the inelastic collision. Eliminating the momentum p' using the relation $\mathscr{E}'^2 = \mathscr{E}_0'^2 + + p'^2 c^2$, we obtain for the internal energy of the object formed

$$\mathscr{E}_0' = \sqrt{2\mathscr{E}_0 (\mathscr{E} + \mathscr{E}_0)} = \sqrt{2\mathscr{E}_0 (2\mathscr{E}_0 + e\varphi)}$$

The kinetic energy of the object formed

$$K' = \mathscr{E}' - \mathscr{E}_0' = 2\mathscr{E}_0 + e\varphi - \sqrt{2\mathscr{E}_0 (2\mathscr{E}_0 + e\varphi)}$$

For a proton ($\mathscr{E}_0 = 0.938$ GeV) with a kinetic energy of 10 GeV we obtain

$$\mathscr{E}_0' = 4.7 \,\text{GeV}, \quad K' = 7.2 \,\text{GeV}$$

For a proton with a kinetic energy of 76 GeV we obtain the values

$$\mathscr{E}_0' = 12.1 \,\text{GeV}, \quad K' = 65.8 \,\text{GeV}$$

13.7. For a proton-antiproton pair to be born out of a cluster, its rest energy should be at least twice that of the rest energy of a proton: $\mathscr{E}_0' \geqslant 2 \times 0.938 = 1.88$ GeV. Noting that the rest energy of an electron is $\mathscr{E}_0 = 0.511$ MeV (see Problem 8.1), we obtain

$$e\varphi \geqslant \frac{\mathscr{E}_0'^2}{2\mathscr{E}_0} - 2\mathscr{E}_0 \approx \frac{\mathscr{E}_0'^2}{2\mathscr{E}_0} = 3.46 \,\text{TeV}$$

At present there are no such accelerators.

13.8. In this case the cluster formed as the result of an inelastic collision is at rest, i.e. the entire kinetic energy of the original particles has been transformed into the internal energy. The internal energy of the cluster is $\mathscr{E}_0' = 2K + 2\mathscr{E}_0^{el} = 2\mathscr{E}_0^{prot}$, therefore

$$K = e\varphi = \mathscr{E}_0^{prot} - \mathscr{E}_0^{el} = 938.3 - 0.511 = 937.8 \text{ MeV} \approx 1 \text{ GeV}$$

Such accelerators do already exist.

13.9. The internal energy of a cluster in a conventional accelerator with a stationary target is $\mathscr{E}_0' = \sqrt{2\mathscr{E}_0(2\mathscr{E}_0 + e\varphi)}$ (see Problem 13.6), in a colliding-beam accelerator it is $\mathscr{E}_0' = 2e\varphi_c + 2\mathscr{E}_0$. Equating both expressions, we obtain

$$\varphi = 2\varphi_c(2 + e\varphi_c/\mathscr{E}_0)$$

where φ is the accelerating potential in a conventional accelerator, and φ_c is the accelerating potential in a colliding-beam accelerator.

Clearly, for $e\varphi_c \ll \mathscr{E}_0$ a colliding-beam accelerator is ineffective since the accelerating potential of a conventional accelerator is only four times greater than in the case of a colliding-beam accelerator. But in the ultra-relativistic case, when $e\varphi_c \gg \mathscr{E}_0$, the colliding-beam accelerator is very effective.

14. Rotational Dynamics of a Rigid Body

14.1. From an arbitrary point O draw an axis perpendicular to the plane in which the forces lie (Fig. 14.1). The moment of the force couple

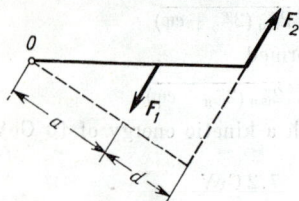
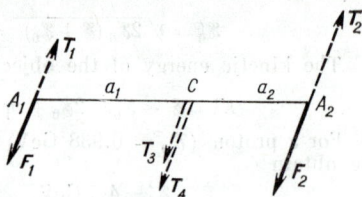

Fig. 14.1.   Fig. 14.2.

(the torque) is equal to the algebraic sum of the moments of each force about the axis. We have

$$M = F_1 a + F_2(a + d) = F_1 a + F_2 a + F_2 d$$

However, $F_1 = F$ and $F_2 = -F$, so $M = -Fd$. The minus sign shows that this couple makes a left-hand screw about the axis.

14.2. The solid arrows in Fig. 14.2 show the forces $\mathbf{F}_1$ and $\mathbf{F}_2$ applied to a rigid body at points A_1 and A_2. Apply the forces $\mathbf{T}_1$ and $\mathbf{T}_2$ at the same points and the forces $\mathbf{T}_3$ and $\mathbf{T}_4$ at the point C so that $T_1 = T_3 = F_1$ and $T_2 = T_4 = F_2$. The point C is chosen so that $F_1 a_1 = F_2 a_2$. Show that the new system of six forces is equivalent to the old one, i.e. that

$$(\mathbf{F_1},\ \mathbf{F_2},\ \mathbf{T_1},\ \mathbf{T_2},\ \mathbf{T_3},\ \mathbf{T_4}) \sim (\mathbf{F_1},\ \mathbf{F_2})$$

Indeed, the system of these forces reduces to the former forces $\mathbf{F_1}$ and $\mathbf{F_2}$ and to two force couples $(\mathbf{T_1},\ \mathbf{T_3})$ and $(\mathbf{T_2},\ \mathbf{T_4})$ whose moments are

$$M_1 = T_1 a_1 \sin \alpha \quad \text{and} \quad M_2 = -T_2 a_2 \sin \alpha$$

But point C was chosen so that $|M_1| = |M_2|$. Therefore these moments are compensated and do not act on the rigid body.

On the other hand, the system of six forces is equivalent to the system of forces $\mathbf{T_3}$ and $\mathbf{T_4}$, i.e.

$$(\mathbf{F_1},\ \mathbf{F_2},\ \mathbf{T_1},\ \mathbf{T_2},\ \mathbf{T_3},\ \mathbf{T_4}) \sim (\mathbf{T_3},\ \mathbf{T_4})$$

Indeed, the forces $\mathbf{F_1}$ and $\mathbf{T_1}$, as well as $\mathbf{F_2}$ and $\mathbf{T_2}$, are compensated, only the forces $\mathbf{T_3}$ and $\mathbf{T_4}$ remaining uncompensated.

Hence, the system of forces $(\mathbf{F_1},\ \mathbf{F_2})$ is equivalent to the system $(\mathbf{T_3},\ \mathbf{T_4})$, and this gives the solution to the problem.

14.4. The work done in twisting the spring by an angle α is equivalent to the work done in extending it by a length x, which is expressed by the formula $W = 1/2 Fx = 1/2 kx^2$. Therefore the work sought is

$$W = \frac{1}{2} M\alpha = \frac{1}{2} f\alpha^2$$

Note that the torsion modulus $f = M/\alpha$ is an analogue of the spring constant $k = F/x$.

14.7. The differential of mass is equal to the mass of a ring of thickness dr. We have

$$\frac{dm}{M} = \frac{2\pi r\, dr}{\pi R^2}, \quad \text{from which} \quad dm = \frac{2Mr\, dr}{R^2}$$

The differential of the moment of inertia is equal to the moment of inertia of this ring:

$$dI = dm \cdot r^2 = \frac{2Mr^3\, dr}{R^2}$$

Hence

$$I = \int_0^R dm \cdot r^2 = \frac{2M}{R^2} \int_0^R r^3\, dr = \frac{2M}{R^2} \left[\frac{r^4}{4} \right]_0^R = \frac{2MR^4}{R^2 \times 4} = \frac{MR^2}{2}$$

14.8. Divide the sphere into thin disks perpendicular to the axis of rotation (Fig. 14.8). The differential of mass is

$$dm = \frac{M\pi r^2\, dz}{4/3\pi R^3} = \frac{3M}{4R^3} (R^2 - z^2)\, dz$$

since $r^2 = R^2 - z^2$. The moment of inertia of such a disk is

$$dI = \frac{r^2\, dm}{2} = \frac{3M}{8R^3} (R^2 - z^2)^2\, dz$$

The moment of inertia of the sphere is

$$I = 2 \int_0^R \frac{3M}{8R^3} (R^4 - 2R^2 z^2 + z^4)\, dz =$$

$$= \frac{3M}{4R^3} \left[R^4 \int_0^R dz - 2R^2 \int_0^R z^2 dz + \int_0^R z^4 dz \right] =$$

$$= \frac{3M}{4R^3} \left[R^4 z - 2R^2 \frac{z^3}{3} + \frac{z^5}{5} \right]_0^R =$$

$$= \frac{3M}{4R^3} \left(R^5 - \frac{2R^5}{3} + \frac{R^5}{5} \right) = \frac{2}{5} MR^2$$

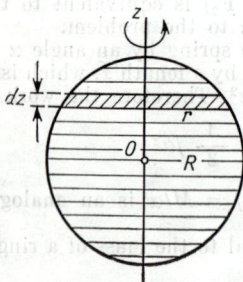
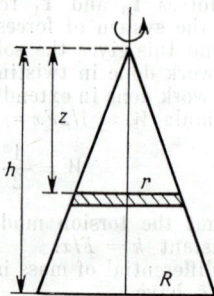

Fig. 14.8.   Fig. 14.9.

14.9. For a cone (Fig. 14.9)

$$dm = \frac{Mr^2\, dz}{1/3\, hR^2}, \quad r = \frac{Rz}{h}, \quad dI = \frac{dm \cdot r^2}{2} = \frac{3MR^2 z^4\, dz}{2h^5}$$

$$I = \int_0^h \frac{3MR^2 z^4\, dz}{2h^5} = \frac{3MR^2}{2h^5} \int_0^h z^4\, dz = \frac{3MR^2 h^5}{2h^5 \times 5} = 0.3 MR^2$$

14.10. It is evident from dimensional considerations that the moment of inertia of a sphere is $I = \alpha MR^2$, where α is a numerical factor. For the purpose of numerical calculation put $M = 1$, $R = 1$ and divide the radius into ten equal parts (see Problem 7.12). The mass of a layer is

$$\Delta m_n = \pi r_n^2\, \Delta x \cdot \rho$$

where

$$\Delta x = 0.1, \quad \rho = \frac{M}{V} = \frac{3M}{4\pi R^3} = \frac{3}{4\pi}$$

Hence $\Delta m_n = 3r_n^2/40$. The moment of inertia of a layer is

$$\Delta I_n = \frac{\Delta m_n r_n^2}{2} = \frac{3r_n^4}{80}$$

The moment of inertia of a sphere is the sum of the moments of inertia of two hemispheres; for $M = 1$ and $R = 1$ we obtain

$$I = \alpha = 2(\Delta I_1 + \Delta I_2 + \ldots + \Delta I_{10}) = \frac{3}{40}(r_1^4 + r_2^4 + \ldots + r_{10}^4)$$

Making use of the data given in Table 7.12, write out the value of the radii raised to the fourth power in Table 14.10, and find their sum. This gives $\alpha = \dfrac{3 \times 5.333}{40} = 0.4$, i.e. numerical calculation yields the same result as integration.

<table>
<tr><td colspan="2">**Table 14.10**</td><td colspan="3">**Table 14.11**</td></tr>
<tr><td>n</td><td>r_n^4</td><td>n</td><td>r_n</td><td>r_n^4</td></tr>
<tr><td>1</td><td>0.995</td><td>1</td><td>0.05</td><td>0.06×10^{-3}</td></tr>
<tr><td>2</td><td>0.956</td><td>2</td><td>0.15</td><td>0.51×10^{-3}</td></tr>
<tr><td>3</td><td>0.880</td><td>3</td><td>0.25</td><td>3.91×10^{-8}</td></tr>
<tr><td>4</td><td>0.770</td><td>4</td><td>0.35</td><td>15.00×10^{-3}</td></tr>
<tr><td>5</td><td>0.636</td><td>5</td><td>0.45</td><td>41.00×10^{-3}</td></tr>
<tr><td>6</td><td>0.486</td><td>6</td><td>0.55</td><td>91.60×10^{-3}</td></tr>
<tr><td>7</td><td>0.333</td><td>7</td><td>0.65</td><td>178.50×10^{-3}</td></tr>
<tr><td>8</td><td>0.191</td><td>8</td><td>0.75</td><td>316.00×10^{-3}</td></tr>
<tr><td>9</td><td>0.077</td><td>9</td><td>0.85</td><td>521.00×10^{-3}</td></tr>
<tr><td>10</td><td>0.009</td><td>10</td><td>0.95</td><td>815.00×10^{-3}</td></tr>
<tr><td>Total</td><td>5.333</td><td>Total</td><td></td><td>$1982.58 \times 10^{-3} = 1.983 \approx 2$</td></tr>
</table>

14.11. For a cone we have from dimensional considerations $I = \beta M R^2$ as we had for a sphere, where β is a numerical factor. For the purpose of numerical calculation put $M = 1$, $h = R = 1$ and divide the height into ten equal parts (see Problem 7.14). We have

$$\Delta m_n = \pi r_n^2 \Delta h \cdot \rho = 0.1 \pi r_n^2 \rho, \qquad \rho = \frac{3M}{\pi R^2 h} = \frac{3}{\pi}$$

$$\Delta I_n = \frac{\Delta m_n r_n^2}{2} = \frac{3r_n^4}{20}, \qquad I = \beta = \frac{3}{20}(r_1^4 + r_2^4 + \ldots + r_{10}^4)$$

Evidently

$$\frac{r_1}{R} = \frac{0.05}{h}, \quad \frac{r_2}{R} = \frac{0.15}{h}, \quad \ldots, \quad \frac{r_{10}}{R} = \frac{0.95}{h}$$

For $R = h = 1$ we obtain Table 14.11. We have

$$I = \beta = \frac{3}{20} \times 1.983 = 0.2975 \approx 0.3$$

The relative error as compared with the precise formula is

$$\varepsilon = \frac{0.3 - 0.2975}{0.3} \times 100\% = 0.8\%$$

14.12. Making use of the law of conservation of energy for a rotating rigid body, let us first express the angular velocity in terms of the angle. We have

$$K = U_0 - U, \quad \text{where } K = \frac{1}{2} I \omega^2, \quad U_0 = mgh_0 \text{ and } U = mgh$$

The moment of inertia of a rod about an axis passing through one end is $I = \frac{1}{3} ml^2$. In the course of oscillations the centre of gravity of the rod rises to a height

$$h_0 = \frac{1}{2} l (1 - \cos \alpha_0), \quad h = \frac{1}{2} l (1 - \cos \alpha)$$

Substituting the values obtained into the equation for the energy balance, we obtain

$$\omega = \sqrt{\frac{3g}{l} (\cos \alpha - \cos \alpha_0)}$$

the speed of the end of the rod is $v = \omega l$.

14.13. From the law of conservation of energy

$$U - W_{\mathrm{fr}} = K, \quad \text{or} \quad mg (l \sin \alpha + r \cos \alpha) - T_{\mathrm{rol}} l = \frac{mv^2}{2} + \frac{I\omega^2}{2}$$

The force of rolling friction is $T_{\mathrm{rol}} = kmg \cos \alpha / r$; the moment of inertia of a solid cylinder is $I = 1/2 mr^2$, and the angular velocity is $\omega = v/r$. We have

$$mg (l \sin \alpha + r \cos \alpha) - \frac{lkmg \cos \alpha}{r} = \frac{mv^2}{2} + \frac{mv^2}{4}$$

from which

$$v = \sqrt{\frac{4g}{3} \left(l \sin \alpha + r \cos \alpha - \frac{lk \cos \alpha}{r} \right)}$$

In principle the friction may not be neglected since in the absence of friction the disk will not roll down, but will slide down, and in this case the kinetic energy of rolling should not be taken into account. But if the friction is small enough, the work of the force of friction may be neglected. The necessary condition for this is

$$\frac{lk}{r} \ll l \tan \alpha + r$$

For the numerical example contained in the problem we have

$$\frac{lk}{r} = \frac{1 \times 5 \times 10^{-4}}{10^{-1}} = 5 \times 10^{-3}, \quad l \tan \alpha + r = \frac{\sqrt{3}}{3} + 0.1 = 0.68$$

i.e. the work of the force of rolling friction may be neglected in the calculation.

When the cylinder slides down

$$mg \, (l \sin \alpha + r \cos \alpha) = \frac{1}{2} \, mv^2, \quad v = \sqrt{2g \, (l \sin \alpha + r \cos \alpha)}$$

14.14.
$$v = \sqrt{g \left(l \sin \alpha + r \cos \alpha - \frac{lk \cos \alpha}{r} \right)}.$$

14.15. The work of the force of friction is responsible for the loss of the entire kinetic energy of the flywheel. We have

$$\Delta K = \frac{I \omega^2}{2} = \frac{mr^2 \omega^2}{4}, \quad W_{\text{fr}} = Tl = \mu N v_{\text{av}} t = \frac{\mu N \omega r t}{2}$$

Hence

$$N = \frac{mr\omega}{2\mu t} = \frac{\pi m r n}{\mu t}$$

Try to solve this problem with the aid of the fundamental equation of rotational dynamics of a rigid body.

14.16. As the weight sinks, its potential energy transforms into the kinetic energies of the weight and of the rotating flywheel:

$$mgh = \frac{1}{2} \, mv^2 + \frac{1}{2} \, I \omega^2$$

The flywheel and the cylinder rotate at the same angular velocity $\omega = v/r$, therefore $2mgh = v^2 \, (m + I/r^2)$. Hence

$$v = \sqrt{\frac{2mgh}{m + I/r^2}}$$

14.17. Since the pulley rotates with an acceleration, there must be a torque acting on it due to the difference in the tensions of the left and the right parts of the rope (see Fig. 14.7). It follows from the fundamental equation of dynamics that

$$m_2 g - T_2 = m_2 a, \quad -m_1 g + T_1 = m_1 a, \quad M = I \Delta \omega / \Delta t$$

The torque is $M = (T_2 - T_1) \, r$. The variation of the angular velocity is

$$\Delta \omega = \omega_2 - \omega_1 = \frac{v_2}{r} - \frac{v_1}{r} = \frac{a \Delta t}{r}$$

We have

$$m_2 g - T_2 = m_2 a, \quad -m_1 g + T_1 = m_1 a, \quad T_2 - T_1 = \frac{Ia}{r^2}$$

Hence

$$a = \frac{(m_2 - m_1) g}{m_1 + m_2 + I/r^2}, \quad T_1 = \frac{2 m_1 m_2 g \, (1 + I/2 m_2 r^2)}{m_1 + m_2 + I/r^2}$$

$$T_2 = \frac{2 m_1 m_2 g \, (1 + I/2 m_1 r^2)}{m_1 + m_2 + I/r^2}$$

For $I/r^2 \ll m_1 + m_2$ we obtain the answer to Problem 3.2.

14.18. The method of solving the problem is the same as for Problem 12.7, the only exception being that in this case one should take into account the kinetic energy of rotation of the ball:

$$N = \frac{mg}{7} \, (17 \cos \alpha - 10)$$

14.19. From the law of conservation of momentum

$$(I_{\mathrm{man}} + I_{\mathrm{b}} + 2 m r_1^2) \, \omega_1 = (I_{\mathrm{man}} + I_{\mathrm{b}} + 2 m r_2^2) \, \omega_2$$

14.21. Applying the law of conservation of momentum we can find the relation between the pulsar radius and its period of revolution. We have

$$I_{\odot} \omega_{\odot} = I \omega, \quad \text{or} \quad \frac{2}{5} M R_{\odot}^3 \frac{2\pi}{T_{\odot}} = \frac{2}{5} M R_{\odot}^2 \frac{2\pi}{T}$$

Hence

$$\frac{R_{\odot}^2}{T_{\odot}} = \frac{R^2}{T}$$

To prevent the escape of matter as the speed of rotation is increased the force of gravity should exceed the centrifugal force, i.e. $m \omega^2 R < F_{\mathrm{gr}}$. Hence $\dfrac{4\pi^2 m R}{T^2} < \dfrac{\gamma m M_{\odot}}{R^2}$.

Therefore the second relation sought between the pulsar radius and its period of revolution is of the form

$$\frac{R^3}{T^2} < \frac{\gamma M_{\odot}}{4\pi^2}$$

Eliminating the pulsar period from both equations, we obtain

$$R \geqslant \frac{4\pi^2 R_{\odot}^4}{\gamma M_{\odot} T_{\odot}^2} = \frac{4\pi^2 \times 7^4 \times 10^{32}}{6.67 \times 10^{-11} \times 2 \times 10^{30} \times 2.2^2 \times 10^{12}} \approx 15 \text{ km}$$

$$T \approx R^2 T_{\odot} / R_{\odot}^2 \approx 10^{-3} \text{ s}$$

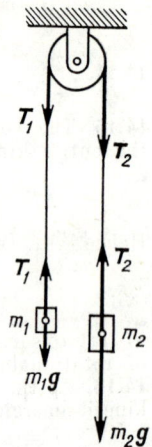

Fig. 14.17.

14.22. The kinetic energy of Sun's rotation is

$$K_\odot = \frac{I_\odot \omega_\odot^2}{2} = \frac{4\pi^2 M_\odot R_\odot^2}{5 T_\odot^2}$$

The kinetic energy of pulsar's rotation is

$$K = 4\pi^2 M_\odot R^2 / 5 T^2$$

The ratio of these quantities is $\dfrac{K}{K_\odot} = \dfrac{T_\odot^2}{T^2} \approx 2 \times 10^9$.

The increase in the kinetic energy of rotation of a star in the process of its contraction (collapse) is at the expense of the work of gravitational forces.

14.23. The moment of the ball's momentum is $L = I\omega = \dfrac{2}{5} mr^2 \dfrac{v}{r} = \dfrac{2}{5} mvr$, where v is the orbital velocity on the equator. Since $v < c$, $L < \dfrac{2}{5} mcr$, whence

$$r > \frac{5L}{2mc}, \quad \text{or} \quad r > \frac{5\hbar}{4mc} = 4.8 \times 10^{-13} \text{ m}$$

This dimension does not agree with experimental data, according to which the effective electron radius is two orders of magnitude less.

15. Non-inertial Frames of Reference and Gravitation

15.1. The reference frame fixed to the wedge moves with an acceleration **a** in the x-direction and therefore is non-inertial. There are four forces acting on the block: the force of gravity $m\mathbf{g}$, the reaction **Q**,

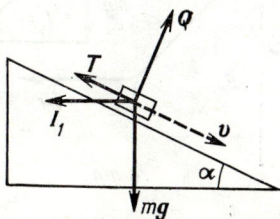

Fig. 15.1a.

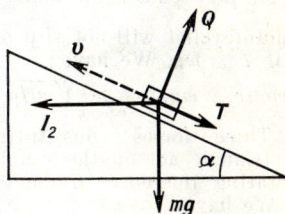

Fig. 15.1b.

the friction force **T**, and the inertial force $\mathbf{I} = -m\mathbf{a}$. To solve the problem one should consider the same two cases as in Problem 5.7 (see Fig. 15.1a and 15.1b). The block is not accelerated with respect to the non-inertial frame, and for this reason the sum of the projections of forces on both coordinate axes is zero. We have for both cases

y-axis:
$$Q \cos \alpha + T \sin \alpha - mg = 0, \qquad Q \cos \alpha - T \sin \alpha - mg = 0$$
x-axis:
$$-I_1 - T \cos \alpha + Q \sin \alpha = 0, \qquad -I_2 + T \cos \alpha + Q \sin \alpha = 0$$

The equations obtained are equivalent to the equations of Problem 5.7, therefore we shall obtain the same answer.

15.2. Four forces act on the body in the rotating coordinate system: the force of gravity mg, the reaction Q, the centrifugal inertial force

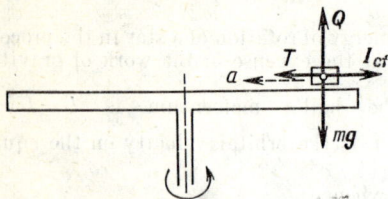

Fig. 15.2.

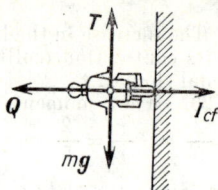

Fig. 15.3.

$I_{cf} = m\omega^2 r$ and the force of friction T (Fig. 15.2). To prevent the disk from sliding the following condition should be satisfied:
$$I_{cf} \leqslant T^{\text{stat}}, \qquad \text{or} \qquad m\omega^2 r \leqslant \mu^{\text{stat}} mg$$
hence $r \leqslant \mu^{\text{stat}} g/\omega^2$.

15.3. The forces acting on the motorcyclist in the rotating reference frame are mg, Q, T and I_{cf} (Fig. 15.3).
Evidently
$$Q = I_{cf} = m\omega^2 r,$$
$$T = \mu Q = \mu m\omega^2 r = \mu m v^2/r$$

The motorcyclist will not slip off the wall, if $T \geqslant mg$. We have
$$\mu m v^2/r \geqslant mg, \qquad v \geqslant \sqrt{gr/\mu}$$

15.4. Three forces constituting a closed triangle act on the weight in the rotating reference frame (Fig. 15.4). We have

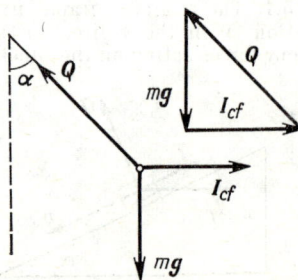

Fig. 15.4.

$I_{cf} = mg \tan \alpha, \qquad \text{or} \qquad m\omega^2 r = mg \tan \alpha$

Noting that $r = l \sin \alpha$ and $\omega = 2\pi/T$, we obtain
$$T = 2\pi \sqrt{\frac{l}{g} \cos \alpha}$$

15.5. From the condition that the centrifugal force of inertia is equal to the elastic force, we obtain the same result as in Problem 3.9.

15.6. The forces acting on material particles on the star's equator in the rotating reference frame are the force of gravity $F = \dfrac{\gamma m M}{R^2}$ and the centrifugal force of inertia $I_{cf} = m\omega^2 R$. Matter will start to escape, if $I_{cf} \geqslant F$, i.e. $\omega \geqslant \sqrt{\gamma M/R^3}$.

15.7. The time needed for the oil droplets to rise in the gravitational field is (see § 11.9)

$$\tau = \frac{9l\eta}{2r^2 g\,(\rho_f - \rho)} = \frac{9 \times 0.2 \times 10^{-3}}{2 \times 10^{-10} \times 9.8 \times 10^2} = 9 \times 10^3 \text{ s} = 2.5 \text{ h}$$

In the centrifuge the part of the gravitational field, in accordance with the principle of equivalence (§ 24.5), is played by the field of centrifugal forces of inertia. Consequently, in the above formula one must simply substitute $\omega^2 R$ for g. We obtain

$$\tau \approx \frac{9l\eta}{2r^2 \omega^2 R\,(\rho_f - \rho)} = \frac{9 \times 0.2 \times 10^{-3}}{2 \times 10^{-10} \times 4 \times 10^2 \times \pi^2 \times 0.8 \times 10^2} = 28 \text{ s}$$

The centrifuge is $\omega^2 R/g = 320$ times more efficient.

15.8. When the system is at rest, the spring is undeformed and its length is maximum, $l_0 = 2a$. When the system rotates, the weights move away from the rotation axis, and the length of the spring becomes $l = 2a \cos \alpha$. The change in length is

$$\Delta l = l_0 - l = 2a\,(1 - \cos \alpha) = 4a \sin^2 \frac{\alpha}{2}$$

To relate the deflection angle to the rotation speed, we employ a rotating reference frame. In compressing the spring, work is performed, equal to

$$W_{el} = \frac{1}{2}\,k\,(\Delta l)^2 = 8ka^2 \sin^2 \frac{\alpha}{2}$$

This work was performed by the centrifugal forces of inertia, which displaced each weight by a distance $r = a \sin \alpha$. The work of the inertial forces is

$$W_{cf} = 2 \times \frac{1}{2}\,I_{cf} r = m\omega^2 a^2 \sin^2 \alpha$$

Equating the two expressions for the work, we obtain

$$8ka^2 \sin^2 \frac{\alpha}{2} = m\omega^2 a^2 \sin^2 \alpha \quad \text{whence} \quad \tan \frac{\alpha}{2} = \sqrt{\frac{m\omega^2}{2k}}$$

Obviously the governor will work in conditions of weightlessness, for the presence of gravity was mentioned nowhere.

The maximum rotation speed may be found from the condition $\Delta l \leqslant 0.1 \times 2a$. From this $2a\,(1 - \cos \alpha) \leqslant 0.2a$, or $0.9 \leqslant \cos \alpha < 1$. Expressing the cosine in terms of the tangent of half the angle and substituting the value obtained into the condition of equilibrium, we obtain

$$\omega_{max} \leqslant \sqrt{2k/19m}$$

15.9. Fix the reference frame to the rotating liquid. Then there will be three forces acting on every particle: the force of gravity mg, the reaction of the liquid $\mathbf{N}$ and the centrifugal force of inertia $\mathbf{I}_{cf} = m\omega^2\mathbf{x}$ (Fig. 15.9). The angle between the reaction and the y-axis is equal to the angle between the tangent and the x-axis (since the edges of the angles are mutually perpendicular). We have

$$\tan\alpha = \frac{I_{cf}}{mg} = \frac{\omega^2 x}{g}$$

It was shown in Problem 3.14 that the tangent to a parabola $x^2 = 2py$ makes an angle of $\tan\alpha = x/p$ with the x-axis. Therefore we may conclude that the surface of a liquid

in a rotating vessel is a paraboloid formed by the parabola $x^2 = \dfrac{2g}{\omega^2}y$ rotating about the y-axis.

15.10. A spacecraft orbiting a planet forms a non-inertial reference frame moving with an acceleration $g = \gamma M/R^2$ directed towards the centre of the planet. Two forces act on an object inside the spacecraft: the force of gravity $F = \gamma mM/R^2$, directed towards the centre of the planet, and the oppositely directed centrifugal force of inertia $I_{cf} = mv^2/R$. The resultant of these forces is zero, therefore the object is weightless with respect to the spacecraft.

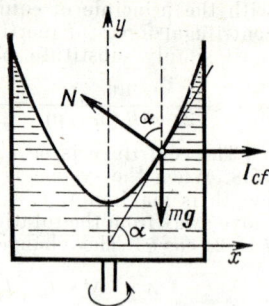

Fig. 15.9.

15.12. The slowing down of time measured by the "plane" clock is due to two effects: to the decrease in gravitation and to the speed of flight. We have

$$t_{pl} = t_{Earth}\sqrt{1-\frac{2\varphi}{c^2}}\cdot\sqrt{1-\frac{v^2}{c^2}} =$$

$$= t_{Earth}\sqrt{1-\frac{2gh}{c^2}}\cdot\sqrt{1-\frac{v^2}{c^2}}$$

(φ is the potential of the gravitational field). Since $\dfrac{gh}{c^2}\ll 1$ and $\dfrac{v^2}{c^2}\ll 1$, the expression for the time assumes the form

$$t_{pl} = t_{Earth}\left(1-\frac{gh}{c^2}\right)\left(1-\frac{v^2}{2c^2}\right) =$$

$$= t_{Earth}\left(1-\frac{gh}{c^2}-\frac{v^2}{2c^2}\right)$$

The time dilation is

$$\Delta t = t_{Earth} - t_{pl} = t_{Earth}\left(\frac{gh}{c^2}+\frac{v^2}{2c^2}\right)$$

Here
$$\frac{gh}{c^2} = \frac{9.81 \times 10^4}{9.0 \times 10^{16}} = 1.09 \times 10^{-12},$$

$$\frac{v^2}{2c^2} = \frac{10^{12}}{2 \times 3.6^2 \times 10^6 \times 9.0 \times 10^{16}} = 0.43 \times 10^{-12}$$

Since $t_{\text{Earth}} = 2.5$ days $= 2.5 \times 8.64 \times 10^4$ s, the time dilation is
$$\Delta t = 2.5 \times 8.64 \times 10^4 \times 1.52 \times 10^{-12} = 3.3 \times 10^{-6} \text{ s} = 330 \text{ ns}$$

The effect of the general theory of relativity (of the gravitational field) turns out to be 2.5 times more pronounced than that of the special theory (of the speed).

15.13. For the Sun and for the white dwarf $\frac{\Delta v}{v} = \frac{\varphi}{c^2} = \frac{\gamma M}{c^2 R}$. For the pulsar we can make use of the precise formula

$$\frac{\Delta v}{v} = 1 - \sqrt{1 - \frac{2\gamma M}{c^2 R}}$$

15.14. Light cannot escape from the star's gravitational field, if the gravitational potential on the surface is so high that $2\varphi/c^2 \geqslant 1$. Hence the radius of a black hole is $R \leqslant 2\gamma M/c^2$.

16. An Ideal Gas

16.1. No matter what the shape of the vessel is, one can always imagine it to be made up of small vertical columns of liquid for which the formula $p = \rho gh$ was derived (see Fig. 16.1). But since the pressure

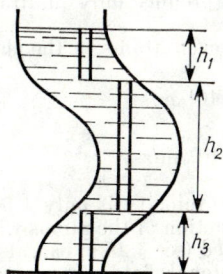
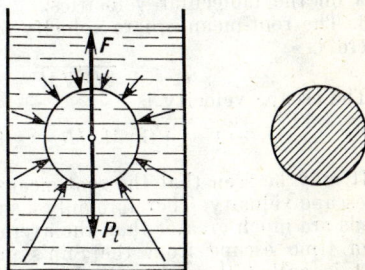

Fig. 16.1.   Fig. 16.2.

at all points at a given depth is the same (a corollary of Pascal's law), to compute the pressure at the depth h one should add up the pressures of all the upper layers:

$$p = p_1 + p_2 + p_3 + \ldots = \rho g\,(h_1 + h_2 + h_3 + \ldots) = \rho gh$$

16.2. One of the possible arguments is as follows. Consider separately the volume in the liquid which will be filled by the object being immersed (Fig. 16.2). The volume is acted upon by the forces of hydrostatic pressure, indicated by small arrows. The resultant of these forces is the buoyancy F. Since the liquid is in a state of equilibrium, $F = P_1$ where P_1 is the weight of the respective volume of the liquid. It is obvious that if we place the object of interest into the liquid, the same hydrostatic forces will act on it and, consequently, its buoyancy will be equal to the weight of the liquid displaced by the object.

16.4. The total displacement of the image is $l = 2r_2 \omega t$, where t is the time of transit of the molecule between the cylinders, i.e. $t = = (r_2 - r_1)/\bar{v}$. The root-mean-square velocity of the silver atoms is

$$\bar{v} = \sqrt{\frac{3RT}{M}} = \sqrt{\frac{3 \times 8.3 \times 10^3 \times 1233}{108}} = 532 \text{ m/s}$$

Hence

$$l = 2\omega r_2 (r_2 - r_1)/\bar{v}$$

To assess the error, calculate the width of the undisplaced image of the slit:

$$\frac{a}{b} = \frac{r_2}{r_1}, \quad \text{whence} \quad a = \frac{br_2}{r_1} = \frac{0.5 \times 8}{2} = 2 \text{ mm}$$

The broadening of the displaced images is still greater because of the Maxwell distribution of the molecular velocities. Hence the error in measurement is $\Delta \geqslant 2a/2 = a$, the relative error being

$$\varepsilon = -\frac{\Delta}{l} \geqslant \frac{a}{l} = \frac{2 \times 100\%}{5} = 40\%$$

This shows that the Stern experiment could produce only qualitative data on the molecular velocities.

16.6. The root-mean-square velocity of hydrogen atoms in the photosphere is

$$\bar{v} = \sqrt{3RT/M} = 1.2 \times 10^4 \text{ m/s}$$

The escape velocity is

$$v = \sqrt{2\gamma M_\odot/R_\odot} = 6.1 \times 10^5 \text{ m/s}$$

It may be seen that the root-mean-square velocity is only 1/51 of the escape velocity. Therefore only a small fraction of the atoms whose speeds are much greater than the average speed (see § 25.2) can at any given time escape from the Sun's gravitational field. They create what is called the solar wind.

16.7. Since the thickness of the photosphere is small, its density, as well as the acceleration due to gravity, may be assumed constant. for the photosphere to be in a state of equilibrium the hydrostatic pressure must be compensated by the gas pressure, i.e. $p = \rho g h = = \rho RT/M$, where M is the molar mass of the gas. Hence

$$h = RT/Mg_\odot$$

16.9. In this problem, as in Problem 16.7, we shall make use of the fact that the gas pressure is equal to the hydrostatic pressure, which may be approximately calculated as follows:

$$p = \bar{\rho}_\odot g_\odot h = \bar{\rho}_\odot \frac{\gamma M_\odot}{2R_\odot^2} \cdot \frac{R_\odot}{2}$$

where the average density of matter is $\bar{\rho}_\odot = \dfrac{M_\odot}{V_\odot} = \dfrac{3M_\odot}{4\pi R_\odot^3}$.

16.10. At the temperature of 100°C the root-mean-square velocity of the hydrogen molecules is 2.15×10^3 m/s. The escape velocity for the Moon is 2.4 km/s (see Problem 12.14). Naturally, the Moon's gravitational field is unable to retain hydrogen. The root-mean-square velocities of molecules of other gases are several times smaller. But in accordance with the Maxwell distribution there is always a considerable fraction of the molecules whose velocity is several times the average (see § 25.2). Because of this Moon's gravitational field is also unable to retain other gases, and they disperse in space.

16.12. The atmospheric pressure close to the Earth's surface is, according to Table 26.3, equal to 1.01×10^5 Pa, the air density is 1.23 kg/m³ and the absolute temperature is 288 K. The helium pressure inside the envelope is the same, as the envelope communicates with the atmosphere. The density of helium in these conditions is $\rho_{He} = = pM/RT = 0.16$ kg/m³. The lift is equal to the difference between the Archimedean force and the force of gravity:

$$F = (\rho_{at} - \rho_{He}) Vg$$

16.13. First find the molar mass of ammonia:

$$M = \rho RT/p = 17 \text{ kg/kmole}$$

Noting that the atomic masses of the elements which make up ammonia are $M_1 = 14$ kg/kmole (nitrogen) and $M_2 = 1$ kg/kmole (hydrogen), we obtain the equation

$$M = x_1 M_1 + x_2 M_2, \quad \text{i.e.} \quad 17 = 14x_1 + x_2$$

Its solution in integral numbers is: $x_1 = 1$, $x_2 = 3$. Hence the molecular formula of ammonia is NH_3.

16.14. In thermodynamical equilibrium the temperature of all the components of a mixture of gases is the same. The pressure of the individual component is

$$p_1 = n_1 kT = N_1 kT/V, \quad p_2 = n_2 kT = N_2 kT/V, \text{ etc.}$$

The sum of partial pressures is

$$p_1 + p_2 + p_3 + \ldots = (N_1 + N_2 + N_3 + \ldots) \frac{kT}{V}$$

Since the total number of molecules N is the sum of the numbers of molecules of all the components making up the mixture, $N = N_1 +$

$+ N_2 + N_3 + \ldots$, the sum of the partial pressures is equal to the pressure of the gas:

$$p_1 + p_2 + p_3 + \ldots = NkT/V = p$$

16.15. In the course of the chemical reaction in which water is produced, 48 g of oxygen react with 6 g of hydrogen. Consequently the container contains 54 g of water vapour and 4 g of hydrogen. To find the pressure apply Dalton's law.

16.16. Using Dalton's law one can easily obtain the equation $\dfrac{m}{M} =$

$= \dfrac{m_1}{M_1} + \dfrac{m_2}{M_2}$. On the other hand, the mass of a gas is the sum of the masses of its components: $m = m_1 + m_2$. Putting $x = m_1/m$, $y = m_2/m$, we obtain a system of two equations:

$$\frac{1}{M} = \frac{x}{M_1} + \frac{y}{M_2}, \qquad 1 = x + y$$

Solving this system we find the percentage composition of the gases.

16.17. Small gumboge gum balls take part in random thermal motion, behaving like gigantic molecules. Therefore their distribution over height corresponds to the barometric distribution

$$\frac{N_1}{N_2} = e^{\frac{mg\,(h_2 - h_1)}{kT}}, \qquad \log \frac{N_1}{N_2} = \frac{0.434 mg\,(h_2 - h_1)}{kT}$$

One should take into account that in addition to the force of gravity, the particles are acted upon by the Archimedean force. Expressing the Boltzmann constant in terms of the gas constant and the Avogadro number, we obtain for the latter

$$N_A = \frac{3RT \log (N_1/N_2)}{0.434 \times 4\pi r^3 g\,(\rho - \rho_0)\,(h_2 - h_1)}$$

Substituting the known data, we obtain the working formula

$$N = 5.79 \times 10^{22}\, \frac{\log (N_1/N_2)}{h_2 - h_1}$$

The values obtained for the Avogadro number are: 6.32×10^{26}, 5.98×10^{26} and 5.45×10^{26}. The average value is 5.92×10^{26}, the maximum error is 0.3×10^{26}. Hence from data obtained in this experiment

$$N_A = (5.9 \pm 0.3) \times 10^{26} \text{ kmol}^{-1}$$

16.18. To solve the problem one should calculate the potential energy in the field of centrifugal forces:

$$U = -W = -\frac{1}{2} Fl = -\frac{1}{2} I_{cf} r = -\frac{1}{2} m\omega^2 r^2$$

Substituting it into formula (26.26), we obtain the result sought.

16.19. A gaseous uranium-fluorine compound, uranium hexafluoride UF_6, is used for isotope separation. The molar masses of the compounds are: $M_1 = 349$ kg/kmole and $M_2 = 352$ kg/kmole. Their concentration ratio prior to the rotation of the vessel is

$$n_{02} : n_{01} = 99.28 : 0.715 = 139 : 1$$

During the rotation of the centrifuge, the isotope of greater mass due to the action of centrifugal forces concentrates near the walls of the vessel. Using the result obtained in the previous problem, we have*

$$n_1 = n_{01} \exp\left(\frac{m_1 \omega^2 r^2}{2kT}\right) = n_{01} \exp\left(\frac{M_1 \omega^2 r^2}{2RT}\right)$$

$$n_2 = n_{02} \exp\left(\frac{M_2 \omega^2 r^2}{2RT}\right)$$

The concentration ratio close to the vessel's walls is

$$\frac{n_2}{n_1} = \frac{n_{02}}{n_{01}} \exp\left[\frac{(M_2 - M_1)\,\omega^2 r^2}{2RT}\right]$$

Taking logarithms, we obtain

$$\log\left(\frac{n_2}{n_1}\right) = \log\left(\frac{n_{02}}{n_{01}}\right) + \frac{0.434\,(M_2 - M_1)\,\omega^2 r^2}{2RT}$$

$$= \log 139 + \frac{0.434 \times 3 \times 4\pi^2 \times 4 \times 10^6 \times 25 \times 10^{-4}}{2 \times 8.3 \times 10^3 \times 3 \times 10^2}$$

$$= 2.143 + 0.103 = 2.246$$

Hence $n_2 : n_1 = 176 : 1$. The enrichment factor is

$$x = \left(\frac{n_2}{n_1}\right) : \left(\frac{n_{02}}{n_{01}}\right) = \exp\left[\frac{(M_2 - M_1)\,\omega^2 r^2}{2RT}\right]$$

The obvious result is $\log x = 0.103$, giving $x = 1.27$.

16.21. $\dfrac{p}{p_0} = (1 - \alpha h)^{\frac{mg}{\alpha k T_0}} = \left[(1 - \alpha h)^{-\frac{1}{\alpha h}}\right]^{-\frac{mgh}{kT_0}} \to e^{-\frac{mgh}{kT_0}}$

16.22. The forces acting on a vertical gas column are the force of gravity $\rho g S\,dh$ and force of pressure $F = -S\,dp$. Since these forces are in equilibrium, $\rho g\,dh = -dp$. We can eliminate the density using the Mendeleev-Clapeyron equation: $p = \frac{1}{M}\rho R T$. From the relation $T = T_0\,(1 - \alpha h)$ we obtain $dT = -\alpha T_0\,dh$. Hence

$$\frac{dp}{p} = \frac{Mg}{\alpha R T_0} \cdot \frac{dT}{T}$$

Integrating, we obtain

$$\ln p = \frac{Mg}{\alpha R T_0} \ln T + \text{const}$$

---

* The exponential function, e^x, is usually written in the form $\exp x$ when the power index x is a lengthy expression.

Since the equation is valid at any point of the gravitational field, we have on the planet's surface

$$\ln p_0 = \frac{Mg}{\alpha R T_0} \ln T_0 + \text{const}$$

Subtracting this from the preceding equation, we eliminate the integration constant to obtain

$$\ln p - \ln p_0 = \frac{Mg}{\alpha R T_0} (\ln T - \ln T_0)$$

whence the formula sought for the barometric distribution.

16.23. Find the molar mass of the gas from the barometric distribution:

$$M = \frac{\alpha R T_0 \log (p_0/p)}{g \log (T_0/T)}, \quad \text{where} \quad \alpha = \frac{T_0 - T}{h T_0} = 1.05 \times 10^{-5} \text{ m}^{-1}$$

Noting that for Venus $g = 8.52$ m/s^2 (see Problem 4.7), we can obtain the values of the molar mass at four altitudes. The average value is

$$M_{\text{av}} = \frac{40.0 + 43.2 + 44.4 + 46.0}{4} = 43.4 \text{ kg/kmole}$$

The molar mass of CO_2 is 44 kg/kmole. This leads to the conclusion that the atmosphere of Venus consists mainly of carbon dioxide gas. Other experimental methods corroborate this conclusion.

17. The First Law of Thermodynamics

17.1. For an isobaric process $Q : \Delta U : W = C_{mp} : C_{mV} : R$. For a monoatomic gas $C_{mp} : C_{mV} : R = 5 : 3 : 2$.

17.2. The work of expansion of a gas is

$$W = m_{\text{w}} g h = p (V_2 - V_1) = \frac{m}{M} R (T_2 - T_1)$$

Therofore

$$\Delta T = m_{\text{w}} g h M / m R$$

The quantity of heat is obtained from the equation

$$\frac{Q}{W} = \frac{C_{mp}}{R} = \frac{7}{2}$$

(diatomic gas!).

17.3. It follows from the relations $C_{mp} - C_{mV} = R$ and $\gamma = \frac{C_{mp}}{C_{mV}}$ that $C_{mV} = \frac{R}{\gamma - 1}$. Hence the molar heat of a monoatomic gas at constant volume lies within the limits

$$1.24 \times 10^4 \leqslant C_{mV} \leqslant 1.28 \times 10^4 \text{ J/(kmole·K)}$$

Accordingly
$$2.07 \times 10^4 \leqslant C_{mp} \leqslant 2.11 \times 10^4 \text{ J/(kmole}\cdot\text{K)}$$
To obtain the specific heats, divide the molar heats by the molar mass.

17.4. For diatomic gases in the specified temperature range we have
$$\frac{R}{0.41} \leqslant C_{mV} \leqslant \frac{R}{0.39}$$
i.e.
$$2.02 \times 10^4 \leqslant C_{mV} \leqslant 2.13 \times 10^4 \text{ J/(kmole}\cdot\text{K)}$$
$$2.85 \times 10^4 \leqslant C_{mp} \leqslant 2.96 \times 10^4 \text{ J/(kmole}\cdot\text{K)}$$

17.6. The work $W = \frac{1}{2}(p_2 + p_1)(V_2 - V_1)$. The change in the internal energy is
$$\Delta U = \frac{m}{M} C_{mV}(T_2 - T_1) = \frac{C_{mV}}{R}(p_2 V_2 - p_1 V_1)$$
The quantity of heat is $Q = \Delta U + A$.
The molar heat is
$$C_m = \frac{Q}{T_2 - T_1} = \frac{QR}{p_2 V_2 - p_1 V_1}$$
and its ratio to the gas constant is
$$\frac{C_m}{R} = \frac{Q}{p_2 V_2 - p_1 V_1} = 2.06$$
The corresponding value for a monoatomic gas is $C_{mp}/R = 2.5$, $C_{mV}/R = 1.5$. Clearly
$$C_{mV} \leqslant C_m \leqslant C_{mp}$$

17.7. Divide the change in volume into 10 equal parts so that $\Delta V = 0.1$ m³. The element of work along a short path is $W_i = \overline{p_i}\,\Delta V$ (Fig. 17.7). Therefore the total work is
$$W = \Delta V(\overline{p_1} + \overline{p_2} + \ldots + \overline{p_{10}})$$
Write the data in the form of a table (Table 17.7). It follows that the work done by a gas expanding at constant temperature is

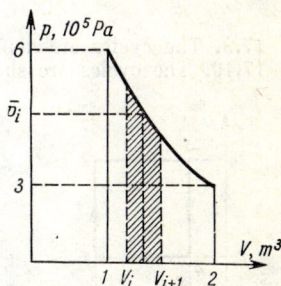

Fig. 17.7.

$$W = 0.1 \times 41.58 \times 10^5 = 4.16 \times 10^5 \text{ J}$$

Using the formula of § 27.6, we have
$$W = 2.3 \times 6 \times 10^5 \times 1 \times \log 2 =$$
$$= 2.3 \times 6 \times 0.301 \times 10^5 = 4.17 \times 10^5 \text{ J}$$
The relative error in the numerical calculation is
$$\varepsilon = \frac{0.001 \times 100\%}{4.17} = 0.24\%$$

Table 17.7

n	V_i, m³	$\overline{V}_i$, m³	$\overline{p}_i = \dfrac{p_0 V_0}{\overline{V}_i}$, 10^5 Pa
0	1.0	1.05	5.71
1	1.1	1.15	5.22
2	1.2	1.25	4.80
3	1.3	1.35	4.45
4	1.4	1.45	4.14
5	1.5	1.55	3.87
6	1.6	1.65	3.64
7	1.7	1.75	3.43
8	1.8	1.85	3.24
9	1.9	1.95	3.08
10	2.0		
		Total	41.58

17.8. The work done by a gas expanding at constant temperature is

$$W = \int_{V_1}^{V_2} p \, dV = \frac{m}{M} RT \int_{V_1}^{V_2} \frac{dV}{V} = \frac{m}{M} RT \ln \frac{V_2}{V_1} = p_1 V_1 \ln \frac{V_2}{V_1}$$

17.9. The cycles are depicted in Figs. 17.9b, 17.9c, 17.9d.
17.10. The cycles are shown in Figs. 17.10b, 17.10c, 17.10d.

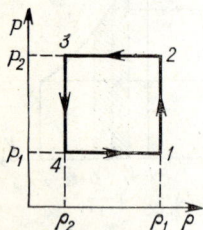
Fig. 17.9b.

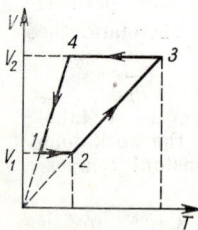
Fig. 17.9c.

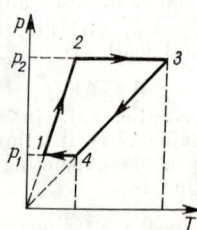
Fig. 17.9d.

17.11. It follows from the first law of thermodynamics for an adiabatic process $(Q = 0)$, that

$$\frac{m}{M} C_{mV} \, dT + p \, dV = 0$$

Differentiating the Mendeleev-Clapeyron equation, we obtain

$$p\, dV + V\, dp = \frac{m}{M}\, R\, dT$$

Eliminating dT from these expressions, we obtain after some trans-

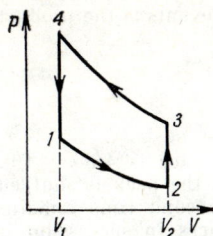

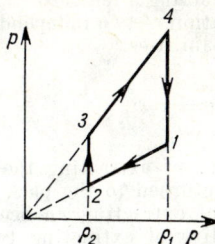

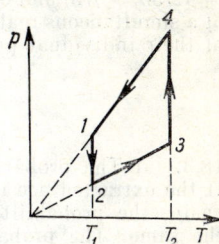

Fig. 17.10b.   Fig. 17.10c.   Fig. 17.10d.

formations

$$\gamma \frac{dV}{V} + \frac{dp}{p} = 0$$

Integrating, we obtain

$$\gamma \int_{V_0}^{V} \frac{dV}{V} + \int_{p_0}^{p} \frac{dp}{p} = 0$$

from which

$$\gamma \ln V - \gamma \ln V_0 + \ln p - \ln p_0 = 0, \quad \text{or} \quad \ln (pV^\gamma) = \ln (p_0 V_0^\gamma)$$

Therefore, $pV^\gamma = p_0 V_0^\gamma$.

17.13. From the Poisson equation, we obtain $p_{ad} = p_0 (V_0/V)^\gamma = 4 \times 10^5 \times 4^{1.4} = 4^{2.4} \times 10^5$. For the case of isothermic compression we obtain $p_{isot} = 4p_0$, i.e. a pressure almost twice as small.

The work of adiabatic compression of a gas is

$$W_{ad} = (p_2 V_2 - p_1 V_1)/(\gamma - 1) = 1.87 \times 10^6 \text{ J}$$

The work of isothermic compression of a gas is

$$W_{isot} = 2.3 p_1 V_1 \log (V_1/V_2) = 1.11 \times 10^6 \text{ J}$$

18. The Second Law of Thermodynamics

18.2. (a) There are three court-cards of each suit: the jack, the queen, the king. Therefore the total number of court-cards is $3 \times 4 = 12$.

(b) The number of red court-cards is $3 \times 2 = 6$. One can also reason as follows. The probability of extracting a red court-card is the probability of the compound event: extracting a court-card ($w_1 = 12/36 = 1/3$) and extracting a red card ($w_2 = 1/2$). The probability of a simultaneous realization of two independent events is the product of their individual probabilities:

$$w = w_1 w_2 = \frac{1}{3} \cdot \frac{1}{2} = \frac{1}{6}$$

18.3. (a) The probability of extracting the first ace is $4/36 = 1/9$. If the extracted ace is returned to the pack and the pack is shuffled again, the probability of extracting an ace a second time remains the same. The probability of extracting two aces in succession is equal to the product of the two equal probabilities.

(b) If the extracted ace is not returned to the pack, the probability of extracting the second ace will be $3/35$. The probability of extracting two aces in succession is equal to the product of the probabilities.

18.4. Imagine the balls to be designated by the letters a, b, c, d. Write out all the possible distributions of the balls in both halves of the vessel (Table 18.4a). We see that there are altogether $2^4 = 16$ distributions, the first and the fifth of which may be realized in one way, the second and the fourth in four ways, the third in six ways. These directly give us the thermodynamic probabilities.

To obtain the mathematical probabilities, divide the values obtainted by the total number of cases.

Use the data obtained to compile Table 18.4b, which shows the thermodynamic and mathematical probabilities of interest to us.

18.5. (a) Let the probability of finding the given ball in one part of the vessel be p; then the probability of finding it in the other part of the vessel is $q = 1 - p$. The probability of finding k particular balls in the first part of the vessel is p^k; the probability of finding the rest in the other half is q^{n-k}. Consequently the probability of the event when k particular balls are found in the first part of the vessel and $n - k$ are found in the second part of the vessel is $p^k q^{n-k}$. However, we assume all the balls to be identical, and because of that this result may be realized in C_n^k ways—in other words, the thermodynamic probability W of this state is C_n^k.

To obtain the mathematical probability w, one should multiply the number of ways by the probability of a favourable combination; therefore

$$w_k = C_n^k p^k q^{n-k} = C_n^k (1-p)^{n-k} p^k$$

Such a distribution of probabilities is called *binomial distribution*.

Table 18.4a

	Left part	Right part	
1	a, b, c, d		First state
2	a, b, c	d	Second state
3	a, b, d	c	
4	a, c, d	b	
5	b, c, d	a	
6	a, b	c, d	Third state
7	a, c	b, d	
8	a, d	b, c	
9	b, c	a, d	
10	b, d	a, c	
11	c, d	a, b	
12	a	b, c, d	Fourth state
13	b	a, c, d	
14	c	a, b, d	
15	d	a, b, c	
16		a, b, c, d	Fifth state

Table 18.4b

State	Thermodynamic probability W	Mathematical probability w
First	$C_4^0 = 1$	$1/16 = 6\%$
Second	$C_4^1 = 4$	$4/16 = 1/4 = 25\%$
Third	$C_4^2 = 6$	$6/16 = 3/8 = 38\%$
Fourth	$C_4^3 = C_4^1 = 4$	$4/16 = 1/4 = 25\%$
Fifth	$C_4^4 = C_4^0 = 1$	$1/16 = 6\%$
		100%

(b) If the probability of finding the ball in both parts of the vessel is the same, then $p = q = 1/2$, and we have

$$w_h = C_n^k \left(\frac{1}{2}\right)^h \left(\frac{1}{2}\right)^{n-h} = C_n^k \left(\frac{1}{2}\right)^n$$

We have generalized the result of Problem 18.4 for the case of n balls.

18.6. See Fig. 18.6. It may be seen from the figure that the probability of a uniform distribution increases rapidly with n.

18.7. *First method.* Since both parts of the vessel are equivalent (this is the consequence of the homogeneity and the isotropy of space) the

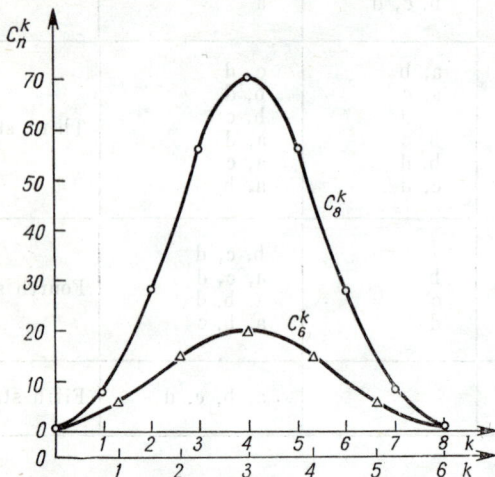

Fig. 18.6.

probability of finding a particle inside a volume $V < V_0$ is equal to the ratio of volumes:

$$p = \frac{V}{V_0}, \qquad q = 1 - p = \frac{V_0 - V}{V_0}$$

In the present problem $k = n$, i.e. all the molecules are contained inside V. The answer is obtained from the solution of Problem 18.5.

For a large number of molecules the probability of such an event is negligible.

Second method. The problem may be solved without the binomial distribution, but directly on the basis of the theorem for compound probability (see problem 18.2). Specifically, the probability of finding a molecule inside the given volume is $p = V/V_0$. The probability of finding simultaneously all the n molecules in it is the product of the individual probabilities: $w = p^n = (V/V_0)^n$.

18.8. Let $\Delta S > 0$, then (see § 28.8, Fig. 28.5) $-\dfrac{Q}{T_1} + \dfrac{Q}{T_2} > 0$, therefore $\dfrac{Q}{T_2} > \dfrac{Q}{T_1}$, whence $T_1 > T_2$. Hence the law of entropy increase leads to the Clausius principle (see §§ 28.9 and 29.5).

18.9. Consider 10 successive steps starting with the lower left. Measure their lengths in millimetres as accurately as possible and transform them to scale into actual dimensions (see Table 18.9).

Table 18.9

i	Dimensions in the figure L_i, mm	True dimensions L_i, μm	L_i^2, μm²
1	8	10	100
2	4	5	25
3	8	10	100
4	7	8.8	77
5	12	15	225
6	9.5	11.9	142
7	14	17.5	301
8	4	5	25
9	4	5	25
10	3	3.8	14
			$\Delta^2 = 1038 \times 10^{-12}$ m²

Hence the square of the r.m.s. displacement is $\Delta^2 = 1.04 \times 10^{-9}$ m². Substituting Δ^2 and $t = 300$ s into Einstein's formula, we obtain

$$k = \frac{\pi \eta r \Delta^2}{Tt} = \frac{\pi \times 8.9 \times 10^{-4} \times 4.4 \times 10^{-7} \times 1.04 \times 10^{-9}}{300 \times 300} = 1.4 \times 10^{-23} \text{ J/K}$$

The Avogadro number is

$$N_A = \frac{R}{k} = \frac{8.3 \times 10^3}{1.4 \times 10^{-23}} = 5.9 \times 10^{26} \text{ kmole}^{-1}$$

We would advise the reader to carry out similar calculations using other parts of the graph and to assess the inherent error in the method.

18.10. See Figs. 18.10a and 18.10b.

18.11. By definition, $\Delta S = \dfrac{\Delta Q}{T}$, therefore a small quantity of heat $\Delta Q = T \, \Delta S$ (see Fig. 18.11).

3*

The total quantity of heat in the process is numerically equal to the area of the curvilinear trapezoid shown in the figure (to the specified scale). The problem may be solved by numerical methods or by integration.

18.13. Since $dS = \dfrac{\Delta Q}{T}$ and $\Delta Q = dU + p\,dV = \dfrac{m}{M} C_{mV}\,dT + p\,dV$, it

follows that $dS = \dfrac{m}{M} C_{mV} \dfrac{dT}{T} + \dfrac{m}{M} R \dfrac{dV}{V}$. Integrating, we obtain

$$S_2 - S_1 = \frac{m}{M} \int_{T_1}^{T_2} C_{mV} \frac{dT}{T} + \frac{m}{M} R \ln \frac{V_2}{V_1}$$

For a small temperature range the isochoric heat capacity may be

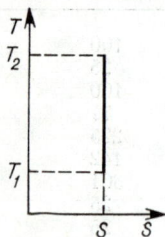

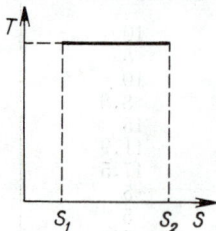

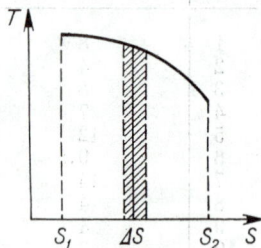

Fig. 18.10a.   Fig. 18.10b.   Fig. 18.11.

assumed to be a constant. In this case

$$S_2 - S_1 = \frac{m}{M} \left(C_{mV} \ln \frac{T_2}{T_1} + R \ln \frac{V_2}{V_1} \right)$$

18.14. For an isochoric process

$$S_2 - S_1 = \frac{m}{M} C_{mV} \ln \frac{T_2}{T_1}$$

For an isobaric process

$$S_2 - S_1 = \frac{m}{M} C_{mp} \ln \frac{T_2}{T_1}$$

For an isothermal process

$$S_2 - S_1 = \frac{m}{M} R \ln \frac{V_2}{V_1}$$

18.15. (a) $W = p_2 (V_2 - V_1) - p_1 (V_2 - V_1) = (p_2 - p_1)(V_2 - V_1)$.

(b) $W = \dfrac{m}{M} RT_1 \ln \dfrac{V_2}{V_1} - \dfrac{m}{M} RT_2 \ln \dfrac{V_2}{V_1} = \dfrac{m}{M} R (T_1 - T_2) \ln \dfrac{V_2}{V_1}$.

18.16. Plot the graph of the Carnot cycle in the T-S variables (Fig. 18.16).

$$\eta = \frac{Q_1 - Q_2}{Q_1} = \frac{T_1(S_2 - S_1) - T_2(S_2 - S_1)}{T_1(S_2 - S_1)} = \frac{T_1 - T_2}{T_1}$$

18.17. The efficiency of the cycle is $\eta = W/Q$. Since the work in isochoric sections is zero, the useful work is equal to the difference between the work of adiabatic expansion and that of adiabatic compression:

$$W = \frac{m}{M} C_{mV}(T_3 - T_4) -$$

$$- \frac{m}{M} C_{mV}(T_2 - T_1) =$$

$$= \frac{m}{M} C_{mV}(T_3 - T_2 + T_1 - T_4)$$

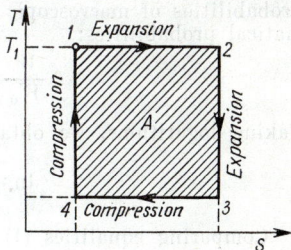

The working medium receives heat in the process of isochoric combustion of fuel:

Fig. 18.16.

$$Q = \frac{m}{M} C_{mV}(T_3 - T_2)$$

Hence

$$\eta = 1 - \frac{T_4 - T_1}{T_3 - T_2}$$

Making use of the result of Problem 17.12, express the temperatures in terms of the volumes. We have $V_2^{\gamma-1} T_2 = V_1^{\gamma-1} T_1$ and $V_2^{\gamma-1} T_3 = V_1^{\gamma-1} T_4$. Dividing the first equality by the second, we obtain $T_2/T_3 = T_1/T_4$. Transform the expression for the efficiency and reduce it to the following form:

$$\eta = 1 - \frac{T_4}{T_3} \cdot \frac{1 - (T_1/T_4)}{1 - (T_2/T_3)}$$

But the second fraction is, evidently, unity and the first fraction $T_4/T_3 = (V_2/V_1)^{\gamma-1} = x^{\gamma-1}$. Hence $\eta = 1 - x^{\gamma-1}$.

18.19. Suppose an ideal gas experiences spontaneous isothermal compression. In the process quantity of heat is liberated to the environment equal to

$$Q_T = W_T = \frac{m}{M} RT \ln \frac{V}{V_0}$$

(see Problem 17.8). Therefore the change in the entropy is

$$\Delta S = S - S_0 = \frac{Q_T}{T} = \frac{m}{M} R \ln \frac{V}{V_0} = Nk \ln \frac{V}{V_0} \qquad (1)$$

Here N is the number of molecules. Since the compression of the gas took place at a constant temperature, the energy of molecular motion does not change, and the change in the entropy is due solely to the change in the volume. Estimate the probabilities of the initial and final states. The mathematical probability of a gas occupying the entire volume V_0 is unity because this is a certainty; hence $w_0 = 1$. The mathematical probability of the gas occupying volume $V < V_0$ was found in Problem 18.7; it is $w = (V/V_0)^N$. The thermodynamic probabilities of macroscopic states are proportional to their mathematical probabilities:

$$\frac{W}{W_0} = \frac{w}{w_0} = \left(\frac{V}{V_0} \right)^N$$

Taking logarithms, we obtain

$$\ln \frac{W}{W_0} = N \ln \frac{V}{V_0} \qquad (2)$$

Comparing equalities (1) and (2), we obtain

$$S - S_0 = k \ln W - k \ln W_0$$

whence the relation between the entropy and the thermodynamic probability.

19. Fundamentals of Fluid Dynamics

19.2. Apply the Bernoulli equation for an incompressible fluid:

$$\Delta p = \frac{1}{2} \rho v_2^2 - \frac{1}{2} \rho v_1^2$$

The velocity of fluid in the fire-hose may be found from the continuity equation.

19.3. Applying the Bernoulli equation for an incompressible fluid to both cross sections and expressing the velocity in the narrowing in terms of the gas velocity in the pipeline, we obtain

$$\Delta p = \frac{\rho v^2}{2} \left(\frac{D^4}{d^4} - 1 \right)$$

where D and d are the diameters of the pipeline and of the narrowing. The flow rate is

$$\mu = \rho S v = \frac{1}{4} \pi \rho v D^2$$

and the pressure drop $\Delta p = \rho_0 g h$, where ρ_0 is the density of water. After some simple transformations we obtain the final expression for the flow rate.

19.4. Apply the law of conservation of energy in conservative systems. In our case the work of the forces of pressure is accompanied by the change in the total mechanical energy of the system: $W = W_2 - W_1 = (K_2 + U_2) - (K_1 + U_1)$. Consider separately a volume of liquid $V = l_1 S_1 = l_2 S_2$ (Fig. 19.4); the mass of this volume is $m = \rho V$. The work of the forces of pressure is

$$W = F_1 l_1 - F_2 l_2 = p_1 S_1 l_1 - p_2 S_2 l_2 = (p_1 - p_2) V$$

Substituting the result obtained into the expression for the change in energy, we obtain

$$(p_1 - p_2) V = \frac{mv_2^2}{2} + mgh_2 - \frac{mv_1^2}{2} - mgh_1$$

whence

$$p_1 + \frac{\rho v_1^2}{2} + \rho g h_1 = p_2 + \frac{\rho v_2^2}{2} + \rho g h_2$$

19.5. Suppose that the volume of fluid flowing out through an orifice during a short time interval is so small that the drop in its level in the wide section of the vessel can be neglected. Taking into account that in our case the pressure drop is determined entirely by the hydrostatic pressure, we conclude that the Bernoulli equation assumes the form $\rho g h = \rho v^2/2$ from which we get the Torricelli formula for the velocity of fluid flowing out through a small orifice.

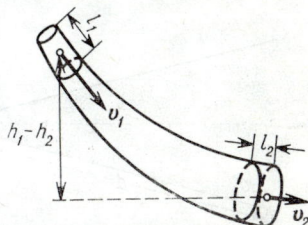

Fig. 19.4.

19.6. Making use of formulas (30.9) and (30.17), we obtain the result sought.

19.7. The velocity of the shock wave is $u = \sqrt{\dfrac{\rho(p - p_0)}{\rho_0(\rho - \rho_0)}}$. Here $p_0 = 1.01 \times 10^5$ Pa, $\rho_0 = 1.29$ kg/m^3, $p = 200 p_0$. The density at the front of the shock wave may be found from the Hugoniot equation. Denoting

$$a = \sqrt{\frac{\gamma_0 p_0}{\rho_0}}, \quad y = \frac{p}{p_0} = 200, \quad \alpha = \frac{\gamma_0 + 1}{\gamma_0 - 1} = 3.5$$

we obtain after some transformations:

$$u = \sqrt{\frac{\alpha y + 1}{\alpha - 1} \cdot \frac{a^2}{\gamma_0}} = a \sqrt{\frac{280}{1.4}} = a \sqrt{200}$$

19.9. It is evident from Fig. 19.9 that $d = \dfrac{h}{\sin \alpha} = Mh$, where M is the Mach number.

19.10. Consider the cycle depicted in Fig. 19.10. Since the gas returns to the original state, the change in the entropy during the complete cycle is zero. But during the quasi-static adiabatic expansion of gas (section *2-3*) its entropy does not change, during the isochoric cooling of the gas (section *3-1*) its entropy decreases. Therefore its entropy must have increased during the shock compression (section *1-2*). Perform the calculation for the compression ratio of the gas $x = \rho_2/\rho_1$. Putting, as in Problem 19.7, $\alpha = \dfrac{\gamma+1}{\gamma-1}$, we obtain with the aid of the Hugoniot and the Poisson equations

$$\frac{p_2}{p_1} = \frac{\alpha x - 1}{\alpha - x}, \qquad \frac{p_2}{p_1} = x^\gamma; \quad \text{therefore} \quad \frac{p_3}{p_1} = \frac{\alpha x - 1}{(\alpha - x)\, x^\gamma}$$

The change in entropy as a result of the shock compression is equal to the change in entropy as a result of the isochoric cooling,

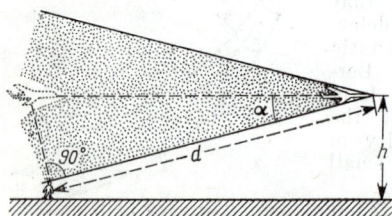

Fig. 19.9.

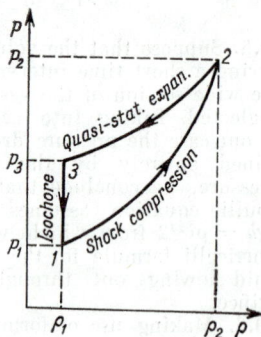

Fig. 19.10

only with the opposite sign. Making use of the result of Problem 18.14, we obtain

$$\Delta S_{\text{sh}} = -\Delta S_V = -\frac{m}{M}\, C_{mV}\, \ln \frac{T_1}{T_3} = \frac{m}{M}\, C_{mV} \ln \frac{p_3}{p_1}$$

$$= \frac{m}{M}\, C_{mV} \ln \left[\frac{\alpha x - 1}{(\alpha - x)\, x^\gamma} \right]$$

19.11. The flow velocity in the critical cross section is equal to the local velocity of sound; in the boiler the flow velocity is zero. Using the result of Problem 19.6, we obtain

$$\frac{a_0^2}{\gamma - 1} = \frac{v_{\text{cr}}^2}{2} + \frac{v_{\text{cr}}^2}{\gamma - 1}, \quad \text{whence} \quad v_{\text{cr}} = a_0 \sqrt{\frac{2}{\gamma + 1}}$$

To find the velocity of steam leaving the nozzle, we make use of the Bernoulli equation in the form of (30.8) and obtain $v = \sqrt{2c_p\, (T_0 - T)}$.

19.13. The thrust may be found from Newton's second law: $F - mg = ma$, whence $F = 4mg$. The consumption of fuel together with the oxidant is

$$\mu = F/u = 4mg/u$$

The density of the gas is found from the continuity equation:

$$\rho = \frac{\mu}{Su} = \frac{16mg}{\pi D^2 u^2}$$

The pressure is found from the Mendeleev-Clapeyron equation.
19.16. To begin with, find the Reynolds number assuming the characteristic dimension to be equal to the pipeline diameter:

$$\text{Re} = \frac{\rho v d}{\eta} = \frac{8 \times 10^2 \times 0.8 \times 1.1}{10^{-2}} = 7 \times 10^4$$

This is much greater than 2320, and therefore the hydraulic friction coefficient should be determined from the empirical formula

$$\lambda = \frac{0.316}{\sqrt[4]{\text{Re}}} = 1.94 \times 10^{-2} \approx 0.02$$

This enables us to find the pressure drop in the section using formula (30.32).

To find the power, use formula $P = Fv = \Delta p S v$.

Note that this calculation was made for an ideally smooth pipe; in a real pipe the required pressure drop, and consequently the pump power, is substantially greater.
19.17. The continuity equation follows from the law of conservation of mass. Hence it is valid for an arbitrary stationary fluid flow. The equation of momenta and the Bernoulli equation were derived for an ideal fluid, i.e. a fluid whose viscosity may be neglected. At the same time viscosity of fluid plays an important part in pipelines and the friction forces cannot be neglected.

20. Solids

20.1. The stress $\sigma = F/S$, where F is the applied force and S is the area of the section where this force is distributed. Making use of the definition of the bulk modulus, we obtain

$$F = KS\varepsilon = KS \left| \frac{\Delta V}{V} \right|$$

20.3. The sag in the cable is $h = \sqrt{(l/2)^2 - (d/2)^2} = 0.625$ m. The force extending the cable is $F = mgl/4h = 1.57 \times 10^4$ N, the cross-sectional area of the cable is $120\pi D^2/4 = 30\pi D^2 = 9.4 \times 10^{-5}$ m^2. Hence applying Hooke's law we find the extension of each section of the cable:

$$\Delta l = \frac{Fl}{ES} = \frac{mgl^2}{4ESh}$$

The force capable of rupturing the cable is found from the breaking stress: $F_m = \sigma_m S$. The load capable of rupturing the cable is

$$M = 4\sigma_m Sh/gl$$

20.4. The force sought is of the form

$$F = -\frac{e^2}{4\pi\varepsilon_0 a^2}\left(1 - \frac{1}{2^2} + \frac{1}{3^2} - \frac{1}{4^2} + \ldots\right) =$$

$$= -\frac{e^2}{4\pi\varepsilon_0 a^2}\left(\frac{3}{1^2 \cdot 2^2} + \frac{7}{3^2 \cdot 4^2} + \frac{11}{5^2 \cdot 6^2} + \ldots\right)$$

Compute the value of the series in the brackets to three significant digits. To obtain the required accuracy, we may discard all terms below 0.001, i.e. we may take the sum of the first ten terms in the series. We obtain

$$\frac{3}{1^2 \cdot 2^2} + \frac{7}{3^2 \cdot 4^2} + \ldots + \frac{39}{19^2 \cdot 20^2} =$$

$$= 0.82128 \approx 0.82$$

Hence

$$F = -0.82\,\frac{e^2}{4\pi\varepsilon_0 a^2}$$

This means that neglecting the interactions with all the ions except the nearest neighbours results in an error of no greater than 20%.

20.5. For the purpose of calculation consider a plane with ions arranged in staggered rows

Fig. 20.5.

(chessboard order) (Fig. 20.5). In this case the breaking stress is $\sigma_m = = F_0 n$, where $F_0 = e^2/(4\pi\varepsilon_0 a^2)$ is the force of interaction between neighbouring ions, $n = a^{-2}$ is the ion concentration per unit area. Hence

$$\sigma_m = \frac{e^2}{4\pi\varepsilon_0 a^4}$$

20.7. We shall solve the problem in a rotating reference frame. Consider a segment of the flywheel which subtends small angle α at its centre (Fig. 20.7). The forces acting on this metallic segment are the centrifugal force of inertia and two elastic forces. The relation between them follows from the condition for equilibrium: $I_{cf} = T\alpha$. Here $T = \sigma S$, where S is the cross-sectional area of the flywheel rim, and σ is the stress. The volume of the separated segment is $V = lS = = \alpha S R_{av}$, where $R_{av} = (R + r)/2$ is the average radius of the flywheel rim. The centrifugal force of inertia is

$$I_{cf} = m\omega^2 R_{av} = \omega^2 R_{av}\rho V = \alpha\rho S\omega^2 R_{av}^2$$

where ρ is the density of the metal. Substituting into the condition for equilibrium, we obtain the dependence of the stress in the metal

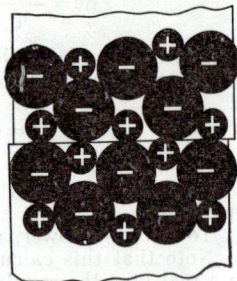

on the speed of rotation:

$$\sigma = \rho \omega^2 R_{av}^2$$

The speed is safe when the stress does not exceed the elastic limit. In this case the elastic forces will return the flywheel to its original state when the speed of rotation is reduced. Therefore the maximum safe speed of rotation of the flywheel is

$$\omega = \sqrt{\frac{\sigma_E}{\rho R_{av}^2}} = \frac{2}{R+r} \sqrt{\frac{\sigma_E}{\rho}}$$

The flywheel will fly apart when the stress in it reaches the breaking stress, i.e. when

$$\omega_{br} = \frac{2}{R+r} \sqrt{\frac{\sigma_{fw}}{\rho}}$$

20.8. Imagine a small spherical segment with a radius of the base of $a = R \sin \alpha$ to be cut out of the sphere (Fig. 20.8). An elementary

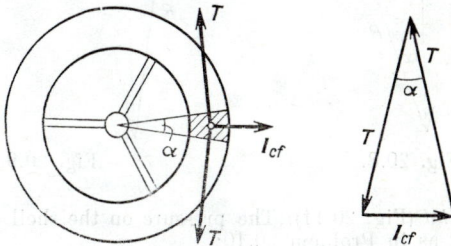

Fig. 20.7.

elastic force $\Delta T = \sigma \, \Delta S = \sigma d \Delta l$ acts on an element of area $\Delta S = d \Delta l$ on the periphery of this segment. The normal component of the elementary force is $\Delta T_n = \Delta T \sin \alpha = \sigma d \, \Delta l \sin \alpha$. Summing over the complete circumference of the segment, we obtain the total force of the normal pressure:

$$T_n = \sigma d \cdot 2\pi a \sin \alpha = 2\pi \sigma R d \sin^2 \alpha$$

This force compensates the force of the gaseous pressure $F = pS$ acting on the segment. For a small angle the segment's area is $S = \pi a^2 = \pi R^2 \sin^2 \alpha$, and the force of pressure is $F = \pi p R^2 \sin^2 \alpha$.

It follows from the balance of forces that $p = 2\sigma d/R$.

20.9. Imagine a small area along a generatrix to be cut out of the cylindrical surface (Fig. 20.9). Four elastic forces are seen to act on the area. Two of them are parallel to the generatrix; their normal components are zero and so they offer no resistance to the gas pressure and should not be taken into account. The remaining two are perpendicular to the generatrices; the sum of their normal components is the normal force $T_n = 2\sigma l d \sin \alpha$. The force of pressure is $F = pS = 2pal = 2plR \sin \alpha$.

It follows from the balance of the forces that $p = \sigma d/R$ which was to be proved (compare with Problem 20.8).

20.10. In the specified temperature range the relative change in length is proportional to the change in temperature: $\varepsilon = \Delta l/l = \alpha \Delta t$. From Hooke's law $\sigma = E\varepsilon = E\alpha \Delta t$.

20.11. The problem is solved in the same way as Problem 20.8. Consider a segment of the shell subtending a small angle α and obtain $F = T\alpha$ where $F = \sigma_1 S_1$ is the force of pressure of the cylinder on the shell, $T = \sigma S_2$ is the tensile force in the ring. But $S_1 =$

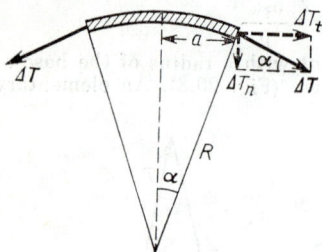

Fig. 20.8.

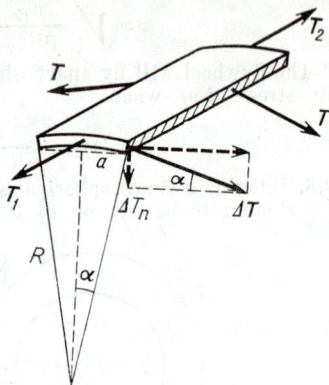

Fig. 20.9.

$= hr\alpha$, $S_2 = hd$ (Fig. 20.11). The pressure on the shell is found in the same way as in Problem 20.10:

$$p = \sigma_1 = E_1 \varepsilon = E_1 \frac{\Delta r_1}{r} = E_1 \alpha_1 \Delta t$$

Here E_1 is the Young modulus for steel, α_1 is the thermal expansion coefficient for steel. Hence $E_1 \alpha_1 \Delta t r \alpha h = \sigma_2 h \alpha d$, and the stress in the shell is

$$\sigma = E_1 \alpha_1 r \Delta t/d$$

20.12. To find the stress, apply Hooke's law: $\sigma = E\varepsilon = E \Delta\rho/\rho$. The change in the density is found from the data of § 33.5. The stress appearing in the ice is equal to the pressure it exerts on the rock.

20.13. The condition for the equilibrium of a fluid in communicating vessels (Fig. 20.13) is $p_1 = p_2$, or $\rho_1 h_1 g = \rho_2 h_2 g$. But $\rho = \rho_0/(1 + \beta t)$, whence

$$\frac{h_1}{1 + \beta t_1} = \frac{h_2}{1 + \beta t_2}, \qquad \beta = \frac{h_2 - h_1}{h_1 t_2 - h_2 t_1}$$

20.14. In the simple cubic lattice the atoms occupy the corners of the cube (Fig. 20.14). There are altogether eight atoms at the eight corners, but the atom at each corner belongs to the eight cubes sharing the corner. Therefore there is one atom to each cube.

20.15. In a face-centered lattice, the atoms occupy positions at the eight corners and in the six faces (Fig. 20.15). A corner has 1/8 of

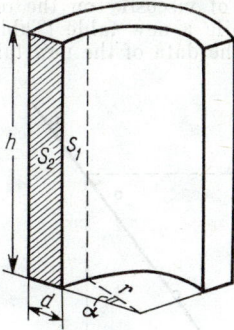

Fig. 20.11.

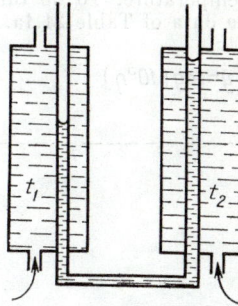

Fig. 20.13.

an atom, a face 1/2 of an atom. Altogether a cell has $8 \times \frac{1}{8} + 6 \times \frac{1}{2} = 4$ atoms.

20.16. In a hexagonal lattice three neighbouring atoms are completely inside the cell (Fig. 20.16). Two atoms at the centres of the bases are

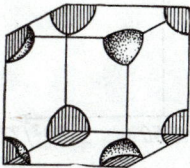

Fig. 20.14

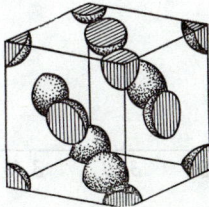

Fig. 20.15.

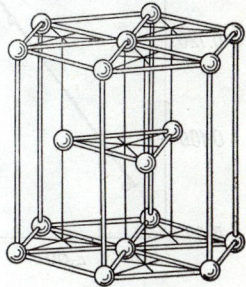

Fig. 20.16.

shared by two cells, and the twelve atoms at the apexes of the prism are each shared by the six cells adjoining each apex. Hence an elementary cell contains $3 \times 1 + 2 \times \frac{1}{2} + 12 \times \frac{1}{6} = 6$ atoms.

21. Liquids

21.1. To check the exponential dependence of viscosity on temperature, find the dependence of the logarithm of viscosity on the reciprocal of the temperature. To do this, compile a new table (Table 21.1b) using the data of Table 21.1a. Using the data of the new table, plot

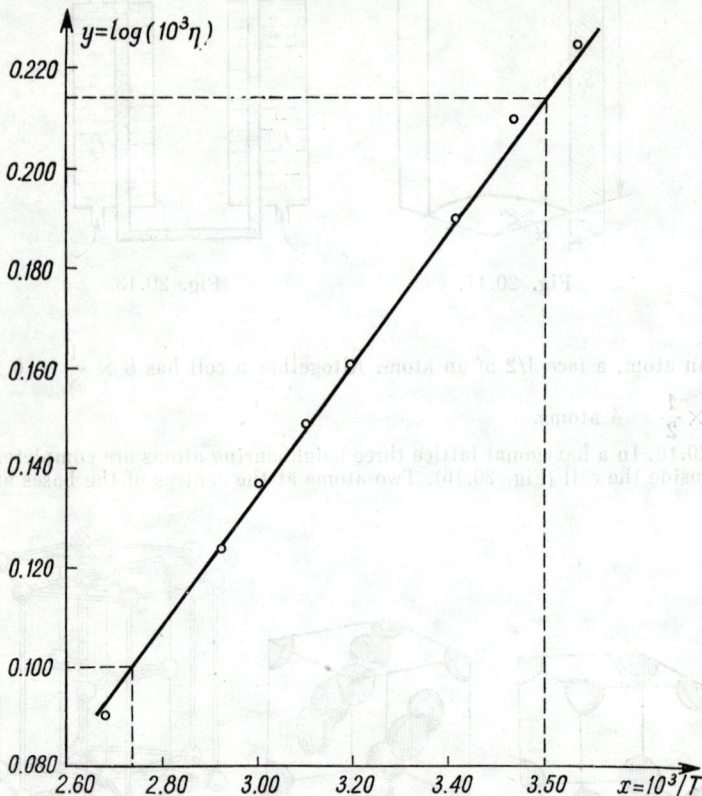

Fig. 21.1.

a graph on millimetre graph paper (Fig. 21.1). Almost all the points are seen to fall on the straight line

$$y = a + bx, \quad \text{or} \quad \log(10^3 \eta) = a + 10^3 \frac{b}{T} = a + \frac{B}{T}$$

Table 21.1b

T, K	$x = 10^3/T$	$y = \log(10^3\eta)$	T, K	$x = 10^3/T$	$y = \log(10^3\eta)$
273	3.66	0.226	323	3.10	0.148
283	3.53	0.210	333	3.00	0.136
293	3.41	0.191	343	2.92	0.123
303	3.30	0.176	373	2.68	0.091
313	3.19	0.161			

Taking antilogarithms we obtain

$$10^3\eta = A \times 10^{B/T}$$

the distinction from formula (34.10) being only in numerical coefficients.

To find the activation energy ε_0 use two points lying on the straight line:

$$x_1 = 2.75, \quad y_1 = 0.100 \quad \text{and} \quad x_2 = 3.60, \quad y_2 = 0.213$$

The temperatures corresponding to these points are $T_1 = 10^3/x_1 = 364$ K and $T_2 = 10^3/x_2 = 278$ K and the corresponding viscosities are $\eta_1 = 10^{-3} \times 10^{y_1} = 1.26 \times 10^{-3}$ Pa·s and $\eta_2 = 1.63 \times 10^{-3}$ Pa·s.

The ratio of the viscosities is

$$\eta_2 : \eta_1 = e^{\varepsilon_0/kT_2} : \varepsilon^{\varepsilon_0/kT_1} = \exp\left\{\frac{\varepsilon_0\,(T_1 - T_2)}{kT_1T_2}\right\}$$

Hence we obtain after taking the logarithms

$$\frac{\varepsilon_0\,(T_1 - T_2)}{kT_1T_2} = \ln\frac{\eta_2}{\eta_1}$$

or

$$\varepsilon_0 = \frac{kT_1T_2\ln(\eta_2/\eta_1)}{T_1 - T_2} = \frac{2.3kT_1T_2\log(\eta_2/\eta_1)}{T_1 - T_2}$$

21.3. Water will start rising and will reach the upper end of the capillary. Here the radius of curvature will decrease until the pressure of the curved surface becomes equal to the hydrostatic pressure of the water column. Then the water will stop rising. The condition for equilibrium is

$$\Delta p = \frac{2\sigma \cos\theta}{r} = \rho g h$$

For the contact angle we obtain

$$\cos\theta = \frac{r\rho g h}{2\sigma} = 0.544, \quad \theta = 57°$$

21.4. The total surface area of all the droplets is $S_0 = 400\pi r^2 = 100\pi d^2$, their total volume is $V_0 = 100\pi a^3/6$. After the droplets merge, the volume remains unchanged, but the surface area decreases: $V = \pi D^3/6 = V_0$, $S = \pi D^2$. From the condition of equality of the volumes, find the diameter of the large drop:

$$\frac{100\pi d^3}{6} = \frac{\pi D^3}{6}, \quad \text{whence} \quad D = d\sqrt[3]{100}$$

The surface area of the large drop is $S = \pi d^2 \sqrt[3]{10^4}$. The decrease in the surface layer energy corresponding to the decrease in the surface area of $\Delta S = S_0 - S = \pi d^2 (10^2 - 10^{4/3})$ is

$$\Delta\mathscr{E}_{\text{sur}} = \alpha\Delta S \approx \sigma\Delta S = \pi\sigma d^2 (10^2 - 10^{4/3})$$

21.5. Two forces act on a fluid in conditions of weightlessness: the force of surface tension $S_{\text{sur}} = \pi\sigma d$ and the force of hydraulic resistance $F_{\text{res}} = \lambda \dfrac{l}{d} \cdot \dfrac{\rho v^2}{2} \cdot \dfrac{\pi d^2}{4}$ (see § 30.17). Since the velocity

of the fluid is small, for small Reynolds numbers $\lambda = \dfrac{64}{\text{Re}} = \dfrac{64\eta}{\rho v d}$. Equating the forces, we obtain after some simplifications

$$v = \sigma d/8\eta l$$

Compute the velocity to find the Reynolds number, and make sure that it is much less than 2320.

21.7. When the fluid reaches the lower end of the tube, a convex meniscus will be formed there with a shape identical to that of the upper meniscus (Fig. 21.7). The excess pressure is $\Delta p = 2 \times 2\sigma/r$. But $2\sigma/r = \rho gh$, $\Delta p = \rho gH$, from which $H = 2h$.

21.9. Suppose the drop spreads evenly and as seen from above has the shape of a circle of radius R (Fig. 21.9). The area of this circle is $S = V/d = m/\rho d$. The force of attraction between the plates is $F = \Delta p S$, where $\Delta p = 2\sigma/d$ is the excess pressure under the curved surface. Therefore

Fig. 21.7.

$$F = 2\sigma m/\rho d^2$$

21.10. The pressures from the left and from the right are equal, i.e.

$$\Delta p_1 + \Delta p = \Delta p_2, \quad \text{or} \quad \frac{4\sigma}{R_1} + \frac{4\sigma}{R} = \frac{4\sigma}{R_2}$$

Here $\Delta p = 4\sigma/R$, for the film has two surfaces—the external and the internal. Hence

$$\frac{1}{R} = \frac{1}{R_1} - \frac{1}{R_2}$$

Since at the point of contact of the three films we have a system of three forces of equal magnitude in equilibrium in a plane, the angle

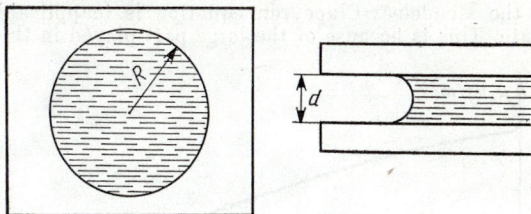

Fig. 21.9.

between the forces is found from the condition that they form a closed triangle.

22. Vapours

22.2. As distinct from an ideal gas, whose molecular concentration (and density) does not change in an isochoric process, the molecular concentration (and density) of a saturated vapour rises with temperature because of additional evaporation of the liquid.

22.3. The density of saturated vapour at 55 °C is 104.3 g/m³. Therefore at this temperature 8 g of saturated vapour occupies a volume of $\frac{8}{104.3} = 7.6 \times 10^{-3}$ m³ = 7.6 litres. In a smaller volume there will be a precipitation of dew.

22.7. Find first the mass of moisture in each volume of air, i.e. the absolute humidity of the volumes which are mixed. We have in 5 m³ of air

$$m_1 = f_1 V_1 = \rho_1^{sat} B_1 V_1 = 12.8 \times 0.22 \times 5 = 14.1\,g$$

In 3 m³ of air

$$m_2 = \rho_2^{sat} B_2 V_2 = 27.2 \times 0.46 \times 3 = 37.5\,g$$

Next find the absolute humidity of the mixture:

$$f = (m_1 + m_2)/(V_1 + V_2) = 6.45 \text{ g/m}^3$$

To find the relative humidity we must find the temperature of the mixture. Neglecting the vapour mass we may write the equation of heat balance in the form

$$\rho_0 V_1 c_0 (t - 15) = \rho_0 V_2 c_0 (28 - t)$$

where the subscripts 0 show that the density and the specific heat refer to air. We have $t = 20$ °C. Now it is easy to compute the relative humidity.

22.8. $\frac{R}{M} \rho_{cr} T_{cr} = 9.8 \times 10^7$ Pa; at the same time $p_{cr} = 218$ atm $= 2.2 \times 10^7$ Pa.

Hence the Mendeleev-Clapeyron equation is inapplicable to the critical state. This is because of the large part played in this case by

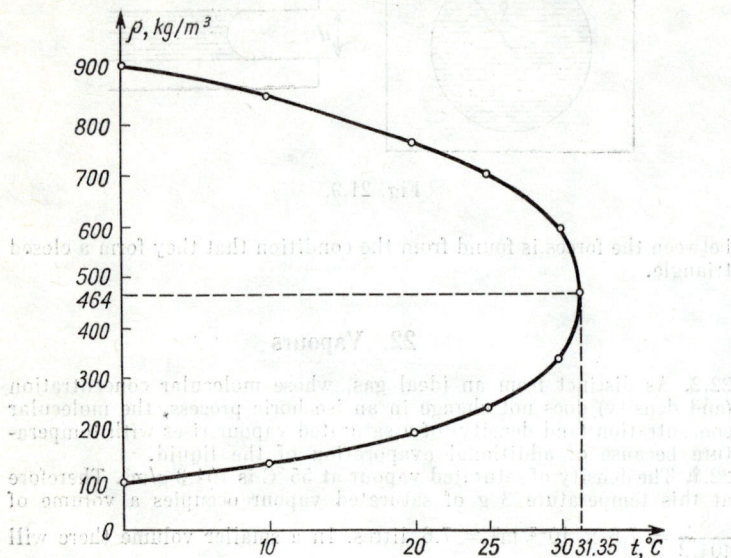

Fig. 22.9.

molecular interactions, which are neglected in the case of an ideal gas.

22.9. See Fig. 22.9.

23. Phase Transitions

23.1. Since evaporation takes place at a constant pressure, $W = p(v_0^{vap} - v_0^{liq})$, where $v_0 = 1/\rho$ is the specific volume, i.e. the volume of 1 kg of the substance. Hence

$$W = p\left(\frac{1}{\rho_{vap}} - \frac{1}{\rho_{liq}}\right)$$

The density of steam at 100 °C may be found from Table 35.1 (see § 35.3). Since the specific volume of vapour is almost a thousand times greater than the specific volume of liquid, it follows with better than 1% accuracy that $W = p/\rho_{vap}$.

The energy spent on breaking the bonds between the molecules can be found from the first law of thermodynamics: $\Delta U = L - W$ where L is the specific heat of evaporation.

23.2. Ice melts under the pressure of the wire, and the wire sinks; the water formed above the wire immediately freezes again.

23.3. The heat liberated in the processes of condensation of water vapour and of cooling of water down to the melting point of ice is $Q = m_3 (L + c\Delta t) = 5.2 \times 10^5$ J. This is not enough to melt all the ice. For this the required heat is $Q_m = m_2\lambda = 10^6$ J. Therefore the ice will only partially melt.

23.7. The heat of fusion liberated in the process of freezing of water will be spent to heat the remaining water to $0\,°C$. Let the total mass of supercooled water be m, the mass of ice formed m_1, the mass of remaining water $m_2 = m - m_1$. From the heat balance equation we have $m_1\lambda = (m - m_1) c\Delta t$, whence

$$x = \frac{m_1}{m} = \frac{c\Delta t}{\lambda + c\Delta t}$$

23.8. The outflow velocity is $v = \mu/\rho S$, where μ is the amount of water that evaporates per second. Obviously, $\mu = \dfrac{Q}{Lt} = \dfrac{\eta P}{L}$, where P is the power of the hot-plate and η is its efficiency. Hence

$$v = \eta P/\rho L S$$

23.9. First find the melting point: $t = -\Delta p/k = -4.35\,°C$. As the ice is cooled to this temperature, the heat liberated is $Q = mc\Delta t = mc \mid t \mid$. This heat will be spent to melt the ice: $Q_m = m_1\lambda$. Hence the fraction of the ice that will melt will be $x = \dfrac{m_1}{m} = \dfrac{c\mid t\mid}{\lambda}$.

In the calculation assume that the specific heat of ice and the heat of melting remain constant.

23.10. The heat flowing to the Dewar vessel is $Q = \alpha\,(T_{air} - T)$, where α is a certain coefficient, and T is the temperature inside the flask. For ice and liquid nitrogen we obtain the ratio

$$\frac{Q_1}{Q_2} = \frac{T_{air} - T_1}{T_{air} - T_2}$$

But for nitrogen $Q_2 = m_2 L$, where L is its heat of evaporation, the respective value for ice being $Q_1 = m_1\lambda$. Hence

$$\frac{m_1\lambda}{m_2 L} = \frac{T_{air} - T_1}{T_{air} - T_2}, \quad \text{from which} \quad m_2 = \frac{m_1\lambda\,(T_{air} - T_2)}{L\,(T_{air} - T_1)}$$

24. A Field of Fixed Charges in a Vacuum

24.1. It is evident from Fig. 24.1 for the case of charges of different signs that the actual force of interaction of the charges is greater than it would have been, if the charges were concentrated in the centres of the spheres, and less than if the charges were concentrated at the nearest points of the spheres:

$$\frac{q^2}{4\pi\varepsilon_0 r^2} < F < \frac{q^2}{4\pi\varepsilon_0 (r-2r_0)^2}$$

The absolute error is less than the difference between the bounding values, the relative error being less than the ratio of this difference

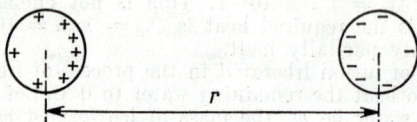

Fig. 24.1.

to the minimum force. Hence,

$$\varepsilon < \frac{F_2 - F_1}{F_1} = \frac{r^2 - (r-2r_0)^2}{(r-2r_0)^2} = \frac{4r_0 (r-r_0)}{(r-2r_0)^2}$$

24.2. Direct the coordinate axes as shown in Fig. 24.2. Let M be one of the points where the potential is zero:

$$\varphi = \varphi_1 - \varphi_2 = \frac{q}{4\pi\varepsilon_0 r_1} - \frac{2q}{4\pi\varepsilon_0 r_2} = 0$$

Hence $r_2 = 2r_1$.

Substituting $r_1 = \sqrt{(3a - x)^2 + y^2}$ and $r_2 = \sqrt{(3a + x)^2 + y^2}$, we obtain after some manipulations

$$(x - 5a)^2 + y^2 = 16a^2$$

This is the equation of a circle of radius $4a$, with centre at $(5a, 0)$.

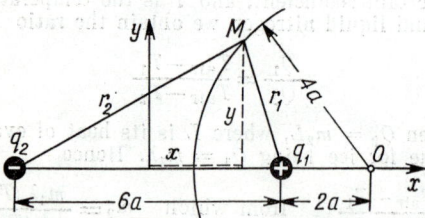

Fig. 24.2.

24.4. A force of gravity directed downwards and equal to $mg = 1/6\pi D^3 \rho g$ acts on the droplet. It is counterbalanced by an electric force $F = qE = q\varphi/d$ (Fig. 24.4). The charge of the droplet is found from the balance of forces.

24.5. In this case equipotential surfaces are spheres with a common centre at the source, and radii normal to the surfaces. If the potential is $\varphi = q/4\pi\varepsilon_0 r$, the field strength is

$$E = -\frac{d\varphi}{dr} = -\frac{d}{dr}\left(\frac{q}{4\pi\varepsilon_0 r}\right) = \frac{q}{4\pi\varepsilon_0 r^2}$$

and just this was to be proved.

24.6. $\quad \varphi = -\int E\,dr = -\frac{q}{4\pi\varepsilon_0}\int\frac{dr}{r^2} = \frac{q}{4\pi\varepsilon_0 r} + \text{const.}$

24.7. To find the potential, divide the ring into small segments and add up the potentials of these segments. The field strength is

$$E = -\frac{d\varphi}{dx} = -\frac{q}{4\pi\varepsilon_0}\frac{d}{dx}(x^2 + a^2)^{-1/2}$$

$$= \frac{1}{2}\cdot\frac{q}{4\pi\varepsilon_0}(x^2+a^2)^{-3/2}\cdot 2x = \frac{qx}{4\pi\varepsilon_0\sqrt{(x^2+a^2)^3}}$$

24.8. (a) It is evident from Fig. 24.8a that in this case a force couple acts on the dipole. The resultant of the couple is zero. To obtain the torque, multiply the force by the dipole separation.

(b) It is evident from Fig. 24.8b that in this case two forces act on the dipole in the direction of the radius vector. Hence it is clear that in the latter case the torque is zero, and the resultant acts in the direction of the radius to the source. The resultant can be found by two methods.

One may use the Coulomb law:

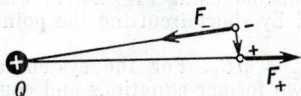

Fig. 24.4.

$$F = F_- + F_+ = -\frac{Qq}{4\pi\varepsilon_0\,(r-l/2)^2} + \frac{Qq}{4\pi\varepsilon_0\,(r+l/2)^2}$$

$$= -\frac{2Qrql}{4\pi\varepsilon_0\,(r^2-l^2/4)^2}$$

Fig. 24.8a.

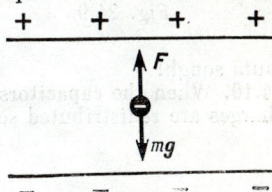

Fig. 24.8b.

Noting that the problem stipulates that $l \ll r$, we obtain

$$F = -\frac{2Qrql}{4\pi\varepsilon_0 r^4} = -\frac{2Qp_e}{4\pi\varepsilon_0 r^3}$$

The same result may be obtained from formula (37.15), if the derivative is substituted for the ratio of increments. We have

$$F = p_e \frac{dE}{dr} = p_e \frac{d}{dr}\left(\frac{Q}{4\pi\varepsilon_0 r^2}\right) = -\frac{2Qp_e}{4\pi\varepsilon_0 r^3}$$

24.9. When the capacitors are connected in parallel (Fig. 24.9), all their interconnected plates have the same potential, therefore $q_1 = C_1(\varphi_1 - \varphi_2)$ and $q_2 = C_2(\varphi_1 - \varphi_2)$, where q_1 and q_2 are the charges of the respective capacitors. The charge of the system is $q = q_1 + q_2 = (C_1 + C_2)(\varphi_1 - \varphi_2)$. On the other hand, $q = C(\varphi_1 - \varphi_2)$, where C is the equivalent capacitance. Hence the formula sought.

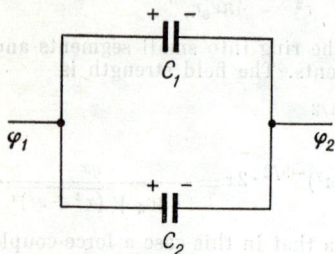

Fig. 24.9.

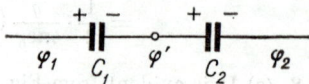

Fig. 24.10.

24.10. When the capacitors are connected in series (Fig. 24.10), their charges are redistributed so that the charges of all the capacitors are

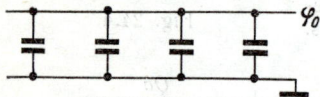

Fig. 24.11a.

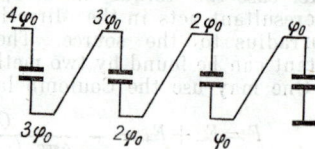

Fig. 24.11b.

equal. To make sure that this is so, consider using Fig. 24.10, what will happen if the system is discharged by shortcircuiting the points at potentials φ_1 and φ_2.

We have $\varphi_1 - \varphi' = q/C_1$, $\varphi' - \varphi_2 = q/C_2$. For the system as a whole, $\varphi_1 - \varphi_2 = q/C$. Adding the two former equations and comparing the result with the third, we obtain the formula sought.

24.11. The solution is obvious from Figs. 24.11a and 24.11b, which give the diagrams of the parallel and series connections of four identical capacitors. The energy in the case of parallel connection is

$$W_{par} = \frac{C_{par}\varphi_{par}^2}{2} = \frac{nC_0\varphi_0^2}{2}$$

and of series connection

$$W_{\text{ser}} = \frac{C_{\text{ser}}\varphi_{\text{ser}}^2}{2} = \frac{(C_0/n)\, n^2\varphi_0^2}{2} = \frac{nC_0\varphi_0^2}{2} = W_{\text{par}}$$

24.12. A possible circuit diagram is shown in Fig. 24.12 for the case of a five-capacitor system. It follows from the diagram that a ten-position switch is required. When the knob is in the upper position,

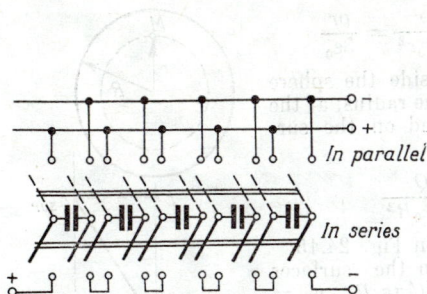

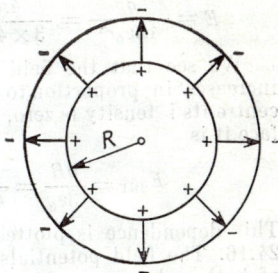

Fig. 24.12.   Fig. 24.14.

the capacitors are connected in parallel; when the knob is in the lower position, they are connected in series.

24.13. Suppose that there is a field inside the sphere. It is obvious from considerations of symmetry that in this case equipotential surfaces must be spherical surfaces concentric with the charged sphere. Accordingly, the lines of force coincide with the radii, i.e. they must either begin or end at the centre of the sphere. This would have been possible, if there were a positive or a negative charge at the centre of the sphere. But since there is no charge inside the sphere, the lines of force cannot begin or end there. Consequently there is no field inside the sphere.

24.14. Construct a second sphere around the sphere under consideration and suppose it carries a charge equal in magnitude, but opposite in sign (Fig. 24.14). According to the result obtained in the previous problem, the charge of the outer sphere does not create a field inside it. Therefore the field between the spheres is created only by the charge of the internal sphere. If there is little difference between the radii of these spheres (i.e. if $R_1 - R \ll R$), the field in between will be almost homogeneous, and its strength will be (see § 37.5)

$$E = \frac{\sigma}{\varepsilon_0} = \frac{Q}{\varepsilon_0 S} = \frac{Q}{4\pi\varepsilon_0 R^2}$$

24.15. Let the volume density of the charge be $\rho = \frac{Q}{V} = \frac{3Q}{4\pi R^3}$, where R is the radius of the sphere. Choose a point M inside the sphere at a distance $r < R$ from its centre and consider a concentric sphere through it. From the results obtained in Problem 24.13 it is evident that the spherical layer lying outside point M does not create a field at this point. The field is created solely by the charge $q = \frac{4}{3} \pi r^3 \rho$ contained inside the smaller sphere. By the result of the previous problem, the field at the surface of this sphere, i.e. at point M, will be

$$E = \frac{q}{4\pi\varepsilon_0 r^2} = \frac{4\pi r^3 \rho}{3 \times 4\pi\varepsilon_0 r^2} = \frac{\rho r}{3\varepsilon_0}$$

We see that the field inside the sphere increases in proportion to the radius; at the centre its intensity is zero, and on the surface it is

$$E_{\text{sur}} = \frac{\rho R}{3\varepsilon_0} = \frac{Q}{4\pi\varepsilon_0 R^2}$$

This dependence is plotted in Fig. 24.15.

24.16. The field potentials on the surfaces of both spheres are $\varphi = q/(4\pi\varepsilon_0 R)$, $\varphi_1 = q/(4\pi\varepsilon_0 R_1)$, respectively. The potential difference is

$$\varphi - \varphi_1 = \frac{q}{4\pi\varepsilon_0} \left(\frac{1}{R} - \frac{1}{R_1} \right) = \frac{q (R_1 - R)}{4\pi\varepsilon_0 R R_1}$$

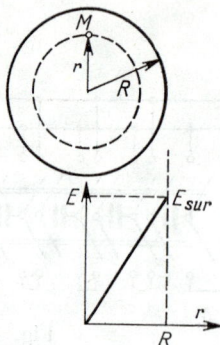

Fig. 24.15.

The capacitance is

$$C = \frac{q}{\varphi - \varphi_1} = \frac{4\pi\varepsilon_0 R R_1}{R_1 - R}$$

If $d = R_1 - R \ll R$, we obtain the approximation

$$C = \frac{4\pi\varepsilon_0 R^2}{d} = \frac{\varepsilon_0 S}{d}$$

which is the expression for the capacitance of a plane capacitor. The error is

$$\delta = \frac{C_{\text{sp}} - C_{\text{pl}}}{C_{\text{sp}}} = \frac{R_1 - R}{R} = \frac{d}{R}$$

24.17. A ball of radius a carrying a surface charge may be regarded as a spherical capacitor whose external sphere is infinitely far away (i.e. $R = a$, $R_1 \to \infty$). Making use of the result of the previous problem, we obtain

$$C = \lim_{R_1 \to \infty} \frac{4\pi\varepsilon_0 a R_1}{R_1 - a} = \lim_{R_1 \to \infty} \frac{4\pi\varepsilon_0 a}{1 - (a/R_1)} = 4\pi\varepsilon_0 a$$

The energy of the field is

$$W = \frac{e^2}{2C} = \frac{e^2}{8\pi\varepsilon_0 a}$$

Equating it to the rest energy of an electron $\mathscr{C}_0 = m_e c^2$, we obtain

$$a = \frac{e^2}{8\pi\varepsilon_0 m_e c^2} = 1.4 \times 10^{-15}\,\text{m}$$

As is shown in § 72.5, the term "classical electron radius" usually applies to a quantity twice as large $r_{cl} = 2a = 2.8 \times 10^{-15}$ m. Comparing this result with the result obtained in Problem 14.23 we see that the latter was two orders of magnitude greater. This implies the incorrectness of the solutions of the two problems. In modern science the problem of the dimensions of elementary particles, including the electron, is far from being solved.

24.18. The mechanical stress is equal to the energy density of the electric field (see § 37.8). We have $p = w_0 = \varepsilon_0 E^2/2$. But we have already found the field on the surface of a sphere (see Problem 24.14): $E = q/(4\pi\varepsilon_0 R^2)$. Hence the result sought.

24.19. The electrical forces extending the film must exceed the surface tension forces:

$$\frac{q^2}{32\pi^2\varepsilon_0 R^4} \geqslant \frac{4\sigma}{R}$$

24.21. Before the connection is made there is a charge $q_1 = C\varphi_1$ on the first capacitor, and $q_2 = C\varphi_2$ on the second. After the upper plates of the capacitors are connected, the charge $q = q_1 + q_2$ is equipartitioned between them. The potential of the unearthed plates is

$$\varphi_{\text{sys}} = \frac{q}{C_{\text{sys}}} = \frac{q_1 + q_2}{2C} = \frac{\varphi_1 + \varphi_2}{2}$$

The energy of the system before the connection is

$$W = W_1 + W_2 = \frac{C\varphi_1^2}{2} + \frac{C\varphi_2^2}{2}$$

while the energy of the battery is

$$W_{\text{sys}} = \frac{C_{\text{sys}}\varphi_{\text{sys}}^2}{2} = \frac{2C\,(\varphi_1+\varphi_2)^2}{2\times 4} = \frac{C\,(\varphi_1+\varphi_2)^2}{4}$$

This is less than before the connection. The lost energy is transformed into other types of energy (heating the conductors, forming a spark, electromagnetic radiation, etc.).

25. Dielectrics

25.1. If the plates are connected to the power supply all the time, the charge on the plates, and consequently the electric field strength, remain constant. The density of the polarization charge is equal to the magnitude of the polarization vector of the dielectric:

$$\sigma_{\text{pol}} = P = \chi_e \varepsilon_0 E = (\varepsilon - 1)\,\varepsilon_0 \varphi/d$$

25.2. If the capacitor is disconnected from the source, the quantity remaining constant is the charge on the plates; the potential and the field strength change by a factor of $1/\varepsilon$ when the dielectric is inserted between the plates. Therefore

$$\sigma_{pol} = \frac{(\varepsilon - 1)\,\varepsilon_0 \varphi}{\varepsilon d}$$

25.3. The aluminium foil sheets are connected alternately to form a system of capacitors connected in parallel (Fig. 25.3). The number of capacitors is equal to the number of dielectric layers.

The breakdown voltage is $U_{bn} = E_M d$, so the working voltage is chosen to be $1/3$ to $1/2$ of this.

25.4. The capacitance of a capacitor will remain unchanged, if we place a very thin piece of foil on top of the insulating layer. For this

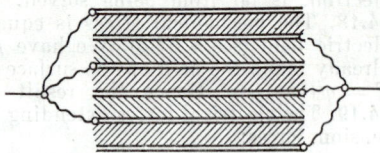

Fig. 25.3.

reason the capacitance sought should be regarded as made up of the capacitances of two capacitors connected in series, with capacitances

$$C_1 = \frac{\varepsilon \varepsilon_0 S}{d} \quad \text{and} \quad C_2 = \frac{\varepsilon_0 S}{d_0 - d}$$

25.5. Here we have two capacitors connected in parallel, with capacitances

$$C_1 = \frac{\varepsilon_0 S_1}{d} = \frac{\varepsilon_0 S\,(l_0 - l)}{d l_0}$$

and

$$C_2 = \frac{\varepsilon \varepsilon_0 S_2}{d} = \frac{\varepsilon \varepsilon_0 S l}{d l_0}$$

25.6. The droplet is polarized in the electric field and acquires a dipole moment $p_e = PV$, where $P = \chi_e \varepsilon_0 E$ is the magnitude of the polarization vector and V is the volume of the droplet. In a non-uniform field a force

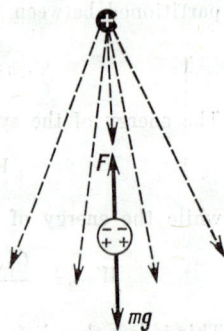

Fig. 25.6.

$F = p_e \dfrac{dE}{dr}$ acts on the droplet. We have

$$F = \chi_e \varepsilon_0 V E \frac{dE}{dr} = (\varepsilon - 1)\,\varepsilon_0 V \frac{Q}{4\pi \varepsilon_0 r^2}\left(-\frac{2Q}{4\pi \varepsilon_0 r^3}\right) = -\frac{(\varepsilon - 1)\,V Q^2}{8\pi^2 \varepsilon_0 r^5}$$

This force is directed upwards (Fig. 25.6). The force of gravity $mg = \rho V g$ acts downwards. The problem requires that the magnitude of the electric force exceed the magnitude of the force of gravity:

$$\frac{(\varepsilon-1)\,VQ^2}{8\pi^2\varepsilon_0 r^5} \geqslant \rho\,Vg, \quad \text{from which} \quad r \leqslant \sqrt[5]{\frac{(\varepsilon-1)\,Q^2}{8\pi^2\varepsilon_0\rho g}}$$

25.7. When the liquid flows through a strongly non-uniform electric field close to the edges of the plates, it is polarized and drawn into the space between the plates. Since the charge on the plates remains unchanged in the process, and the capacitance of the capacitor increases, this is accompanied by a decrease in the energy of the field. This decrease is compensated by the increase in the potential energy of the column of liquid held between the plates. From the law of conservation of energy

$$\frac{q^2}{2C_0} = \frac{q^2}{2C} + \frac{mgh}{2}$$

Here $C_0 = \dfrac{\varepsilon_0 ab}{d}$, $C = \dfrac{\varepsilon_0 b}{d}\,[a + (\varepsilon - 1)\,h]$ (see Problem 25.5), $m = {}= \rho bhd$. Substituting these values into the first formula we obtain, after some simplifications,

$$(\varepsilon-1)\,q^2 = \varepsilon_0\rho\,ghab^2\,[a+(\varepsilon-1)\,h]$$

Express the charge on the plates in terms of the potential:

$$q = \varphi_0 C_0 = \varepsilon_0\varphi_0\,ab/d$$

After simplifications we obtain a quadratic equation

$$h^2 + \frac{a}{\varepsilon-1}\,h - \frac{\varepsilon_0 a\varphi_0^2}{\rho g d^2} = 0$$

Solving it we obtain the height the liquid rises.

25.8. In this case, too, the capacitance of the capacitor increases as the liquid rises, but the energy of the electric field is not conserved but increases. Besides, the potential energy of the rising water increases as well. Is this not in contradiction with the law of conservation of energy? Of course not. The power supply performs work to raise the liquid, the increase in the energy of the system being equal to the work of the power supply in displacing the charges to the capacitor plates:

$$W_{p.s} = \Delta W_{el} + \Delta W_{pot}$$

But

$$W_{p.s} = \Delta q \cdot \varphi = (C - C_0)\varphi^2$$

$$\Delta W_{el} = \frac{C\varphi^2}{2} - \frac{C_0\varphi^2}{2}, \quad \Delta W_{pot} = \frac{1}{2}\,mgh = \frac{1}{2}\,\rho gbdh^2$$

Substituting, we obtain the result sought after some simple transformations.

25.9. To plot the graph it is convenient to use new variables: $x = {}= 10^3/T$, where T is the absolute temperature, and $y = 10^3\chi_e$ where

χ_e is the electric susceptibility. The respective values are presented in Fig. 25.9, from which it may be seen that the Debye law is well satisfied in the experimental range (see § 38.6). Because of this, let us use formula (38.26) to calculate the dipole moment of the water vapour molecule, and the gas equation to calculate the molecular concentration.

It is advisable to carry out the computations for all four experimental points and average the results.

25.10. A characteristic feature of the inert gases is their deformation polarizability. From the formulas of § 38.5 we have $\chi_e = n\alpha$ where

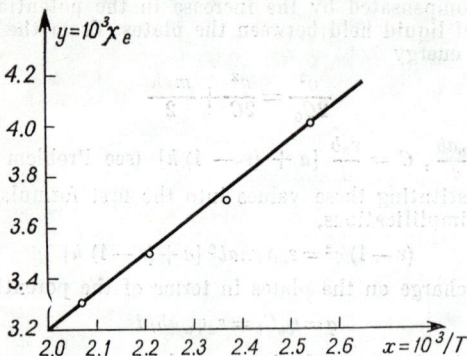

Fig. 25.9.

$n = p/kT$ is the atomic concentration and α is the polarizability of the atom. The dipole moment of an atom in an electric field is

$$p_e = \alpha\varepsilon_0 E = \frac{1}{n}\chi_e\varepsilon_0 E$$

The atomic concentration at standard conditions is $n = N_L$ (the Loschmidt number). Hence

$$p_e = \frac{\chi_e\varepsilon_0 E}{N_L} = \frac{(\varepsilon - 1)\varepsilon_0 E}{N_L}$$

Calculations show that even in such strong fields the dipole moment of an argon atom is six orders of magnitude smaller than that of a water molecule.

26. Direct Current

26.2. From the symmetry of the circuit it is evident that the potentials of points 2 and 4 are equal, so no current flows through the conductor 2-4 and it may be removed. This gives the circuit of Fig. 26.2b, whose resistance is easily found.

26.3. The resistances of the conductors are proportional to their lengths:

$$x = r \, (1 - \cos 36°)$$

26.4. The problem may be solved in stages. First we replace the star connection by an equivalent resistance shown in Fig. 26.4a, and then by an equivalent resistance shown in Fig. 26.4b. It is evident from considerations of symmetry that the potentials of points H and K are equal and so the connection HK may be removed. We obtain a circuit whose resistance is easily found to be a half of the resistance of either of the two parallel links of three conductors.

26.5. It is clear from considerations of symmetry that the potentials at points 2, 4 and 5 coincide, i.e. $\varphi_2 = \varphi_4 = \varphi_5 = \varphi'$. Hence the potentials at points 6, 8 and 3 coincide as well: $\varphi_6 = \varphi_8 = \varphi_3 = \varphi''$. If we shortcircuit the points at equal potential, i.e. connect the points by means of conductors of negligible resistance, the resistance of the

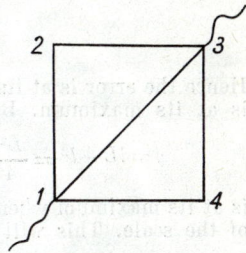

Fig. 26.2b.

circuit remains unchanged. The circuit obtained in this way is shown in Fig. 26.5b. Its resistance is equal to the sum of the resistances of

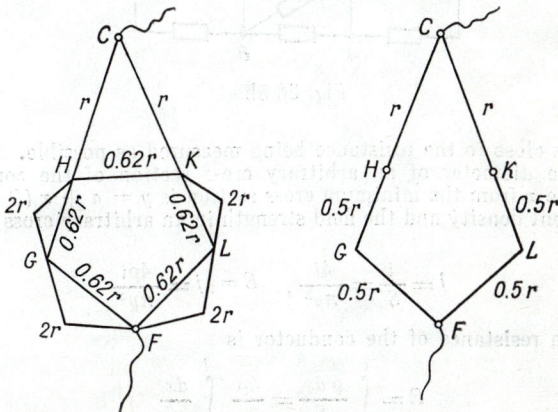

Fig. 26.4a.

three series-connected sections of three, six, and three parallel-connected branches each.

26.6. In a balanced bridge the current flowing through the galvanometer is zero, so $\varphi_C = \varphi_D$. According to Ohm's law for a homogeneous section, we have $\varphi_A - \varphi_C = IR$; $\varphi_C - \varphi_B = IR_x$; $\varphi_A - \varphi_D = = iR_1 = i\rho l_1/S$; $\varphi_D - \varphi_B = iR_2 = i\rho l_2/S$. Hence we find the unknown resistance.

26.7. The relative error is $\delta = \dfrac{h_R}{R} + \dfrac{h}{l} + \dfrac{h}{L-l}$, where h_R is the error in the value of the calibrating resistance, h is the error in the position of the slide wire. We have

$$\delta = \frac{h_R}{R} + \frac{hL}{l(L-l)}$$

Hence the error is at its minimum when the expression $y = l(L - l)$ is at its maximum. But

$$y = lL - l^2 = \frac{L^2}{4} - \frac{L^2}{4} + 2l\frac{L}{2} - l^2 = \frac{L^2}{4} - \left(l - \frac{L}{2}\right)^2$$

is at its maximum when $l = L/2$, i.e. when the slide is in the middle of the scale. This will be the case, if the calibrating resistance is

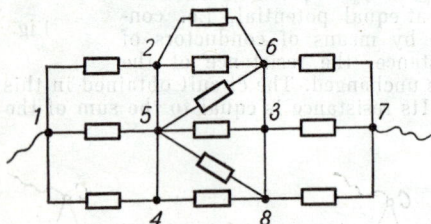

Fig. 26.5b.

chosen as close to the resistance being measured as possible.

26.8. The diameter of an arbitrary cross section of the conductor a distance x from the minimum cross section is $y = a + x(D - a)/l$. The current density and the field strength in an arbitrary cross section are

$$j = \frac{i}{S} = \frac{4i}{\pi y^2} , \quad E = \rho j = \frac{4\rho i}{\pi y^2}$$

26.9. The resistance of the conductor is

$$R = \int_0^l \frac{\rho \, dx}{S} = \frac{4\rho}{\pi} \int_0^l \frac{dx}{y^2}$$

Let us change the variables, noting that $y = a$ for $x = 0$ and $y = D$ for $x = l$. Differentiating, we obtain

$$dy = dx\frac{D-a}{l}, \quad \text{so} \quad dx = \frac{l \, dy}{D-a}$$

Substituting into the expression for the resistance, we obtain

$$R = \frac{4\rho l}{\pi (D-a)} \int_a^D \frac{dy}{y^2} = \frac{4\rho l}{\pi (D-a)} \left[-\frac{1}{y} \right]_a^D = \frac{4\rho l}{\pi a D}$$

26.10. (a) When the cells are connected in series, their e.m.f. and internal resistances are added.

(b) When the cells are connected in parallel, the e.m.f. remains unchanged, but the internal conductances are added.

(c) In a mixed connection we calculate first the e.m.f. and the internal resistance of a group, and then the same parameters for the battery as a whole.

26.11. The accumulators should best be connected in series in two groups of 100 cells each, both groups being connected in parallel and the entire battery connected through a rheostat to the terminals of a dynamo (Fig. 26.11). The e.m.f. of the battery is $\mathscr{E} = ne/2 = 100 \times 1.4 = = 140$ V, the internal resistance is $R_i = nr/4 = 0.5$ ohm. The current in the circuit is $I = 2i = 60$ A. Ohm's law can be written in the following form: $\Delta \varphi - \mathscr{E} = I (R + R_i)$, from which

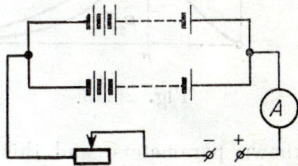

Fig. 26.11.

$$R = \frac{\Delta \varphi - \mathscr{E}}{I} - R_i$$

26.13. The power $P_{\text{tot}} = \mathscr{E}^2/(R + r)$ is at its maximum in conditions of short-circuit $(R = 0)$. The short-circuit power is $P_{\text{sh.c}} = \mathscr{E}^2/r$.

The power in the external circuit is at its maximum when $R = r$. To check this consider the extremum of the expression

$$P_{\text{ex}} = \frac{\mathscr{E}^2}{r} \cdot \frac{Rr}{(R+r)^2} = \frac{\mathscr{E}^2}{ry}$$

We have

$$y = \frac{(R+r)^2}{Rr} = \frac{R}{r} + 2 + \frac{r}{R} = \frac{R}{r} - 2 + \frac{r}{R} + 4 =$$

$$= \left(\sqrt{\frac{R}{r}} - \sqrt{\frac{r}{R}} \right)^2 + 4$$

Obviously, $y = 4$ for $R = r$ is minimum value. In this case the power in the external circuit is maximum. The corresponding graphs are shown in Fig. 26.13.

26.14. Connect all the tubes in series (Fig. 26.14) together with a series resistor $R = (U - n \Delta \varphi)/i = 573$ ohm. The power dissipated is $P = iU = 66$ W. The ratio of the power dissipated in the tubes

to that in the series resistor is

$$\frac{n\Delta\varphi}{U-n\Delta\varphi}$$

26.15. One possible circuit is that utilizing a five-position switch (Fig. 26.15). In positions 5 and 4 the instrument is an ammeter with terminals "+" and A, in the other three it is a voltmeter with terminals "+" and V.

26.16. The voltage drop of 40 V takes place in a two-wire line of

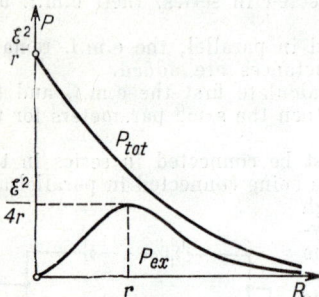

Fig. 26.13.

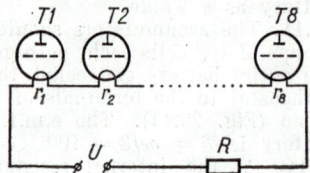

Fig. 26.14.

known parameters, and this makes it possible to find the current in the circuit. The number of lamps connected in parallel is equal to the ratio of the current flowing in the circuit to the current in one lamp.

26.17. The circuit shown in the diagram of Fig. 26.17 enables any one of the three powers desired to be obtained.

26.18. The length of the wire is $l = \dfrac{0.6\pi t U^2 d^2}{4\rho m c\Delta T}$.

26.19. (a) *Numerical calculation.* Compile Table 26.19 from the available data. The quantity of heat dissipated in time $\Delta t = 1$ s is $\Delta Q_n = i_n^2 R \ \Delta t$. The quantity of heat dissipated during the whole time is equal to the sum of the individual quantities of heat:

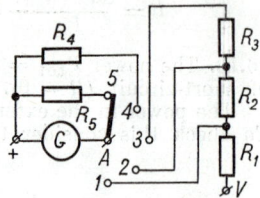

Fig. 26.15.

$$\Delta Q = \Delta Q_1 + \Delta Q_2 + \ \ldots \ + \Delta Q_9 = (i_{1\mathrm{av}}^2 + i_{2\mathrm{av}}^2 + \ \ldots \ + i_{9\mathrm{av}}^2)\,R \ \Delta t = $$

$$= 2580 \times 40 \times 1 = 1.03 \times 10^5 \ \mathrm{J}$$

(b) *Integration.* The current changes according to the law $i = 5 + 2t$. The quantity of heat is

$$Q = \int_0^{10} i^2 R \ dt = 40 \int_0^{10} (5+2t)^2 \ dt = 20 \int_0^{10} (5+2t)^2 d\,(5+2t) =$$

Table 26.19

t, s	i, A	i_{av}, A	i^2_{av}, A^2
0	5	6	36
1	7	8	64
2	9	10	100
3	11	12	144
4	13	14	196
5	15	16	256
6	17	18	324
7	19	20	400
8	21	22	484
9	23	24	576
10	25		
		Total	2580

$$= \frac{20}{3}(5+2t)^3 \Big|_0^{10} = \frac{20}{3}(25^3 - 5^3) = \frac{20 \times 775 \times 20}{3} = 1.03 \times 10^5 \text{ J}$$

We see that the result of the numerical calculation was accurate.
26.20. For this circuit the parameters present in Ohm's law $\Delta\varphi = iR$

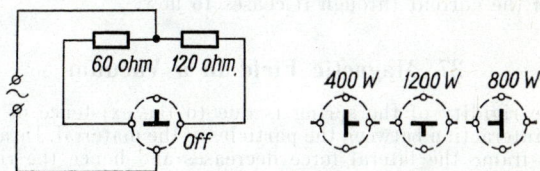

Fig. 26.17.

take the form

$$\Delta\varphi = \frac{q}{C}, \quad i = \lim_{\Delta t \to 0}\left(-\frac{\Delta q}{\Delta t}\right) = -\frac{dq}{dt}$$

The minus sign is due to the decrease in the capacitor's charge in the process of its discharge. Substituting into the expression for Ohm's law, we obtain

$$\frac{q}{RC} = -\frac{dq}{dt}, \quad \text{or} \quad \frac{dt}{RC} = -\frac{dq}{q}$$

Integrating, we obtain

$$\frac{t}{RC} = -\ln q + \ln A$$

where A is a constant. Noting that for $t = 0$, $q = q_0$, we obtain $0 = -\ln q_0 + \ln A$, from which $A = q_0$. Hence

$$\frac{t}{RC} = -\ln q + \ln q_0$$

Denoting the *time constant* (the relaxation time) $\tau = RC$, we obtain

$$\ln \frac{q}{q_0} = -\frac{t}{\tau}, \qquad \text{giving} \qquad q = q_0 e^{-t/\tau}$$

For the current we have

$$i = -\frac{dq}{dt} = \frac{q_0}{\tau} e^{-t/\tau} = i_0 e^{-t/\tau}, \quad \text{where} \quad i_0 = \frac{q_0}{\tau} = \frac{q_0}{RC} = \frac{U_0}{R}$$

26.21. (a) When the e.m.f. of the battery is less than the breakdown potential of the voltage stabilizer, its resistance is infinite and the current in the circuit is zero.

(b) When the e.m.f. of the battery exceeds the firing potential of the voltage stabilizer, its resistance drops to zero and the current in the circuit is determined by the resistance of the resistor and the difference between the e.m.f. and the firing potential of the voltage stabilizer.

26.22. The current in a circuit containing a barretter is determined by the transconductance of the device and is independent of the circuit's resistance. However, current flows only if $\mathscr{E} - i_0 R > 0$, i.e. if $\mathscr{E} > i_0 R$. Otherwise the voltage across the barretter drops to zero, and the current through it ceases to flow.

27. Magnetic Field in a Vacuum

27.1. The rigidity of the spring is due to the existence of electrical forces of interaction between the particles of the material. In a moving reference frame the lateral force decreases and hence the rigidity of the lateral spring decreases as well:

$$k_\perp = k_{0\perp} \sqrt{1 - v^2/c^2}$$

But if the acting force changes according to the same law as the rigidity (the spring constant) of the spring, the lateral dimension of the spring remains unchanged in full agreement with the theory of relativity.

27.3. Consider the following imaginary experiment. Suppose a current flows in a conductor from the left to the right (Fig. 27.3a) so that the electrons move to the left with a certain velocity v. Let a free electron move in the same direction with the same velocity v. In the reference frame xyz of the conductor there are three forces acting on the electron: the force of repulsion from the electron cloud, F_-, the force of attraction to the ionic lattice, F_+, and the Lorentz force F_m acting in the same direction. It is known from experiment that the resultant of those three forces acts in the direction of the conductor.

Let us consider the reference frame $x_0 y_0 z_0$ of the electrons (Fig. 27.3b). The magnetic field here is exactly the same, but it does not

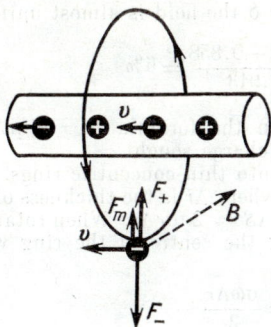 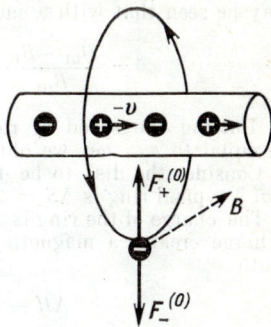

Fig. 27.3a.   Fig. 27.3b.

act on a *stationary* electron. The forces acting on an electron are the force of repulsion from the electron gas, $F_-^{(0)}$, and the force of attraction $F_+^{(0)}$ to the moving ionic lattice. But if in the former reference frame the electron was attracted to the conductor, in accordance with the principle of relativity it will be attracted to it in any other reference frame as well. Therefore $F_+^{(0)} > F_-^{(0)}$ and consequently, $E_+^{(0)} > E_-^{(0)}$. We see that the lateral field intensity of moving charges is greater than that of stationary charges, i.e. greater than the Coulomb field.

27.4. Neglecting the thickness of the wire as compared with the radius of the coil and the other dimensions, we obtain an expression for the field induction on the axis:

$$B = \frac{\mu_0 i w a^2}{2(a^2 + h^2)^{3/2}}$$

where w is the number of turns, a is the radius of a turn, and h is the distance from the centre to the point on the axis of the coil where the field is to be determined.

27.5. The induction of the magnetic field in the centre of a long solenoid is $B = \mu_0 i n = \mu_0 i w / l$. If the wire is closely wound (see Fig. 27.5), the diameter of the insulated wire is $d = l/w$. Hence $B = \mu_0 i / d$. At the end of the solenoid the field is twice as weak.

27.6. Making use of the result of Problem 27.4, we obtain for the field at the centre of the ring

$$B_c = \frac{\mu_0 i w a^2}{2}\left(\frac{1}{a^3} + \frac{1}{(a^2 + a^2/4)^{3/2}}\right) = \frac{\mu_0 i w a^2}{2a^3}\left(1 + \frac{8}{\sqrt{125}}\right) = \frac{0.858\mu_0 i w}{a}$$

The field induction at the midpoint is

$$B_m = \frac{2\mu_0 i w a^2}{2 \left(a^2 + a^2/16\right)^{3/2}} = \frac{0.913\mu_0 i w}{a}$$

It may be seen that with a small error δ the field is almost uniform:

$$\delta = \frac{B_m - B_c}{B_m} = \frac{0.913 - 0.858}{0.913} = 6\%$$

27.8. Putting the speed of rotation in the formula $B = \mu_0 qv/4\pi r^2$ to be equal to $v = \omega r$, we obtain the charge sought.

27.9. Consider the disk to be divided into thin concentric rings. The area of a typical ring is $\Delta S = 2\pi r \, \Delta r$, where Δr is the thickness of the ring. The charge of the ring is $\Delta q = \sigma \, \Delta S = 2\pi \sigma r \Delta r$. When rotating, the charge creates a magnetic field at the centre of the ring with strength

$$\Delta H = \frac{\Delta q \, v}{4\pi r^2} = \frac{\sigma \omega \Delta r}{2}$$

The total intensity of the field at the centre is

$$H = \Delta H_1 + \Delta H_2 + \ldots = \frac{1}{2} \, \sigma \omega \, (\Delta r_1 + \Delta r_2 + \ldots) = \frac{1}{2} \, \sigma \omega R$$

where R is the external radius of the disk.

The magnetic moment of the ring is

$$\Delta p_m = i\pi r^2 = \pi r^2 \, \frac{\Delta q}{T} = \frac{1}{2} \, \Delta q \, \omega r^2 = \pi \sigma \omega r^3 \Delta r$$

To find the total magnetic moment of the rotating disk we must add up all these values. We have

$$p_m = \int\limits_0^R \pi \sigma \omega r^3 \, dr = \frac{1}{4} \, \pi \sigma \omega R^4$$

The moment of momentum $L = I\omega = \frac{1}{2} \, mR^2\omega = \frac{1}{2} \, \pi \omega \rho h R^4$, where ρ is the density of the material. We have

$$\frac{p_m}{L} = \frac{\sigma}{2\rho h}$$

27.10. The magnetic field induction at the point of interest is

$$B = \frac{2\mu_0 p_m}{4\pi r^3} = \frac{\mu_0 p_m}{2\pi} \, \left(a^2 + x^2\right)^{-\frac{3}{2}}$$

The gradient is

$$\frac{dB}{dx} = \frac{\mu_0 p_m}{2\pi} \frac{d}{dx} (a^2 + x^2)^{-3/2} =$$

$$= -\frac{3}{2} \frac{\mu_0 p_m}{2\pi} (a^2 + x^2)^{-5/2} \cdot 2x = -\frac{3\mu_0 p_m x}{2\pi r^5}$$

28. Charges and Currents in a Magnetic Field

28.1. The momentum of the particle may be found from the condition $\frac{mu^2}{R} = 2eBu$, since an alpha-particle is a doubly ionized helium atom. Having established the fact that this is a nonrelativistic particle, we find its velocity and kinetic energy from the equations

$$u = 2eBR/m \quad \text{and} \quad K = 2e^2B^2R^2/m$$

28.2. The momentum of a muon is half that of the alpha-particle of the previous problem. It may easily be established after calculating the quantity $\frac{\beta}{\sqrt{1-\beta^2}} = \frac{p}{m_0 c} = 1.66$, that the muon in this problem is a relativistic particle. We find $\beta = 0.856$, from which the velocity of the particle may be found.

The rest energy of a muon is 207 times that of an electron, i.e. $\mathscr{E}_0 = 207 \times 0.511 = 106$ MeV (see Problem 8.1). The total energy is $\mathscr{E} = \frac{\mathscr{E}_0}{\sqrt{1-\beta^2}}$, and the kinetic energy is $K = \mathscr{E} - \mathscr{E}_0$.

28.3. Since the charge of the particle and the magnetic field induction remain unchanged, the radii of the tracks of the particles are proportional to their momenta: $R_1/R_2 = p_1/p_2$. The relation to the kinetic energy depends on the nature of motion.

(a) Nonrelativistic particles. The momenta of the particle are proportional to the square roots of their kinetic energies, and therefore also proportional to the radii of their tracks.

(b) Relativistic particles. In this case the dependence of the momentum on the kinetic energy of the particle is more complex:

$$p = \frac{1}{c} \sqrt{K (2\mathscr{E}_0 + K)}$$

Hence we obtain the desired ratio of the radii of the tracks.

28.4. This is a relativistic electron, since its total energy $\mathscr{E} = \mathscr{E}_0 + K = 0.511 + 1.5 = 2.0$ MeV is much greater than its rest energy. We obtain from $mu^2/R = euB$

$$T = \frac{2\pi R}{u} = \frac{2\pi m}{eB} = \frac{2\pi \mathscr{E}}{eBc^2}$$

28.5. In the field the electron acquires a kinetic energy of 20 keV, which is much less than its rest energy (511 keV). Therefore in this problem it is a nonrelativistic particle. Resolve the electron velocity into two components: one along the line of induction, $v_{\parallel} = v \cos \alpha$, and the other perpendicular to it, $v_{\perp} = v \sin \alpha$ (Fig. 28.5). No forces act on the electron in the longitudinal direction, therefore the electron will move at a constant speed along the z-axis according to the equation

$$z = z_0 + v_{\parallel} t = z_0 + vt \cos \alpha$$

In the lateral direction (i.e. in the xy plane) the electron is acted upon by the Lorentz force, which makes the projection of its motion in this plane a circle with radius

$$R = \frac{mv_{\perp}}{eB} = \frac{\sqrt{2me\varphi} \sin \alpha}{eB}$$

and with period $T = 2\pi m/eB$. In space the electron moves along a helix which winds around the lines of induction. The radius of the circle, R, was given above. The pitch of the helix is

$$h = v_{\parallel} T = \frac{2\pi mv \cos \alpha}{eB} = 2\pi R \cot \alpha$$

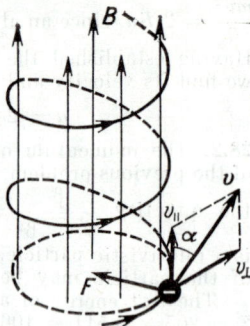

Fig. 28.5.

28.6. An ion entering a uniform magnetic field at an angle to the lines of induction will move along a helix to one of the poles of the magnet, and after some time will strike the dees and leave the bunch. To prevent losses, the magnetic field should be made slightly nonuniform (in the shape of a barrel) (Fig. 28.6). It is easily seen that such a field focusses the ions, concentrating them in the middle plane.

28.7. The electrons in this problem are nonrelativistic, they enter the magnetic field at a speed $u = \sqrt{2e\varphi/m} = 1.33 \times 10^7$ m/s. In the magnetic field they move along an arc of a circle of radius $R = um/eB$ (Fig. 28.7b). The electrons are deflected through an angle $\angle GCE = \alpha$. But the angle $\angle GCE$ is congruent to the angle $\angle COM$ (as angles with mutually perpendicular sides). Therefore

$$\sin \alpha = \frac{MC}{OC} = \frac{l}{R} = \frac{eBl}{m_e u} = \frac{eBl}{\sqrt{2m_e e\varphi}}$$

As is evident from the figure, $GD = GE + ED$, or

$$d = L \tan \alpha + R (1 - \cos \alpha) = L \tan \alpha + l \frac{1 - \cos \alpha}{\sin \alpha} = L \tan \alpha + l \tan \frac{\alpha}{2}$$

Knowing the parameters of the device one may easily calculate the displacement sought.

28.8. Making use of the result of Problem 4.14 we obtain

$$d = \frac{eEl}{2e\varphi} \left(L + \frac{l}{2} \right) = \frac{El}{2\varphi} \left(L + \frac{l}{2} \right)$$

whence

$$E = \frac{2\varphi d}{l\,(L + l/2)}$$

28.9. First we find the charge of the ion using the condition $mu^2/R = = quB$. We have $q = mu/BR$. Taking account of the fact that heavy ions in the energy range of hundreds of megaelectron-volts move at nonrelativistic speeds, we have $m = A \times 1.66 \times 10^{-27}$, where

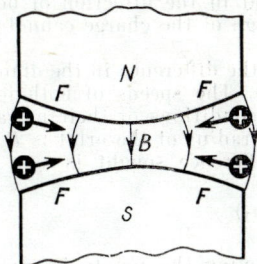

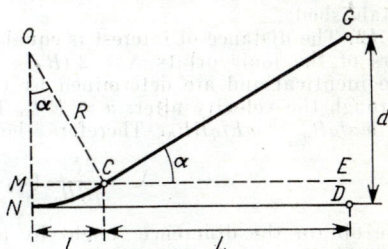

Fig. 28.6.   Fig. 28.7b.

$A = 20.18$ amu is the atomic mass of neon. The momentum of the ion is found from its kinetic energy: $mu = \sqrt{2mK}$. Hence the charge of the ion

$$q = \frac{\sqrt{2mK}}{BR} = \frac{\sqrt{2 \times 20.18 \times 1.66 \times 10^{-27} \times 100 \times 1.6 \times 10^{-13}}}{1.55 \times 1.1} =$$
$$= 6.6 \times 10^{-19} \text{ C}$$

Dividing by the electron charge we find the neon ions to be ionized quadruply.

The total number of revolutions an ion makes is equal to its kinetic energy divided by the energy acquired in the process of passing twice through the accelerating gap:

$$N = \frac{K}{2q\varphi} = \frac{100 \times 10^6}{2 \times 4 \times 300 \times 10^3} = 42$$

The frequency of the change in polarity of the accelerating field is equal to the circular frequency of the ion:

$$n = \frac{u}{2\pi R} = \frac{qB}{2\pi m}$$

28.10. The magnetic induction is found from the condition

$$B = \frac{p}{eB} = \frac{\sqrt{K\,(2\mathscr{E}_0 + K)}}{ecR}$$

and the frequency from the condition

$$n = \frac{c \sqrt{1 - (\mathcal{E}_0/\mathcal{E})^2}}{2\pi R}$$

(see § 41.6). Note that towards the end of the acceleration cycle the proton's energy is so great that $n = c/2\pi R$ approximately.

28.11. The condition for the balance of forces is $eE = euB$ from which we get $u = E/B$. Since the change in the sign of the particle's charge is accompanied by a simultaneous reversal in the direction of both the electric and the magnetic forces, the sign of the charge cannot be established.

28.12. The distance of interest is equal to the difference in the diameters of the ionic orbits $\Delta = 2 (R_2 - R_1)$. The speeds of both ions are identical and are determined by the conditions of their passage through the velocity filter: $u = E/B$. The radius of the orbit is $R = mu/qB_0 = mE/qBB_0$. Therefore the difference sought is

$$\Delta = \frac{2E}{qBB_0} (m_2 - m_1)$$

We obtain the difference sought by assuming the ion to be singly ionized, i.e. by putting $q = e$.

28.13. Making use of the result of the previous problem and noting that $R = l/2$, we obtain the expression for the ionic mass

$$m = \frac{elB^2}{2E} \text{ (kg)} = \frac{elB^2}{2 \times 1.66 \times 10^{-27}E} \text{ (amu)} = \frac{4.82 \times 10^4}{E} \text{ (amu)}$$

28.14. The magnetic moment of the moving coil is $p_m = wiS$, while the torque is $M = p_m B$, since in our problem $\alpha = \pi/2$.

28.15. A torque $M = wiSB$ acts on the moving coil balanced by a torque $M = f\alpha$ due to the elasticity of the twisted thread, where f is the torsion modulus. Equating, we obtain $f\alpha = wiSB$, from which we see that, other conditions being equal, the coil's angle of rotation is proportional to the current.

28.16. It is easily seen that the moving coils hanging freely will arrange themselves so that their planes will be perpendicular to their common axis. The force of interaction is $F = p_m \dfrac{dB}{dx}$. Noting that

$$\frac{dB}{dx} = - \frac{6\mu_0 p_m x}{4\pi (a^2 + x^2)^{5/2}}$$

(see Problem 27.11) and that according to the conditions of the problem $x \approx r \gg a$, we have

$$\frac{dB}{dx} = - \frac{6\mu_0 p_m}{4\pi r^4}$$

The force of interaction is

$$F = p_m \frac{dB}{dx} = - \frac{6\mu_0 p_m^2}{4\pi r^4}$$

It is quite similar to the force of interaction between electric dipoles (see §§ 10.4 and 40.6).

28.17. Making use of the result of the previous problem, we obtain

$$F = -\frac{6\mu_0 w^2 i^2 S^2}{4\pi r^4} = -\frac{3\pi\mu_0 w^2 i^2 a^4}{2r^4}$$

28.18. The positive charge circulates as shown in Fig. 28.18a. The direction of the magnetic moment is established with the aid of the screw driver rule (see §§ 40.5, 40.6). The direction of circulation of

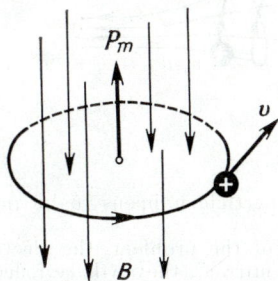

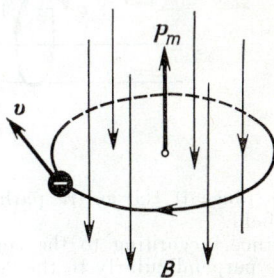

Fig. 28.18a.   Fig. 28.18b.

a negative charge is the opposite (Fig. 28.18b), but the magnetic moment is, just the same, directed against the field.

28.19. As was shown above (see Problem 28.5), the particle will move along a helix winding around the lines of induction. Let us resolve

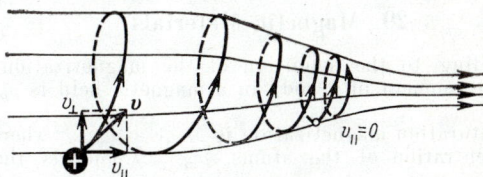

Fig. 28.19b.

the velocity vector into two components: the lateral $v_\perp$ (the orbital velocity) and the longitudinal $v_\parallel$ (the drift velocity). Since the orbital moment of the circulating charge is directed against the field, the magnetic forces tend to push the charge out into the region of the weak field (compare with §§ 37.4 and 41.10, where the dipole and magnetic moments are arranged in the direction of the field). We see that as the charge approaches the magnetic mirror, its drift velocity decreases, becoming zero in the case of a sufficiently high field gradient (Fig. 28.19b). From this moment it begins to drift in the opposite direction towards the weaker field (Fig. 28.19c).

28.20. A charged particle entering a magnetic field perpendicularly to the lines of induction will move along the arc of a circle of radius $R = p/eB$, where p is the momentum of the particle. Mirror reflection

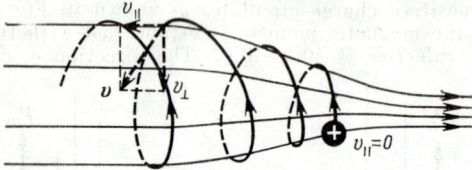

Fig. 28.19c.

takes place if the entire path of the particle happens to lie inside the field.

Since, according to the conditions of the problem, the electrons move perpendicularly to the "magnetic mirror", they will be reflected backwards, provided that the radius of the semicircle is less than the thickness of the "mirror". Hence $\frac{p}{eB} < d$.

The total energy of the electron is $\mathscr{E} = \sqrt{\mathscr{E}_0^2 + p^2 c^2} < \sqrt{\mathscr{E}_0^2 + e^2 B^2 d^2 c^2}$, the kinetic energy is $K = \mathscr{E} - \mathscr{E}_0$.

Finally, we get

$$K < \mathscr{E}_0 \left(\sqrt{1 + (eBd/m_e c)^2} - 1 \right)$$

29. Magnetic Materials

29.1. According to the definition of the magnetization vector **M**, the magnetic moment of a body in a magnetic field is $p_m = MV = \chi_m H V$.

29.3. The saturation magnetization is $M_{sat} = n_0 p_m$, where $n_0 = 4/a^3$ is the concentration of the atoms, $p_m = 7.95 \mu_B$ is the magnetic moment of a single atom. Hence $M_{sat} = 4 \times 7.95 \mu_B / a^3$.

29.4. Making use of the result of § 38.6, we obtain

$$\frac{N_1}{N_2} = \frac{e^{-\mathscr{E}_1/kT}}{e^{-\mathscr{E}_2/kT}} = e^{\frac{\mathscr{E}_2 - \mathscr{E}_1}{kT}} = 1 + \frac{\mathscr{E}_2 - \mathscr{E}_1}{kT}$$

But N_1 is the number of atoms whose magnetic moments are oriented along the field, the energy is $\mathscr{E}_1 = -p_m B$, N_2 is the number of atoms whose magnetic moments are oriented against the field, their energy

is $\mathscr{E}_2 = p_m B$. We have

$$\frac{N_1}{N_2} = 1 + \frac{2 p_m B}{kT}$$

29.6. Since the Curie point of ferromagnetic materials is of the order of hundreds of degrees Celsius, the energy of thermal motion is

$$\bar{\varepsilon} \approx kT = 1.38 \times 10^{-23} \times 400 \approx 5 \times 10^{-21} \ \text{J}$$

The energy of interaction of two magnetic moments is $\mathscr{E}_m = p_m B = 2\mu_0 p_m^2 / 4\pi r^3$. Putting $r \approx 1$ Å, $p_m = \mu_B$, we obtain

$$\mathscr{E}_m \approx \frac{4\pi \times 9.28^2 \times 10^{-48}}{2\pi \times 10^7 \times 10^{-30}} \approx 2 \times 10^{-23} \ \text{J}$$

We see that the interaction energy of magnetic moments is by two orders of magnitude smaller than the energy of thermal motion; therefore magnetic interaction is incapable of causing spontaneous magnetization inside a domain.

29.7. The Curie point for iron is 770 °C, the energy of exchange interaction must exceed the energy of thermal motion at temperatures below

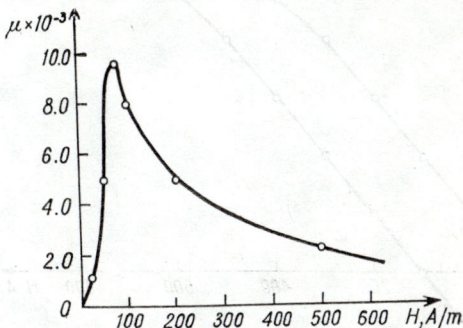

Fig. 29.9b.

the Curie point Θ_C. Hence $\mathscr{E}_{ex} > k\Theta_C$.

29.8. The force acting on an atom whose magnetic moment is $p_m = \pm \mu_B$ is $F = p_m \frac{dB}{dz}$, where $\frac{dB}{dz}$ is the magnetic field gradient. The deflection is $h = at^2/2$, where $a = F/m$, $t = l/v$. Substituting, we obtain

$$h = \frac{p_m l^2}{2mv^2} \frac{dB}{dz}$$

But $1/2 \ mv^2 = 3/2 \ kT$. Therefore the final result is

$$h = \pm \frac{\mu_B l^2}{6kT} \frac{dB}{dz}$$

29.9. From the graph 29.9a we compile the table

H, A/m	50	75	100	200	500	1000	1500
μ	5.0×10^3	9.6×10^3	8.0×10^3	5.0×10^3	2.2×10^3	1.2×10^3	0.8×10^3

The graph for μ is given in Fig. 29.9b.
29.10. The right-hand half of the hysteresis loop is plotted using the data given in the table; the left-hand half is plotted symmetrically

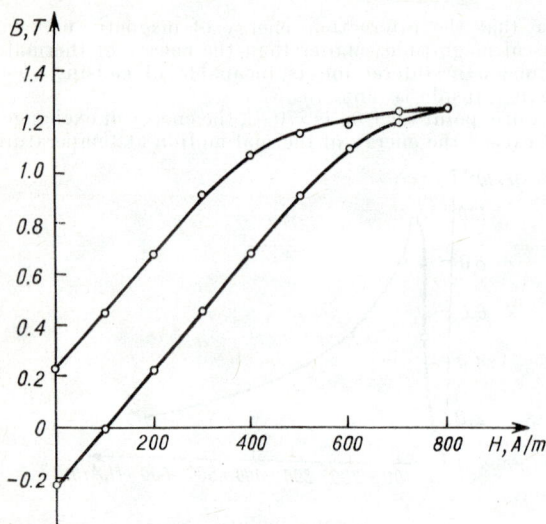

Fig. 29.10.

(Fig. 29.10). The coercive force is determined at the point of intersection of the graph with the H-axis; saturation induction is the point where the upper and lower branches of the loop intersect. The saturation magnetization is

$$M_{\text{sat}} = \frac{B_{\text{sat}}}{\mu_0} - H_{\text{sat}} \approx \frac{B_{\text{sat}}}{\mu_0}$$

for $B_{\text{sat}} \gg \mu_0 H_{\text{sat}}$. The residual magnetization is $M_r = B_r/\mu_0$, where B_r is determined at the point of intersection of the graph with the B-axis.

30. Electromagnetic Induction

30.1. The bulb will not glow because the magnetic flux flowing through the circuit made up of the wings, the wires and the bulb remains unchanged.

30.3. The forces acting on a falling conductor are the force of gravity mg directed downwards and the Ampere force $F = iBl$ directed upwards. By Ohm's law $i = \mathscr{E}/R$ and the induced e.m.f. is $\mathscr{E} = Blv$.

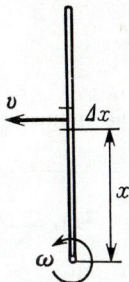

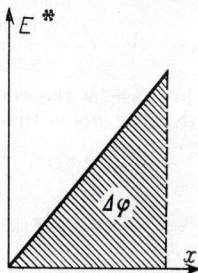

Fig. 30.4a.   Fig. 30.4b.

Hence the Ampere force is $F = B^2l^2v/R$. The equation of motion of the conductor is

$$a = \frac{mg - F}{m} = g - \frac{B^2l^2v}{mR}$$

After a certain moment of time the acceleration becomes zero and the conductor continues to fall uniformly at a constant speed (compare with Problem 5.13).

30.4. The rod moves perpendicularly to the lines of induction of the magnetic field, and in a small section of it an elementary e.m.f. $\Delta\mathscr{E} = Bv\,\Delta x$ is established, Δx being the length of the section and v its velocity (see Fig. 30.4a). The voltage across the rod is the sum of the elementary e.m.f.'s. Since $v = \omega x$, $\Delta\mathscr{E} = B\omega x\,\Delta x$. The result may be found by two methods:

(a) *By integration.* We have

$$\Delta\varphi = \int_0^l B\omega x\,dx = B\omega \left[\frac{x^2}{2} \right]_0^l = \frac{1}{2}\,B\omega l^2$$

(b) *Graphically.* Plot a graph of the strength of the induced field $E^* = \Delta\mathscr{E}/\Delta x = B\omega x$. Since this is a linear function, its graph is of the form shown in Fig. 30.4b. The voltage is numerically equal to the area under the graph:

$$\Delta\varphi = \frac{lB\omega l}{2} = \frac{B\omega l^2}{2}$$

30.5. The force applied to a conductor moving at a constant speed is equal in magnitude to the magnetic force. But the current is $i = \dfrac{\mathcal{E}}{R} = \dfrac{Blv}{R}$. Hence

$$F = iBl = B^2l^2v/R$$

30.6. Since the ring is small, the field inside it may be assumed to be uniform and equal to the field on the axis. Therefore the magnetic flux is

$$\Phi = BS = \frac{2\mu_0 p_m \pi r^2}{4\pi \left(a^2 + x^2\right)^{3/2}}$$

The variable in this case is the coordinate $x = x_0 - vt$, where v is the velocity of fall. The magnitude of the induced e.m.f. is

$$|\mathcal{E}| = \frac{d\Phi}{dt} = \frac{\mu_0 p_m r^2}{2} \frac{d}{dt} \left(a^2 + x^2\right)^{-3/2}$$

$$= -\frac{3}{4} \mu_0 p_m r^2 \left(a^2 + x^2\right)^{-5/2} \cdot 2x \frac{dx}{dt} = \frac{3\mu_0 p_m r^2 xv}{2(a^2 + x^2)^{5/2}}$$

30.7. The induced e.m.f. is $\mathcal{E} = -\dfrac{\Delta\Phi}{\Delta t} = \dfrac{\Phi}{\Delta t}$, since initially the magnetic flux through the ring is zero. The charge flowing through the circuit is

$$q = i\Delta t = \frac{\mathcal{E}}{R} \Delta t = \frac{\Phi}{R}$$

It is equal to the galvanometer constant multiplied by the number of scale divisions: $q = CN$.

30.9. A change in magnetic flux is accompanied by an induced electric field of strength $E^* = \mathcal{E}/2\pi r$, where r is the radius of the ring. This field causes the polarization of the dielectric, i.e. a preferential orientation of its dipoles in the direction of the induced electric field.

30.11. The current in the circuit is $I = (\mathcal{E} - \mathcal{E}_{\text{ind}})/R$, where $\mathcal{E}$ is the e.m.f. of the accumulator battery, R is the resistance of the circuit (including the internal resistance of the battery) and $\mathcal{E}_{\text{ind}}$ is the e.m.f. induced in the armature in the course of its rotation. When the armature is stopped, $\mathcal{E}_{\text{ind}} = 0$ and the current is $I_0 = \mathcal{E}/R$, from which we find the resistance of the circuit. The power of the motor is

$$P = I\mathcal{E} - I^2R = I\mathcal{E}\left(1 - \frac{I}{I_0}\right)$$

30.14. To find the number of turns divide the length of the torus' internal circumference by the wire diameter. We obtain

$$w = \pi D/d = 80\pi/0.6 = 420$$

The magnetic field strength is

$$H = \frac{iw}{l} = \frac{iw}{\pi D_{\text{m}}} = \frac{iD}{dD_{\text{m}}}$$

where $D_m = 120$ mm is twice the distance from the axis of revolution of the torus to the centre of the generating circle.

Knowing the magnetic field strength and making use of the graph of Fig. 29.9a, we find the induction of the field. Applying the formula $w_m = BH/2$ we find the energy density, and multiplying this by the volume of the core we find the total energy of the magnetic field. The inductance is found using the formula

$$W_m = Li^2/2$$

30.15. The energy of the magnetic field in the absence of the ferromagnetic core is $W_m = 1/2\mu_0 H^2 V$. It is significantly less than the energy of the magnetic field in the presence of a ferromagnetic core, despite the fact that the current flowing through the winding is the same in both cases. The explanation is that in the absence of a ferromagnetic core the current in the coil attains its stationary value very quickly and the work performed by the power supply in inducing the magnetic field is much less than in the presence of such a core.

30.16. In the case of a good contact of the armature with the core, the force of attraction at one pole is $F = w_m S$. Therefore the armature as a whole is attracted with the force $F = 2w_m S = B^2 S/\mu\mu_0$ where $S = 60 \times 60 \times 10^{-6}$ m^2 = 36×10^{-4} m^2 is the core cross section (see Fig. 30.16). Since we assumed the gap between the armature and the core to be negligible, we may assume the induction of the field to be the same in the gap as in the core. The magnetic permeability in the gap, on the other hand, is unity ($\mu = 1$).

We have $F_{sat} = B_{sat}^2 S/\mu_0$ in case of saturation magnetization and $F_r = B_r^2 S/\mu_0$ in the case of residual magnetization. The values of B_{sat} and B_r are presented in the table following Problem 29.10 (see also Fig. 29.10).

30.18. Ohm's law should be written in the form $\mathscr{E} + \mathscr{E}_L = iR$, where $\mathscr{E}$ is the e.m.f. of the power supply and $\mathscr{E}_L = -L\dfrac{di}{dt}$ is the e.m.f. of self-induction. Hence

$$\mathscr{E} - L\frac{di}{dt} = iR$$

Divide by R and introduce the notation $\mathscr{E}/R = I_M$, the stationary current, and $L/R = \tau$, the relaxation time. We obtain the equation

$$I_M - \tau \frac{di}{dt} = i, \quad \text{or} \quad -\tau \frac{di}{dt} = i - I_M$$

Multiplying by dt, we obtain

$$-\tau \, di = (i - I_M)\, dt, \quad \text{or} \quad \frac{di}{i - I_M} = -\frac{dt}{\tau}$$

Integrating, we obtain

$$\int \frac{di}{i - I_M} = -\frac{1}{\tau}\int dt, \quad \text{yielding } \ln(i - I_M) = -\frac{t}{\tau} + \ln C$$

where C is the integration constant. Taking antilogarithms, we obtain

$$\frac{i - I_M}{C} = e^{-\tau/t}$$

When $t = 0$, the current is $i(0) = 0$, so $C = -I_M$. After some simple transformations we obtain

$$i = I_M (1 - e^{-t/\tau})$$

The graph of this function is shown in § 43.12, Fig. 43.6.

30.19. According to the result of the previous problem, we have for $i = 0.9 I_M$ an exponential equation

$$0.9 I_M = I_M (1 - e^{-t/\tau}), \quad \text{or} \quad e^{-t/\tau} = 0.1$$

Taking the logarithms, we obtain

$$-\frac{t}{\tau} \log e = \log 0.1, \quad -\frac{t}{\tau} 0.434 = -1$$

Hence $t = 2.3\tau$.

30.20. The formula obtained in Problem 30.18 is no longer valid when the difference between the stationary and the instantaneous currents becomes equal to the thermal current fluctuations. After that a gradual increase in the current is replaced by the usual thermal fluctuations of the current around its equilibrium value.

31. Classical Electron Theory

31.2. Here the centrifugal force of inertia, $I_{cf} = m\omega^2 r$, where r is the distance from the appropriate point of the conductor to the centre of the disk is the non-electrical force acting on the disk. The strength of this force field is

$$E^* = \frac{I_{cf}}{e} = \frac{m\omega^2 r}{e}$$

The induced e.m.f. may be found either graphically (Fig. 31.2b), or by integration:

$$\Delta\varphi = \mathcal{E} = \int\limits_0^{r_0} E^* \, dr$$

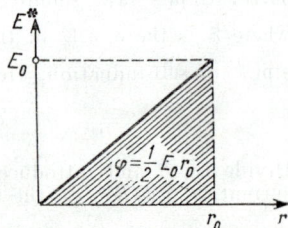

Fig. 31.2b.

$$= \frac{m\omega^2}{e} \int\limits_0^{r_0} r \, dr = \frac{m\omega^2 r_0^2}{2e}$$

31.3. The electron concentration may be computed from the expression for the Hall voltage (see § 44.2) and the electric conductivity of copper found from the data on the dimensions of the plate, the current and the longitudinal voltage. Knowing these quantities, we may easily find the electron mobility from formula (44.8).

31.4. Since silver is a monovalent element, the electron concentration in it is equal to the concentration of atoms. The density is $\rho = m_0 n$, where m_0 is the mass of the atom. But $m_0 = A/N_A$, where A is the atomic mass. Hence $n = \rho N_A/A$ and the Hall constant is

$$R_H = A/e\rho N_A$$

31.9. A thermocouple may be regarded as a heat engine working in the temperature range from T_1 to T_2, where the indices 1 and 2 refer to the hot and the cold junctions. When a charge passes through a thermocouple, work is performed equal to $W = \eta Q_1$. The transported charge is

$$q = \frac{W}{\mathscr{E}} = \frac{\eta Q_1}{\alpha (T_1 - T_2)}$$

31.13. First find the volumetric heat (molar heat capacity). It may easily be established (for instance, by checking the dimensionality) that $C = \rho c$. From § 45.3 we obtain

$$\Lambda = \frac{3K}{aC} = \frac{3K}{a\rho c}$$

32. Electrical Conductivity of Electrolytes

32.1. The electrical conductivity of an electrolyte is $\gamma = qn (b_+ + b_-) = \alpha q n_0 (b_+ + b_-)$, where α is the dissociation coefficient sought. The charge of a monovalent ion is $q = e$. The concentration of the solution is $C = m_0 n_0 = M n_0/N_A$, where M is the molar mass of the dissolved substance. Substituting these values, we obtain

$$\alpha = \frac{\gamma M}{eCN_A (b_+ + b_-)}$$

32.2. The mass of material deposited on the cathode is $\rho Sd = \dfrac{Ait}{eN_A Z}$; the valence of nickel is $Z = 2$. The remaining information is contained in the statement of the problem and in the tables.

32.3. First find the charge passing through the solution, making use of the graph in Fig. 32.3. Since the current changes linearly, the eventual value being $i_{ev} = 6 - 0.03 \times 180 = 2.4$ A, the charge is easily obtained: $q = (i_0 + i_{ev}) t/2$. Incidentally, the same result may be obtained by integrating the expression

$$q = \int_0^{180} i \, dt$$

(check this). Then the mass of copper may be found from Faraday's law.

32.5. The e.m.f. of the power supply should exceed the e.m.f. of polarization, which may be found from the specific energy of the chemical reaction:

$$\mathscr{E}_{pol} = \lambda K = \frac{\lambda A}{eN_A Z}$$

32.6. The capacitor's charge is $q = C\Delta\varphi$, the accumulated energy is $W_{cap} = \frac{1}{2} C (\Delta\varphi)^2 = 1.8$ J. The amount of hydrogen produced is $m = \frac{AC\Delta\varphi}{eN_A Z}$; the quantity of heat liberated in the process of combustion is $Q = m\lambda = 9.1 \times 10^{-3}$ J, which is much less than the energy of the capacitor. Obviously, in the course of the discharge

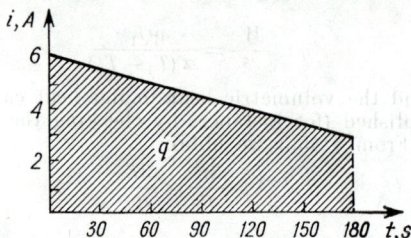

Fig. 32.3.

of the capacitor through the electrolyte, part of the energy stored in it will be liberated in the form of heat, with only a small fraction being spent on the chemical reaction.

32.7. The lift $F = (\rho_0 - \rho_H) Vg$, where ρ_0 is the density of air and ρ_H the density of hydrogen. The mass of hydrogen is

$$m = \rho_H V = \rho_H F/g (\rho_0 - \rho_H).$$

Applying Faraday's law, we find the charge q passing through the electrolyte solution. The energy required to produce the hydrogen is

$$W = q\mathscr{E}_{pol} + Q$$

where Q represents the Joule heat loss. The polarization e.m.f. has already been found in Problem 32.5.

33. Electric Current in a Vacuum and in Gases

33.1. The calculation is done using the Richardson-Dushmann formula. For the sake of convenience one should first find the logarithm of the current:

$$\log i_{sat} = \log \pi + \log d + \log l + \log B + 2 \log T - 0.434 \log A_0/kT$$

33.2. According to the Richardson-Dushmann formula we have

$$x = \frac{i_2}{i_1} = \left(\frac{T_2}{T_1} \right)^2 \exp \left[\frac{A_0 \left(T_2 - T_1 \right)}{k T_1 T_2} \right]$$

For the computation one should find $\log x$.

33.3. The collision of the electrons with the anode is an inelastic one, and this makes it possible to compute the force using formula (17.19) from § 17.5. Noting that the current is $i = enSv$, we obtain

$$F = \frac{imv}{e} = \frac{i}{e} \sqrt{2e\varphi m}$$

33.4. The ratio of the saturation currents of the two cathodes is

$$x = \frac{i_1}{i_2} = \left(\frac{T_1}{T_2} \right)^2 \exp \left(\frac{A_2}{k T_2} - \frac{A_1}{k T_1} \right)$$

33.5. Calculations should be done for the linear section of the characteristic curve. In this case a change in the anode voltage $\Delta U_a = 150$ V, with a constant grid voltage (for instance, with $U_g = 0$), causes a change in the anode current of $\Delta i_a = 75$ mA. The tube's internal resistance is $R_i = \frac{\Delta U_a}{\Delta i a}$. The tube's amplification factor is $\mu = \frac{\Delta U_a}{\Delta U_g}$, i.e. μ is the ratio of the change in the anode voltage to the change in the grid voltage which causes a given change in the anode current. It follows from Fig. 33.5 that a change of anode current equal to 75 mA may be obtained either by changing the anode voltage by $\Delta U_a = 150$ V, or by changing the grid voltage by $\Delta U_g = 7.5$ V. Therefore the grid is 20 times more effective in controlling the current flowing through the tube (on the linear section of its characteristic curve), i.e. amplification factor $\mu = 20$.

33.6. Away from the saturation region the current density is a function of the ion mobility (§ 48.2), from which we get for the ion concentration

$$n = \frac{id}{eUS \left(b_+ + b_- \right)}$$

The concentration of air molecules in normal conditions is equal to the Loschmidt number (§ 26.9), which gives the ionization coefficient $\alpha = n/N_{\mathrm{L}}$.

33.8. Away from the saturation region the current will increase, since the strength of the electric field increases as the plates are brought closer together. In conditions of saturation the current will decrease, since the effective volume of the ionization chamber is smaller. The current-voltage characteristics are shown in Fig. 33.8.

33.9. The saturation current is $i_{\mathrm{sat}} = \beta n_0 eV = \nu eV$, where ν is the number of ions produced per second per unit volume of the chamber.

33.10. Usually the computations are carried out using the relation $3/2 kT = \mathscr{E}_{\mathrm{ion}}$. This, however, yields too large a value for the temperature:

$$T = \frac{2\mathscr{E}_{\text{ion}}}{3k} \approx 10^5 \text{ K}$$

In fact, ionization takes place at lower temperatures. The reason is the Maxwellian molecular speed distribution, according to which in equilibrium conditions there is always a noticeable percentage of molecules with speeds exceeding the average. For example, from Table 25.1 (see § 25.2) it may be seen that $\frac{9}{368} \approx 2.5\%$ of the molecules have a speed more than three times the average. This means that their kinetic energy is more than nine times greater than the average kinetic energy of the molecules.

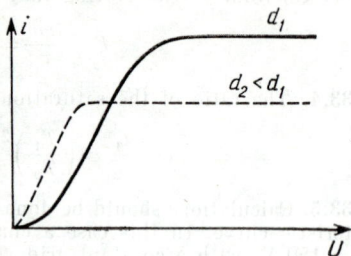

Fig. 33.8.

33.11. Thermal motion of ions and of electrons in a magnetic field takes the form of motion along arcs of circles, whose radii may be computed with the aid of the formula used to compute the radius of the ionic cyclotron orbit (see § 41.2). We can express the momentum of the particle in terms of the gas temperature: $p = \sqrt{3mkT}$ which gives the cyclotron radius $R = \dfrac{\sqrt{3mkT}}{eB}$.

33.12. First find the Reynolds number:

$$\text{Re} = \frac{\rho v l}{\eta} = \frac{13.6 \times 10^3 \times 5 \times 10^{-2} \times 0.2}{1.55 \times 10^{-3}} = 8.8 \times 10^4 \gg 2300.$$

Hence the flow is turbulent and it should be assessed with the aid of the Stewart number:

$$N = \frac{\gamma B^2 l}{\rho v} = \frac{1.05 \times 10^6 \times 0.36 \times 5 \times 10^{-2}}{13.6 \times 10^3 \times 0.2} = 7$$

But the Stewart number represents the ratio of the magnetic force to the resistance of pressure. Hence, in this case the magnetic force will appreciably affect the coefficient of hydraulic friction.

33.13.

$$\text{Re} = \frac{1.02 \times 10^3 \times 5 \times 10^{-2} \times 0.2}{2.44 \times 10^{-3}} = 4200 > 2300$$

$$N = \frac{73.9 \times 0.36 \times 5 \times 10^{-2}}{1.02 \times 10^3 \times 0.2} = 6.5 \times 10^{-3} \ll 1.$$

33.14. Since the lines of induction are frozen into the plasma, the magnetic flux will remain unchanged as the star contracts: $\Phi = \Phi_0$, or $BR^2 = B_0 R_0^2$. Hence we find the magnetic induction of the pulsar. For data on star radii (prior to contraction), and pulsars, see Problem 14.21.

33.15. The pressure of the magnetic field is equal to the energy density:

$$p_m = w_m = B^2/2\mu_0$$

The pressure of the gravitational forces will be assessed in the same way as in Problem 16.7:

$$p_{grav} = \bar{\rho}\bar{g}h = \frac{3M}{4\pi R^3} \cdot \frac{\gamma M}{2R^2} \cdot \frac{R}{2} = \frac{3\gamma M^2}{16\pi R^4}$$

Substituting the values of the pulsar's mass and radius (see Problem 14.21) we obtain the value of the pressure exerted by the gravitational forces.

34. Harmonic Vibrations

34.4. The expression for the kinetic energy is transformed as follows:

$$K = 2.50 \cos^2 \left(20\pi t + \frac{3\pi}{4} \right) = 1.25 \left[1 + \cos \left(40\pi t + \frac{3\pi}{2} \right) \right] =$$
$$= 1.25 \, (1 + \sin 40\pi t)$$

The frequency of energy oscillations is $\nu_K = 40\pi/(2\pi) = 20$ Hz, the period is $T_K = 0.05$ s.

34.5. The law of oscillations is of the form $s = A \cos (\omega t + \varphi)$. Since $s_0 = 0$, it follows that $0 = A \cos \varphi$, giving $\varphi = (2k + 1) \frac{\pi}{2}$. The initial phase is always less than the period of the oscillations $\varphi < 2\pi$. Hence $\varphi = \pi/2$, or $\varphi = 3\pi/2$.

The particle's velocity is $v = -A\omega \sin (\omega t + \varphi)$. The initial velocity $v_0 = -A\omega \sin \varphi = 0.20$ is, according to the statement of the problem, a positive quantity, and this is possible only if $\varphi = 3\pi/2$. Hence, $A\omega = 0.2$. But $\omega = 2\pi\nu = \pi$ rad/s. Hence the amplitude is $A = 0.20/\pi = 0.064$ m. Knowing the amplitude, the frequency and the initial phase we may easily write down the equation of the oscillations.

34.6. The equation of the oscillations is of the form $s = A \cos (\omega t + \varphi)$. The total energy is $W = m\omega^2 A^2/2$, the velocity is $v = -A\omega \sin (\omega t + \varphi)$. At the initial point of time

$$s_0 = A \cos \varphi, \quad v_0 = -A\omega \sin \varphi, \quad W = m\omega^2 A^2/2$$

giving $\sin \varphi = -\frac{v_0}{A\omega} = -v_0 \sqrt{\frac{m}{2W}}$. Since $\sin \varphi > 0$ and $\cos \varphi > 0$, it follows that the initial phase φ lies in the interval $0 < \varphi < \pi/2$.

The circular frequency is $\omega = -\frac{v_0}{s_0} \cot \varphi$, the amplitude $A = \sqrt{s_0^2 + \left(\frac{v_0}{\omega} \right)^2}$. The period of oscillations is 50 ms, so the time of

0.4 s spans 8 periods. During this time the particle will cover a distance equal to 32 amplitudes.

34.8. Apply the vector diagram (Fig. 34.8). Here

$$B = \sqrt{\left(A - \frac{A}{4}\right)^2 + \left(\frac{A}{4} - \frac{A}{8}\right)^2}; \qquad \tan\varphi = \frac{(A/4) - (A/8)}{A - (A/4)} = \frac{1}{2}$$

34.10 Carry out the following transformations:

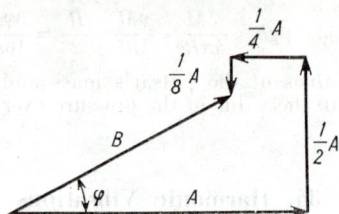

Fig. 34.8.

$$s = 4\cos^2\frac{t}{2} \cdot \sin 1000t = 2(1 + \cos t)\sin 1000t =$$

$$= 2\sin 1000t + 2\sin 1000t \cdot \cos t = 2\sin 1000t + \sin 1001t - \sin 999t$$

The spectrum is shown in Fig. 34.10.

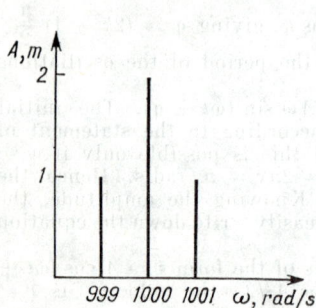

Fig. 34.10.

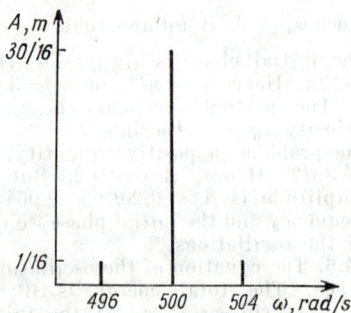

Fig. 34.11.

34.11. We have

$$1 + \cos^2 t + \sin^4 t = 1 + \frac{1}{2}(1 + \cos 2t) + \frac{1}{4}(1 - \cos 2t)^2 =$$

$$= \frac{1}{4}(4 + 2 + 2\cos 2t + 1 - 2\cos 2t + \cos^2 2t) =$$

$$= \frac{1}{4}\left[7 + \frac{1}{2}(1 + \cos 4t)\right] = \frac{1}{8}(15 + \cos 4t)$$

Hence it follows

$$s = \frac{1}{8}(15 + \cos 4t)\sin 500t =$$

$$= \frac{15}{8}\sin 500t + \frac{1}{8}\sin 500t \cdot \cos 4t =$$

$$= \frac{15}{8}\sin 500t + \frac{1}{16}\sin 504t + \frac{1}{16}\sin 496t$$

The spectrum is shown in Fig. 34.11.

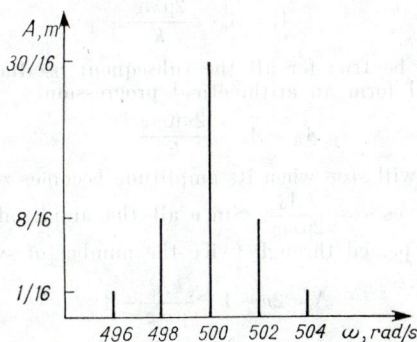

Fig. 34.12.

34.12. We have

$$1 + \cos^2 t + \cos^4 t = 1 + \frac{1}{2}(1 + \cos 2t) + \frac{1}{4}(1 + \cos 2t)^2 =$$

$$= \frac{1}{4}(4 + 2 + 2\cos 2t + 1 + 2\cos 2t + \cos^2 2t) =$$

$$= \frac{1}{4}\left[7 + 4\cos 2t + \frac{1}{2}(1 + \cos 4t)\right] = \frac{1}{8}(15 + 8\cos 2t + \cos 4t)$$

Hence

$$s = \frac{1}{8}(15 + 8\cos 2t + \cos 4t)\sin 500t = \frac{15}{8}\sin 500t + \cos 2t\,\sin 500t +$$

$$+ \frac{1}{8}\cos 4t \cdot \sin 500t = \frac{15}{8}\sin 500t + \frac{1}{2}\sin 502t + \frac{1}{2}\sin 498t +$$

$$+ \frac{1}{16}\sin 504t + \frac{1}{16}\sin 496t$$

The spectrum of the vibrations considered above is shown in Fig. 34.12.

35. Free Vibrations

35.2. $Q = k/h\omega_0$, where $h = F_{\text{fr}}/v = 6\pi r\eta$.

35.3. The friction force $F_{\text{fr}} = \mu mg$ is independent of the velocity, and this makes it possible to discuss the problem from the standpoint of energy. Suppose the weight goes over from the initial state of maximum deflection from the position of equilibrium, characterized by the amplitude A_0, to another, similar state with amplitude A_1. Then, according to the law of conservation of energy,

$$\frac{1}{2} kA_0^2 - \mu mgA_0 = \frac{1}{2} kA_1^2 + \mu mgA_1$$

from which it follows that

$$A_1 = A_0 - \frac{2\mu mg}{k}$$

The same will be true for all the subsequent oscillations, i.e. the amplitudes will form an arithmetical progression:

$$A_n = A_0 - \frac{2n\mu mg}{k}$$

The pendulum will stop when its amplitude becomes zero. Substituting $A_n = 0$ gives $n = \frac{kA_0}{2\mu mg}$. Since all the amplitudes except the initial one are passed through twice the number of swings is

$$N = 2n - 1 = \frac{kA_0}{\mu mg} - 1$$

As may be seen, due to friction the mechanical energy rather quickly transforms into internal energy, and the oscillations cease.

35.4. When the volume of a gas is changed at constant temperature we have, according to the Boyle-Mariotte law

$$p_1 (d - x) S = p_2 (d + x) S = p \, dS$$

The force acting on the piston is

$$F = (p_1 - p_2) S = \frac{2pxSd}{d^2 - x^2} = \frac{2pVx}{d^2 - x^2}$$

where V is the volume of one half of the vessel. As can be seen, the force does not conform to Hooke's law, and the oscillations are not harmonic. But for small deflections of the piston (when $x \ll d$), the force will be quasi-elastic: $F = 2pVx/d^2$, and the oscillations of the piston will be harmonic. The rigidity of the system is $k = F/x = 2pV/d^2$.

35.5. For an adiabatic process we must make use of the Poisson equation, and of the approximations (for $x \ll d$)

$$\frac{d^\gamma}{(d+x)^\gamma} = \left(1 + \frac{x}{d}\right)^{-\gamma} \approx 1 - \frac{\gamma x}{d}, \quad \frac{d^\gamma}{(d-x)^\gamma} = \left(1 - \frac{x}{d}\right)^{-\gamma} \approx 1 + \frac{\gamma x}{d}$$

For the force we obtain

$$F = (p_1 - p_2)\, S = \left[\frac{pd^\gamma}{(d-x)^\gamma} - \frac{pd^\gamma}{(d+x)^\gamma} \right] S \approx \frac{2\gamma pSx}{d} = \frac{2\gamma pVx}{d^2}$$

i.e. $F_{ad} = \gamma F_{isot}$.

35.6. As may be seen from Fig. 35.6 the force which restores the body to its equilibrium positions is $F = \rho g\, \Delta V = 2\rho gSx$. Since this force is proportional to the displacement, the natural frequency of the vibrations can be found from the formula $\omega_0 = \sqrt{k/m}$. Here $k = = F/x = 2\rho gS$, $m = \rho Sl$.

Hence $\omega_0 = \sqrt{2g/l}$.

35.7. The restoring force is $F = \rho_0 gSx$, where $S = 20 \times 20$ cm^2 = $= 4 \times 10^{-2}$ m^2, ρ_0 is the density of water, and x is the increase in the depth of immersion. Since the force is quasi-elastic, the frequency can be obtained using the familiar formula.

35.8. The period of oscillations of the pendulum at the surface of the Earth is $T_0 = = 2\pi \sqrt{l/g_0}$. At an altitude h above the surface of the Earth it is $T = 2\pi \sqrt{l/g}$. We have $\dfrac{\Delta T}{T_0} = \dfrac{\tau}{\tau_0}$, where $\tau_0 = 8.64 \times 10^4$ s is the duration of a complete day and τ is the lag of the clock. Hence

$$\tau = \frac{\tau_0 \Delta T}{T_0} = \tau_0 \left(\frac{T}{T_0} - 1 \right) = \tau_0 \left(\sqrt{g_0/g} - 1 \right)$$

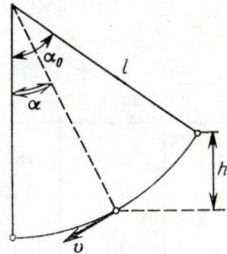

Fig. 35.10.

The acceleration due to gravity at the Earth's surface is $g_0 = \dfrac{\gamma M}{R^2}$ while at an altitude h it is $g = \dfrac{\gamma M}{(R+h)^2}$ where R is the radius of the Earth. After some simple transformations we obtain

$$\tau = \tau_0 h/R$$

35.9. One should find the total acceleration with respect to the Earth: $w = \sqrt{a^2 + g^2}$. Then the period of the pendulum will be $T = = 2\pi \sqrt{l/w}$.

The equilibrium position will be deflected from the vertical by an angle $\varphi = \arctan \dfrac{a}{g}$.

35.10. The particle's velocity at an arbitrary point on the circle is (Fig. 35.10)

$$v = \sqrt{2gh} = \sqrt{2gl(\cos\alpha - \cos\alpha_0)} = x\sqrt{2gl}$$

where $x = \sqrt{\cos \alpha - \cos \alpha_0}$. The body travels along the element of arc $\Delta s = l \, \Delta \alpha$ in time

$$\Delta t = \frac{\Delta s}{v_{\mathrm{av}}} = \frac{l \Delta \alpha}{x_{\mathrm{av}} \sqrt{2gl}} = \frac{\Delta \alpha}{x_{\mathrm{av}} \sqrt{2}} \sqrt{\frac{l}{g}}$$

Put $\Delta \alpha = 3° = \pi/60$ radian. Then

$$\Delta t = 2\pi \sqrt{\frac{l}{g}} \cdot \frac{\sqrt{2}}{240 x_{\mathrm{av}}}$$

The period of oscillations is

$$T = 4 \, (\Delta t_1 + \Delta t_2 + \ldots) = 2\pi \sqrt{\frac{l}{g}} \frac{\sqrt{2}}{60} \left(\frac{1}{x_{1\mathrm{av}}} + \frac{1}{x_{2\mathrm{av}}} + \ldots \right)$$

Table 35.10

i	α	$\cos \alpha$	$\cos \alpha - \cos \alpha_0$	x	x_{av}	$1/x_{\mathrm{av}}$
0	45°	0.7071	0.0000	0.0000		
1	42°	0.7431	0.0360	0.190	0.095	10.50
2	39°	0.7771	0.0700	0.265	0.228	4.38
3	36°	0.8090	0.1019	0.318	0.292	3.43
4	33°	0.8387	0.1316	0.362	0.340	2.94
5	30°	0.8660	0.1589	0.399	0.380	2.63
6	27°	0.8910	0.1839	0.428	0.414	2.42
7	24°	0.9135	0.2064	0.454	0.441	2.27
8	21°	0.9336	0.2265	0.476	0.456	2.15
9	18°	0.9511	0.2440	0.494	0.485	2.06
10	15°	0.9659	0.2588	0.508	0.501	1.99
11	12°	0.9781	0.2710	0.520	0.510	1.96
12	9°	0.9877	0.2806	0.530	0.525	1.91
13	6°	0.9945	0.2874	0.535	0.532	1.88
14	3°	0.9986	0.2915	0.540	0.538	1.89
15	0	1.0000	0.2929	0.541	0.540	1.85
					Total	44.23

Since the formula $T_0 = 2\pi \sqrt{l/g}$ is used to compute the period of small oscillations, it follows that $T = kT_0$, where

$$k = \frac{\sqrt{2}}{60} \left(\frac{1}{x_{1av}} + \frac{1}{x_{2av}} + \dots \right)$$

is the correction factor. Let us compile a table (see Table 35.10) from the computed data. We have

$$k = \frac{\sqrt{2} \times 44.23}{60} = 1.042$$

Hence, the period $T = 2\pi k \sqrt{l/g} = 2.08$ s, the value of T_0 being $T_0 = 2\pi \sqrt{l/g} = 2.00$ s. In this case the relative error due to the use of the formula for small oscillations will be 4%.

35.13. The moment of inertia about the axis is

$$I = \frac{1}{3} m_1 l^2 + \frac{1}{2} m_2 r^2 + m_2 (l+r)^2$$

The distance between the centre of mass and the axis is

$$a = \frac{1/2 m_1 l + m_2 (l+r)}{m_1 + m_2}$$

Hence we find the period.

36. Forced Vibrations. Alternating Current

36.1. Away from resonance, $A = \left| \dfrac{F_M}{m (\omega_0^2 - \omega^2)} \right|$, at resonance $A_{res} = QA_{stat} = QF_M/k$.

36.2. Since $V_M = \omega A$, for $\omega = 0$ and for $\omega \to \infty$ the amplitude of the velocity becomes $V_M = 0$. The resonance curve is shown in Fig. 36.2.

36.3. First we find the natural frequency (see Problem 35.1). We have $\omega_0 = \sqrt{g/A_{stat}}$. The Q factor is found from the time of damping: $Q \approx \omega_0 \tau = \tau \sqrt{g/A_{stat}}$. Hence we find the amplitude at resonance:

$$A_{res} = QA_{stat} \approx \tau \sqrt{gA_{stat}}$$

Clearly, at resonance the system will break down.

36.4. To prevent the merging of two successive impulses the interval between them should be appreciably longer than the time of damping of the first impulse and the build-up time of the second, i.e.

$$\tau_{sp} > 2\tau \approx 4Q/\omega_0$$

To find the maximum volume of information transmitted per second, one should take into account that such information should be made up of N_1 dots and N_2 dashes: $N = N_1 + N_2$, where N is the amount of information. But usually on the average $N_1 \approx N_2 \approx N/2$. We have

$$1 \text{ s} = N_1\tau_1 + N_2\tau_2 + N\tau_{sp} \approx N\tau_{sp}\left(\frac{1.5}{2} + \frac{4.5}{2} + 1\right) = 4N\tau_{sp} \approx 16N\,\frac{Q}{\omega_0}$$

Hence we find the amount of information: $N \leqslant R/16L$.

36.5. Let the voltage be $u = U_M \cos \omega t$, and the current $i = I_M \cos(\omega t + \varphi)$. According to the definition of the back e.m.f., self-induced e.m.f. $\mathscr{E}_L = -L\,\dfrac{di}{dt}$, the voltage drop across the inductive reactance is $u_L = -\mathscr{E}_L = L\,\dfrac{di}{dt}$ (see § 54.2). Substituting $\dfrac{di}{dt} = -I_M\omega \sin(\omega t + \varphi)$ we obtain $U_M \cos \omega t = -I_M L\omega \sin(\omega t + \varphi)$. Hence

$$X_L = \frac{U_M}{I_M} = L\omega, \quad \varphi = -\frac{\pi}{2}$$

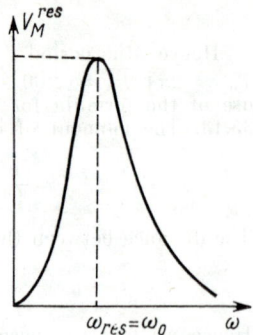

Fig. 36.2.

36.6. Let the voltage be $u = U_M \cos \omega t$ and the current $i = I_M \cos(\omega t + \varphi)$. The voltage drop across the capacitor is $u_C = q/C$, and the current is

$$i = \frac{dq}{dt} = C\,\frac{du}{dt} = -U_M C\omega \sin \omega t$$

Hence $I_M \cos(\omega t + \varphi) = -U_M C\omega \sin \omega t$ from which it follows that

$$X_C = \frac{U_M}{I_M} = \frac{1}{C\omega}, \quad \varphi = \frac{\pi}{2}$$

36.7. When a coil and a resistor are connected in series, the current flowing through them is the same, and there is a phase shift between the voltages. Therefore the vector diagram is plotted with the vector representing the effective or the amplitude value of the current (see Fig. 36.7).

36.8. The vector diagram is shown in Fig. 36.8.

36.9. When a capacitor and a resistor are connected in parallel, the same voltage is applied to them, and there is a phase shift between the currents. Therefore the vector diagram is plotted with the vector representing the effective or the amplitude value of the voltage (see Fig. 36.9).

36.10. In this circuit $Z = \sqrt{R^2 + \left(L\omega - \dfrac{1}{C\omega}\right)^2}$. Let us take the resistance from under the square sign and the capacitive reactance $X_C = 1/C\omega$ out of the brackets, we obtain

$$Z = R\sqrt{1 + \frac{(LC\omega^2 - 1)^2}{R^2 C^2 \omega^2}}$$

The natural frequency is $\omega_0 = \sqrt{\dfrac{1}{LC}}$, $Q = \dfrac{1}{R}\sqrt{\dfrac{L}{C}} = \dfrac{1}{RC\omega_0}$, giving $LC = 1/\omega_0^2$, $R^2C^2 = 1/Q^2\omega_0^2$. Substituting into the expression for the impedance, we obtain

$$Z = R\sqrt{1 + \frac{Q^2\omega_0^2}{\omega^2}\left(\frac{\omega^2}{\omega_0^2} - 1\right)^2} = R\sqrt{1 + \frac{Q^2}{\gamma^2}(\gamma^2 - 1)^2}$$

where $\gamma = \dfrac{\omega}{\omega_0}$.

36.11. The vector diagram is shown in Fig. 36.11b (see Problem 36.9), where

$$Z_0 = \sqrt{R^2 + L^2\omega^2}, \quad \cos\varphi_0 = R/Z_0, \quad \sin\varphi_0 = L\omega/Z_0$$

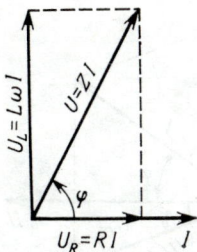

Fig. 36.7.

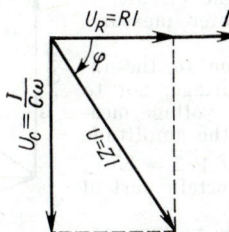

Fig. 36.8.

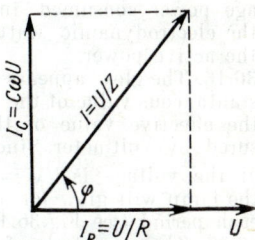

Fig. 36.9.

It is clear from the diagram that

$$I^2 = I_0^2 + I_C^2 - 2I_0I_C\cos\alpha$$

but since $\alpha = (\pi/2) - \varphi_0$, it follows that

$$I^2 = I_0^2 + I_C^2 - 2I_0I_C\sin\varphi_0$$

Substituting the values of the currents and $\sin\varphi_0$, we obtain after some simple transformations the required effective value of the current in the unbranched section of the circuit.

From the vector diagram $\cos\varphi = \dfrac{I_0\cos\varphi_0}{I} = \dfrac{UR}{IZ_0^2}$

36.12. To find the power we apply the formula $P = IU\cos\varphi$. Knowing the amplitude to be $U_M = 312$ V, we must find the effective voltage and substitute the data into the formulae of the previous problem. To simplify computations assume $\pi^2 = 10$.

36.14. An electrodynamic wattmeter has two coils (Fig. 36.14). The stationary coil wound with thick wire is connected in series with the load. It sets up a magnetic field whose induction is proportional to the current:

$$B \propto i, \quad \text{or} \quad B = k_1I_M\cos(\omega t + \varphi)$$

The moving coil is connected in parallel with the load, so the magnetic moment of this coil is proportional to the voltage:

$$p_m \propto u, \quad \text{or} \quad p_m = k_2 U_M \cos \omega t$$

Here k_1 and k_2 are proportionality factors. The instantaneous value of the torque acting on the moving coil is

$$M = p_m B = k_1 k_2 I_M U_M \cos \omega t \cdot \cos (\omega t + \varphi)$$

$$= k_1 k_2 I U \left[\cos \varphi + \cos (2\omega t + \varphi)\right]$$

The average value of the torque is

$$M_{av} = k_1 k_2 I U \left[\cos \varphi + \cos (2\omega t + \varphi)\right]_{av} = k_1 k_2 I U \cos \varphi$$

since the average value of the term $\cos (2\omega t + \varphi)$ is zero. We see that the average value of the torque acting on the moving part of the instrument is proportional to the average power consumed in the circuit, so the electrodynamic wattmeter measures the active power.

36.16. The glow appears due to the instantaneous value of the voltage, not to the effective value of the voltage measured by voltmeter. Since the amplitude of the voltage is $U_M = U \sqrt{2} = 85$ V, the lamp will glow for a certain part of each period (see Fig. 36.16).

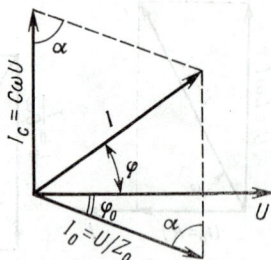

Fig. 36.11b.

36.17. The amplitude of the voltage exceeds the breakdown voltage.

36.19. If we neglect the phase shift we may easily find the current in the secondary $I_2 = k I_1$, and the number of turns $w_2 = w_1 / k$.

Assuming the maximum current density in the wires to be the same, we find the cross section of the wires to be proportional to the currents, therefore $S_2 = k S_1$.

To find the resistance of the secondary we must know the length of the wire. Note that according to the statement of the problem, the winding is wound in a single layer, so the lengths of the wires are proportional to the number of turns:

$$\frac{l_2}{l_1} = \frac{w_2}{w_1} = \frac{1}{k}$$

Since the wires are of the same material, the ratio of their resistances is

$$\frac{R_2}{R_1} = \frac{l_2 S_1}{l_1 S_2} = \frac{1}{k^2}$$

This allows us to find the resistance of the secondary.

The copper losses in the windings are $P_{copper} = I_1^2 R_1 + I_2^2 R_2$, and the efficiency is

$$\eta = \frac{P_2}{P_1} = \frac{P_1 - P_{copper}}{P_1}$$

36.20. In the no-load condition, the secondary does not consume power. Hence $P_{\text{no-load}} = I_{\text{no-load}}^2 r_1 + P_{\text{iron}}$ where r_1 is the resistance of the primary. But the current $I_{\text{no-load}}$ of correctly designed transformers is very small due to the enormous inductive reactance, and also because the resistance of the winding is small. For this reason the first term may be neglected in the power balance and, $P_{\text{no-land}} = $ $= P_{\text{iron}}$.

36.21. Consider the high frequency case when the resistance of a solid copper or aluminium ring is negligible compared with its inductive reactance. Suppose a sinusoidal current flows in the primary. The magnetic flux permeating the ring will also be sinusoidal. The e.m.f. induced in the ring is proportional to the time derivative of the magnetic flux with a minus sign. Hence the phase lag of the induced

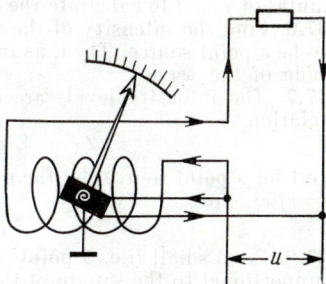

Fig. 36.14.

e.m.f. behind the current in the primary is $\varphi_{\mathscr{E}} = -\pi/2$. The phase

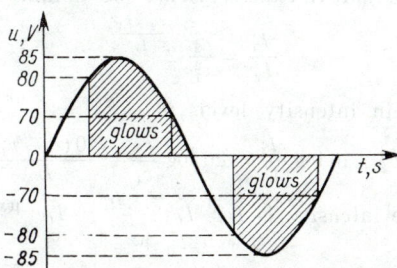

Fig. 36.16.

lag of the current oscillations in the ring, as in any other inductive reactance, will be the same: $\varphi_i = -\pi/2$. Therefore the phase shift between the currents in the ring and in the primary will be $\varphi = $ $= \varphi_{\mathscr{E}} + \varphi_i = -\pi$, i.e. these currents are in *opposite phases*, which means they flow in opposite directions. Such currents, as is well known, repel each other. The force of repulsion balances the force of gravity, with the result that the ring "floats" in the air.

36.22. The secondary feeds a resistive load, so $\varphi_2 = 0$. The power factor is

$$\cos \varphi_1 = P_1/I_1 U_1$$

The active power P_1 is obtained from the efficiency.

37. Elastic Waves

37.5. First we must find the density of air and the velocity of the wave $u = \sqrt{\gamma p/\rho}$ at a temperature of 27 °C, and then apply the formulas of § 55.3 to calculate the energy and the amplitude of the wave.

37.6. Find the intensity of the wave $I = P/4\pi r^2$, assuming the source to be a point source. Then, as in the previous problem, find the amplitude of the wave.

37.7. The intensity levels are connected with the intensities by the relation

$$\mathscr{L}_1 - \mathscr{L}_2 = 10 \log (I_1/I_2)$$

But for a point source, by the results of the previous problem, $I_1/I_2 = r_2^2/r_1^2$. So

$$\mathscr{L}_1 - \mathscr{L}_2 = 20 \log (r_2/r_1)$$

37.8. For a small (i.e. a point) source, the wave intensity is inversely proportional to the square of the distance from the source. If in addition we take into account the attenuation, one would obtain for the wave intensities at distances r_1 and r_2 from the source the expressions

$$I_1 = \frac{I_0 r_0^2}{r_1^2} \cdot 2^{-r_1/L}, \qquad I_2 = \frac{I_0 r_0^2}{r_2^2} \cdot 2^{-r_2/L}$$

where L is the half-thickness. Hence we obtain

$$\frac{I_1}{I_2} = \frac{r_2^2}{r_1^2} \cdot 2^{\frac{r_2 - r_1}{L}}$$

The difference in intensity levels is

$$\mathscr{L}_1 - \mathscr{L}_2 = 10 \log \frac{I_1}{I_2} = 20 \log \frac{r_2}{r_1} + \frac{10 (r_2 - r_1)}{L} \log 2$$

37.9. The wave intensity is $I = I_0 \cdot 2^{-x/L} = I_0 e^{-\mu x}$. Therefore

$$2^{-x/L} = e^{-\mu x}$$

Taking the logarithms, we obtain

$$\frac{x}{L} \ln 2 = \mu x$$

which gives the required relation.

37.11. To solve the problem we should make use of the expression for the frequency of the signal from a moving source as measured by a stationary observer:

$$\nu_1 = \frac{\nu_0}{1 + x} \qquad \text{and} \qquad \nu_2 = \frac{\nu_0}{1 - x}$$

where $x = v/u$ is the ratio of the velocity of the source to the wave velocity. The beat frequency is equal to the difference in frequencies:

$$\nu = \nu_1 - \nu_2 = \frac{2x\nu_0}{1 - x^2} = \frac{2v\nu_0}{u (1 - v^2/u^2)}$$

We obtain a quadratic equation $vx^2 + 2v_0 x - v = 0$, which gives

$$x = \frac{-v_0 + \sqrt{v_0^2 + v^2}}{v} = \frac{v_0^2 + v^2 - v_0^2}{v \left(v_0 + \sqrt{v_0^2 + v^2}\right)} = \frac{v}{v_0 + \sqrt{v_0^2 + v^2}} \approx \frac{v}{2v_0}$$

since the beat frequency v is much lower than the natural frequency of the tuning fork, v_0. Hence

$$\frac{v}{u} \approx \frac{v}{2v_0}, \quad \text{from which} \quad v \approx \frac{uv}{2v_0}$$

37.12. When the source approaches the receiver, the relation

$$v = v_0 \frac{1 + V/u}{1 - v/u}$$

holds, where V and v are respectively the speeds of the receiver and the source relative to the transmitting medium. In the case of the source moving away from the receiver, the signs in the numerator and the denominator should be reversed.

37.18. In the presence of an oil film the ultrasonic vibrations enter the part. In the presence of an air gap between the transducer and the part, the wave is completely reflected by a layer of air back to the transducer, and does not enter the part.

37.19. The reflected and the direct pulses can be seen separately only if there is an interval of more than half the duration of the pulse between them. This interval will be equal to $\tau = 30T = 30/v$. During this time the wave should twice travel through the thickness of the metal in the direct and in the reverse directions, i.e. $\tau = 2l/u$. Hence $l = 30\, u/2v = 15\, \lambda$.

38. Interference and Diffraction

38.1. Let the wave equation in a medium with wave resistance $z_1 = \rho_1 u_1$ be

$$s_1 = A_1 \cos (\omega t - kx)$$

The wave is reflected by the medium with wave resistance $z_2 = \rho_2 u_2$, and the equation of the reflected wave at the boundary is

$$s_{\text{ref}} = A_{\text{ref}} \cos (\omega t + kx)$$

But

$$A_{\text{ref}} = A_1 \frac{z_1 - z_2}{z_1 + z_2}$$

Therefore for $z_2 > z_1$ the amplitude of the reflected wave is negative, i.e. the phase of the wave is reversed. To simplify the computation put $z_2 \gg z_1$. We obtain $A_{\text{ref}} = -A_1$ and the equation of the wave in the first medium in the form

$$s = s_1 + s_{\text{ref}} = A_1 \cos (\omega t - kx) - A_1 \cos (\omega t + kx) = 2A_1 \sin kx \sin \omega t$$

At the boundary $x_0 = 0$ so $s_0 = 0$ for any t. Thus, the node of the standing wave appears here.

Similarly, for $z_2 \ll z_1$ we have $A_{\text{ref}} = A_1$, and the equation of the standing wave is

$$s = 2A_1 \cos kx \cdot \cos \omega t$$

The amplitude at the boundary between the two media ($x_0 = 0$) is $2A_1$, i.e. an antinode appears.

38.2 The wave resistance of quartz is greater than the wave resistance of air (the lower surface) or of water (the upper surface). Therefore there will be antinodes at both boundaries (although their amplitudes will be different). Hence it follows that an integral number of half-waves fits into the plate's thickness: $l = n\lambda/2$, and this enables the fundamental frequency and the harmonics to be found.

If the upper surface of the quartz plate is covered by oil, the frequency will remain unchanged, although the power radiated by the lower and the upper surfaces will be redistributed.

38.5. The beat frequency is equal to the difference in frequencies:

$$\nu = \nu_1 - \nu_2 = \frac{u_1 - u_2}{2l} = \frac{20 \left(\sqrt{T_1} - \sqrt{T_2} \right)}{2l}$$

Hence

$$\sqrt{T_1} - \sqrt{T_2} = \frac{l\nu}{10}, \quad \text{or} \quad \frac{T_1 - T_2}{\sqrt{T_1} + \sqrt{T_2}} = \frac{l\nu}{10}$$

But $T_1 \approx T_2 = T$, therefore $\Delta T = 0.2l\nu \sqrt{T}$.

38.6. Resonance sets in when an odd number of quarter waves fits along the air column: $l = (2n + 1) \lambda/4$. In our case $n = 0; 1; 2$.

38.7. The first-order interference minimum will be observed for an auxiliary angle $\alpha_1 = \pi$. In this case the angular width of the principal maximum will clearly be

$$\gamma = 2\theta_1 = 2 \arcsin \frac{\lambda a_1}{\pi D} = 2 \arcsin \frac{u}{\nu D}$$

39. Electromagnetic Waves

39.2. A standing wave is established along the aerial, as shown in Fig. 39.2. In the middle of the aerial the current is at its maximum (current antinode) and at the ends it is at its minimum (nodes), and since the magnetic field strength is proportional to the current, distribution of the standing wave of the magnetic field vector will be similar. As to the electric field strength, it forms antinodes at the ends of the aerial (why?), and a node in the middle.

Thus $l = \lambda/2$, whence $\lambda = 2l$.

39.3. According to the theory of forced oscillations, the frequency of a wave does not change when it crosses a boundary between two media. The parameters subject to change are the velocity and the wavelength. We have $\nu = \dfrac{u}{\lambda} = \dfrac{c}{\lambda_0}$, where $\lambda = 2l$ is the wavelength in the liquid, λ_0 is the wavelength in air. Noting that $u = c/\sqrt{\varepsilon}$, we obtain $\lambda_0 = 2l\sqrt{\varepsilon}$.

39.4. First find the velocity of the wave and the medium in which it propagates. We have $u = \omega/k = c/\sqrt{\varepsilon}$, and the dielectric constant of the material $\varepsilon = c^2k^2/\omega^2$.

The magnetic permeability of the material is $\mu = 1.0$. Find the amplitude of the magnetic field strength:

$$H_M = E_M\sqrt{\varepsilon\varepsilon_0/\mu\mu_0}$$

The amplitude of the energy density of the electromagnetic wave is

$$w_M = \frac{E_M H_M}{u} = \frac{\varepsilon E_M^2}{c}\sqrt{\frac{\varepsilon_0}{\mu_0}}$$

The average value of the energy is equal to one half of its amplitude value:

$$\overline{w} = \frac{\varepsilon E_M^2}{2c}\sqrt{\frac{\varepsilon_0}{\mu_0}}$$

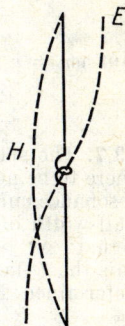

Fig. 39.2.

In the case of an ideal absorbing surface the pressure is equal to the average energy density.

The energy absorbed by an area S in time t is

$$\mathcal{E} = \overline{w}uSt = \frac{E_M^2 St}{2}\sqrt{\frac{\varepsilon\varepsilon_0}{\mu_0}}$$

39.5. The amplitude of the current is $I_M = enSV_M$ where $V_M = \omega A$ is the amplitude of the velocity of the oscillations of the charge. The magnitude of the oscillating charge is $q = enSl$, hence $I_M = qA\omega/l$. The radiation power is

$$P = \frac{\mu_0 q^2 A^2 \omega^2}{12\pi c} = \frac{\mu_0 I_M^2 l^2 \omega^2}{12\pi c}$$

But for a half-wave antenna $\omega l = \pi c$ (see Problem 39.2), so

$$P = \frac{\pi}{12}\mu_0 c I_M^2$$

The power is $P = I^2 R = I_M^2 R/2$, so the antenna is equivalent to a resistance

$$R = \frac{\pi}{6}\mu_0 c = \frac{\pi}{6}\sqrt{\frac{\mu_0}{\varepsilon_0}}$$

39.6. The power of the synchrotron radiation may be found from the formula

$$P = \frac{\mu_0 q^2 a^2}{12\pi c}$$

where a is the acceleration and q the charge of the bunch. Since $a = \omega^2 r$ and the current is $I = q/T = q\omega/2\pi$, where T is the period of circular motion it follows that $q = 2\pi I/\omega$. Substituting into the expression for the power, we obtain

$$P = 4\pi^2 \mu_0 I^2 \omega^2 r^2 /(12\pi c)$$

But $\omega r = v$ is the velocity of the electron, therefore

$$P = \pi\mu_0 I^2 v^2/3c$$

39.7. The spectrum of a modulated signal is shown in Fig. 39.7. For there to be no substantial distortion of the signal the half-width of the resonance curve should not be less than the half-width of the spectrum of the modulated signal: $\Delta v \geqslant v_1 - v$, or $v_0/Q \geqslant v_{aud}$. From this the Q-factor of the resonant circuit is determined:

$$Q \leqslant v_0/v_{aud}$$

Expressing the Q-factor and the natural frequency of the circuit in terms of its parameters, we obtain

$$R/L \geqslant 2\pi v_{aud}$$

where v_{aud} is the maximum frequency of the audio signal which must pass through the circuit without substantial distortion. Noting that $v_{aud} \approx 2 \times 10^3$ Hz, we obtain

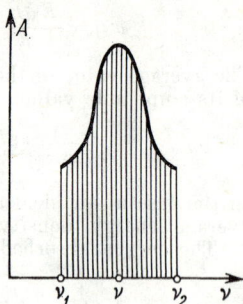

Fig. 39.7.

$$R/L \geqslant 4\pi \times 10^3 \ (\text{ohm} \cdot \text{H}^{-1})$$

The capacitance of the capacitor is $C = \dfrac{1}{4\pi^2 v_0^2 L}$. The natural frequency of the resonance circuit is $v_0 = c/\lambda = 1.2 \times 10^7$ Hz. Hence

$$C = \frac{1}{5.7 \times 10^{15} L} \ (\text{F})$$

If we choose an ohmic resistance of $R = 0.1$ ohm, we obtain reasonable values for the inductance and the capacitance.
39.8. Equation (59.22) follows from the phase invariance (see § 59.8). Applying the Lorentz transformations, we obtain

$$\omega \left(\frac{t_0 + vx_0/c^2}{\sqrt{1 - v^2/c^2}} - \frac{\cos\theta}{c} \cdot \frac{x_0 + vt_0}{\sqrt{1 - v^2/c^2}} - \frac{z_0 \sin\theta}{c} \right)$$

$$= \omega_0 \left(t_0 - \frac{x_0 \cos\theta_0}{c} - \frac{z_0 \sin\theta_0}{c} \right)$$

Removing brackets and regrouping the terms, we have

$$\frac{\omega t_0}{\sqrt{1-v^2/c^2}}\left(1-\frac{v\cos\theta}{c}\right)+\frac{\omega x_0}{c\sqrt{1-v^2/c^2}}\left(\frac{v}{c}-\cos\theta\right)$$

$$-\frac{\omega z_0\sin\theta}{c}=\omega_0 t_0-\frac{\omega_0 x_0\cos\theta_0}{c}-\frac{\omega_0 z_0\sin\theta_0}{c}$$

Noting that x_0, z_0 and t_0 are independent variables we see that equality obtained is possible only if the factors preceding these variables are equal. Hence putting $\beta=v/c$ we obtain

$$\frac{\omega(1-\beta\cos\theta)}{\sqrt{1-\beta^2}}=\omega_0, \qquad \frac{\omega(\cos\theta-\beta)}{\sqrt{1-\beta^2}}=\omega_0\cos\theta_0, \qquad \omega\sin\theta=\omega_0\sin\theta_0$$

The first equality is the expression for the Doppler effect. Dividing the second equation by the first, we obtain the relation for the cosines:

$$\frac{\cos\theta-\beta}{1-\beta\cos\theta}=\cos\theta_0$$

39.9. Let the source and the observer approach each other at a speed $v=\beta c$. According to the classical Doppler effect, the frequency of the approaching source is $\omega'=\omega_0/(1-\beta)$, and of the approaching observer $\omega''=\omega_0/(1+\beta)$. Considering the periods, we obtain

$$T'=T_0(1-\beta), \qquad T''=\frac{T_0}{1+\beta}$$

But we must also take into account the time dilatation. In the first case (that of the moving source), T_0 in the formula should be replaced by the quantity γT_0 where γ is the relativistic factor. In the second case (that of the moving observer), the quantity T'' should be replaced by $\gamma T''$. We obtain

$$T'=\gamma T_0(1-\beta), \qquad \gamma T''=\frac{T_0}{1+\beta}$$

Since, according to the principle of relativity, $T'\equiv T''$, we have

$$\gamma^2 T_0(1-\beta)=T_0/(1+\beta)$$

from which it follows that

$$\gamma=\frac{1}{\sqrt{1-\beta^2}}, \qquad T=T_0\sqrt{\frac{1-\beta}{1+\beta}}, \qquad \omega=\omega_0\sqrt{\frac{1+\beta}{1-\beta}}$$

39.10. The Doppler broadening is

$$\frac{\Delta\nu_{\text{Dop}}}{\nu}=\pm\frac{v}{c}=\pm\sqrt{\frac{3RT}{Mc^2}}$$

where M is the molar mass. The gravitational shift of the spectral line is

$$\frac{\Delta\nu_{\text{grav}}}{\nu}=\frac{\varphi_{\text{grav}}}{c^2}=\frac{\gamma m}{c^2 r}$$

where m and r are the mass and the radius of the star, respectively. On a "white dwarf" $\Delta\nu_{grav}$ exceeds $\Delta\nu_{Dop}$ by about an order of magnitude.

39.11. Since the ions move towards the observer, the wavelength is

$$\lambda = \lambda_0 \frac{1 - \beta\cos\theta}{\sqrt{1-\beta^2}}.$$

The kinetic energy of an ion is 40.0 MeV, the rest energy is four times the rest energy of a proton (Problem 8.1). We have

$$\sqrt{1-\beta^2} = \sqrt{1 - \frac{m^2 u^2 c^2}{m^2 c^4}} = \sqrt{1 - \frac{p^2 c^2}{\mathscr{E}^2}} = \frac{\mathscr{E}_0}{\mathscr{E}}$$

$$= \frac{\mathscr{E}_0}{\mathscr{E}_0 + K} = \frac{3.7284}{3.7684} = 0.989$$

The reciprocal quantity is

$$\gamma = \frac{1}{\sqrt{1-\beta^2}} = 1 + \frac{K}{\mathscr{E}_0} = 1.01$$

Hence we obtain the ratio of the ion velocity to the velocity of light:

$$\beta = u/c = \sqrt{1 - 0.989^2} = \sqrt{0.011 \times 1.989} = 0.148$$

Hence the observed wavelength is

$$\lambda = 410\,(1 - 0.148\cos\theta) \times 1.01 = 361 \text{ nm}$$

39.12. The velocity of rotation of the Sun is much less than the velocity of light, so we may use the classical expression for the Doppler effect. From a surface element moving towards us, $\lambda_1 = \lambda_0\,(1-\beta)$, from the element on the other side of the Sun, $\lambda_2 = \lambda_0\,(1+\beta)$. Therefore

$$\Delta\lambda = 2\beta\lambda_0 = \frac{4\pi\lambda_0 R_\odot}{cT_\odot}$$

where $R_\odot$ is half the Sun's equatorial diameter. The period of rotation is

$$T_\odot = \frac{4\pi\lambda_0 R_\odot}{\Delta\lambda c}$$

39.15. The shift of the spectral lines is a maximum when one star moves in its orbit towards us and the other away from us. Since the orbital velocities of the stars are much less than the velocity of light, the broadening of the spectral lines may be found from the nonrelativistic Doppler formula:

$$\Delta\lambda = \lambda_0\,(1 + \beta) - \lambda_0{}^r\,(1 - \beta) = 2\lambda_0\beta = 2\lambda_0 v/c$$

where v is the projection of the orbital velocity on the line of sight.

39.16. The period of revolution of the stars about their common centre of mass is twice the period of the spectral line broadening.

Knowing the orbital velocity and period, we may find the radius of the orbit:
$$R = vT/2\pi$$

Then, applying the law of gravitation, we have
$$\frac{\gamma M^2}{(2R)^2} = \frac{Mv^2}{R}, \quad \text{giving} \quad M = \frac{4v^2R}{\gamma} = \frac{2v^3T}{\pi\gamma}$$

40. Interference and Diffraction of Light

40.1. Obviously, the principal (the zero-order) maximum will be observed in the centre of the interference pattern (Fig. 40.1). Let us find the coordinate of the m-th maximum, which we shall denote

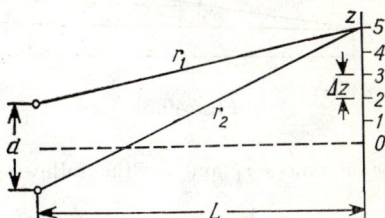

Fig. 40.1.

by z_m. This maximum will be observed when the propagation difference is $r_2 - r_1 = 2m\lambda/2$.

But $r_1^2 = L^2 + \left(z_m - \dfrac{d}{2}\right)^2$, $r_2^2 = L^2 + \left(z_m + \dfrac{d}{2}\right)^2$. Subtracting, we obtain $(r_2 - r_1)(r_2 - r_1) = 2z_m d$, Since $d \ll L$ and since in practice only the interference maxima of low order can be observed (i.e. $z_m \ll L$), we may put $r_2 + r_1 = 2L$. Hence
$$2L (r_2 - r_1) = 2z_m d, \quad \text{or} \quad m\lambda L = z_m d$$

Hence we obtain the coordinates of the maximum: $z_m = m\lambda L/d$. The separation between successive maxima (or minima) is
$$\Delta z = z_{m+1} - z_m = \lambda L/d$$

40.2. The interference pattern will be blurred if the red maximum of order m will coincide with the violet maximum of order $(m + 1)$: $z_m^{\text{red}} = z_{m+1}^{\text{viol}}$. Substituting the values, we obtain

$$m\lambda_{\text{red}} = (m + 1)\,\lambda_{\text{viol}} \quad \text{giving} \quad m = \frac{\lambda_{\text{viol}}}{\lambda_{\text{red}} - \lambda_{\text{viol}}}, \quad \text{i.e. } m = 1.6 < 2$$

This means that the zero- and the first-order maxima will be clearly seen together with the first- and the second-order minima (black bands). The second-order maximum will be blurred, the third-order and the subsequent maxima will not be visible at all. The zero-order

maximum will be white, while the first-order maximum will be
spectrally coloured, with the red outside and the violet inside and
the other parts of the spectrum in between.

The separation on the screen between the red and the violet bands
is

$$\Delta z = \frac{L}{d}\,(\lambda_{\text{red}} - \lambda_{\text{viol}})$$

40.3. As may be seen from Fig. 40.3b, $\dfrac{r_2 - r_1}{d} = \dfrac{h}{l}$. Since we consider here two successive maxima (or minima) and since the light

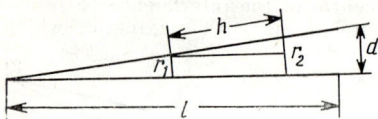

Fig. 40.3b.

twice covers the distances r_1 and r_2, the following relations hold:

$$2r_1 = 2m\,\frac{\lambda}{2}\,, \qquad 2r_2 = 2\,(m+1)\,\frac{\lambda}{2}$$

from which

$$r_2 - r_1 = \frac{\lambda}{2}$$

Thus $\dfrac{\lambda}{2d} = \dfrac{h}{l}$, from which the wavelength of the light can be
found.

40.4. When the mirror is displaced by a half-wave, the pattern shifts
by one band.

40.5. The optical propagation difference is $\Delta = n_2 l_2 - n_1 l_1 =$
$= (n-1)\,l$. This propagation difference accomodates $N = 47.5$ half-
waves. Hence $(n-1)\,l = N\lambda/2$ and $n = 1 + N\lambda/2l$.

40.7. The interference pattern will disappear if the maxima of one
wavelength coincide with the minima of the other.

40.9. It follows from the condition $d\sin\theta = m\lambda$ that $m\lambda/d \leqslant 1$.
Therefore the highest order of the visible maximum is $m \leqslant d/\lambda$,
m being the maximum integer. When computing the total number
of visible maxima one should take into account the presence of the
zero-order (the principal) maximum and the symmetry of the interference pattern about the principal maximum.

40.10. The first-order maximum is visible at an angle θ_1, which is
determined from the condition $d\sin\theta_1 = \lambda$. The second-order maximum is visible at an angle $\theta_2 = \theta_1 + 15°$, determined from the
condition $d\sin\theta_2 = 2\lambda$. Hence it follows that $\sin(\theta_1 + 15°) =$

$= 2 \sin \theta_1$, and this reduces to the equation

$$\tan \theta_1 = \frac{\sin 15°}{2 - \cos 15°} = 0.2503$$

Knowing the deflection angle θ_1 of the first-order maximum, we may easily compute the wavelength.

40.11. Find the total number of slits: $N = \dfrac{l}{d} = \dfrac{12.0 \times 10^3}{15.0} = 8000$.
Since $Nd = l$ is much greater than the wavelength, $\gamma = 2\lambda/l$, which gives the angular width of the principal maximum.

To find the resolving power of the grating we should find the number of maxima that can be obtained with it. We have (see Problem 40.9)

$$m \leqslant \frac{d}{\lambda} = \frac{1.50}{530 \times 10^{-3}} = 2.8, \qquad \text{so} \qquad m = 2$$

i.e. with this grating only the first- and the second-order spectra may be observed. The resolving power is $A = \lambda/\Delta\lambda = mN$.

40.12. The spectral interval that can be resolved is $\Delta\lambda = \lambda_2 - \lambda_1$, the resolving power is $A = \lambda_1/\Delta\lambda = mN$, from which we may find the total number of slits. The length of the grating is $l = Nd = \lambda_1 d/m \, \Delta\lambda$. The highest order of the spectrum is found from the condition $m \leqslant d/\lambda$ (see Problem 40.9). In our case this is 5.

40.13. To see these spectral lines separately, we should have a grating with a resolving power

$$A = \frac{\lambda}{\Delta\lambda} = \frac{5890}{6} = 982$$

The resolving power of our grating for the first-order spectrum is $A = mN = 990$, so the spectral lines will be resolved, but the resolution will be poor. Measurements can be done better from the spectrum of higher orders.

The angular distance between the maxima of the second-order spectrum is found from the conditions $d \sin \theta_1 = 2\lambda_1$ and $d \sin \theta_2 = 2\lambda_2$. The computations should be carried out using four- or five-place sine tables; slide rule accuracy is not enough to solve this problem.

40.14. Let a parallel beam, that is, a plane wave, fall on the grating at a glancing angle of α (Fig. 40.14). The direction of the zero-order interference maximum will obviously be the same. As to the maximum of order m, its direction will be at a glancing angle β, so that the propagation difference is $\Delta = a - b = m\lambda$. Noting that $a = d_0 \cos \alpha$, $b = d_0 \cos \beta$, where d_0 is the grating constant, we obtain

$$d_0 (\cos \alpha - \cos \beta) = m\lambda$$

This is just the condition for the interference maxima when the light rays are incident at an angle to the diffraction grating. Now let us express the interference condition for the angle θ equal to the deflection angle of the diffraction maximum from the original direction of the beam. Since $\beta = \alpha + \theta$, it follows that

$$\cos \alpha - \cos \beta = \cos \alpha - \cos(\alpha + \theta) = \cos \alpha - \cos \alpha \cos \theta + \sin \alpha \sin \theta$$

Since the angle θ is usually very small, $\cos \theta \approx 1$, and $\cos \alpha -$

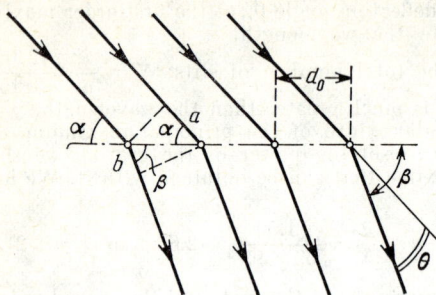

Fig. 40.14.

$- \cos \beta \approx \sin \alpha \sin \theta$. The condition for the maximum assumes the form

$$d_0 \sin \alpha \sin \theta = m\lambda$$

i.e. the instrument behaves with respect to the inclined beam in the way it would have done if a grating with constant $d = d_0 \sin \alpha$ were placed perpendicular to the rays.

41. Dispersion and Absorption of Light

41.1. The condition for Cerenkov radiation which takes account of dispersion is $\cos \theta = c/nv$. Since the protons are relativistic, it follows that

$$\sqrt{1 - \frac{v^2}{c^2}} = \sqrt{1 - \frac{m^2 v^2 c^2}{m^2 c^4}} = \sqrt{1 - \frac{p^2 c^2}{\mathscr{E}^2}} = \frac{\mathscr{E}_0}{\mathscr{E}}$$

Hence

$$\frac{c}{v} = \frac{1}{\sqrt{1 - (\mathscr{E}_0/\mathscr{E})^2}} = \frac{K + \mathscr{E}_0}{\sqrt{K(2\mathscr{E}_0 + K)}}$$

where $\mathscr{E}_0 = 0.939$ GeV is the rest energy of the proton (see Problem 8.1). The refractive indices for these parts of the spectrum are $n_1 = 1.48$ and $n_2 = 1.51$.

41.2. The ratio $\beta = \dfrac{v}{c} = \dfrac{1}{n \cos \theta} = \dfrac{1}{1.3428 \cos 41°10'}$.   The kinetic energy is

$$K = \mathscr{E} - \mathscr{E}_0 = \mathscr{E}_0 \left(\frac{1}{\sqrt{1 - \beta^2}} - 1 \right)$$

41.4. According to the definition, the group velocity is

$$U = \lim_{\Delta k \to 0} \frac{\Delta \omega}{\Delta k} = \frac{d\omega}{dk} = \frac{1}{\dfrac{dk}{d\omega}}$$

But the wave number is $k = \dfrac{\omega}{u} = \dfrac{n\omega}{c}$. Differentiating, we obtain

$$\frac{dk}{d\omega} = \frac{n}{c} + \frac{\omega}{c} \frac{dn}{d\omega} = \frac{1}{c} \left(n + \omega \frac{dn}{d\omega} \right)$$

Hence

$$U = \frac{c}{n + \omega \dfrac{dn}{d\omega}}$$

41.5. In the region of normal dispersion

$$n^2 = 1 + \frac{\alpha}{\omega_0^2 - \omega^2}, \quad \text{where} \quad \alpha = \frac{e^2 n_0}{\varepsilon_0 m_e}$$

The derivative of the refractive index with respect to the frequency is found by differentiating this equation. We have

$$2n \frac{dn}{d\omega} = - \frac{\alpha}{(\omega_0^2 - \omega^2)^2} (-2\omega) = \frac{2\alpha\omega}{(\omega_0^2 - \omega^2)^2}$$

Therefore

$$\frac{dn}{d\omega} = \frac{\omega}{n} \cdot \frac{\alpha}{(\omega_0^2 - \omega^2)^2} > 0$$

i.e. in the region of normal dispersion the derivative of the refractive index with respect to frequency is everywhere positive.

Now let $\omega_0 > \omega$. Then $n > 1$, and it immediately follows from the formula $U = \dfrac{c}{n + \omega \dfrac{dn}{d\omega}}$ (see the previous problem), that $U < c$.

If $\omega_0 < \omega$, then $n < 1$. Substituting the value of the derivative into the expression for the group velocity, we obtain

$$U = \frac{c}{n + \dfrac{\alpha\omega^2}{n \, (\omega_0^2 - \omega^2)^2}} = \frac{cn}{n^2 + \dfrac{\alpha\omega^2}{(\omega_0^2 - \omega^2)^2}} = \frac{cn}{1 + \dfrac{\alpha\omega_0^2}{(\omega_0^2 - \omega^2)^2}}$$

We see that the number in the denominator of the fraction exceeds unity. And since in this case the refractive index is less than unity, it follows that here too $U < c$.

41.6. Since the free electron concentration in the plasma is small, the second term in formula (63.15) at high frequencies is much less than unity, and the dielectric constant is close to unity. Applying the approximate equality $\sqrt{1+x} = 1 + x/2$ (for $x \ll 1$), we obtain the expression for the refractive index.

The group velocity is found by computing the derivative of the refractive index with respect to frequency:

$$\frac{dn}{d\omega} = \frac{e^2 n_0}{\varepsilon_0 m_e \omega^3}$$

and by substituting this value into the formula for the group velocity. Incidentally, it is easier to apply the last formula of the solution of the previous problem, substituting $\omega = 0$ into it.

41.8. There can be no Cerenkov radiation in a plasma because in a plasma the phase velocity exceeds the velocity of light in a vacuum, and because the particles responsible for the Cerenkov radiation must move with a velocity exceeding the phase velocity of light in the medium.

41.10. The concentration of the valence electrons in aluminium is shown in Table 44.1 (§ 44.2). For the refractive index make use of the result of Problem 41.6.

41.13. The transit time of the light pulse from the toothed wheel to the mirror and back is $\tau = 2l/c$. During this time at $n_1 = 283$ r.p.s. the toothed wheel will turn through k teeth, $k = z\tau/T_1 = z\tau n_1$, where $z = 720$ is the number of teeth on the wheel. In this time the toothed wheel rotating at $n_2 = 313$ r.p.s. will turn through $k + 1$ teeth, so $k + 1 = z\tau n_2$. Subtracting, we obtain $1 = z\tau (n_2 - n_1)$, from which

$$c = 2lz (n_2 - n_1)$$

41.15. Make use of the data in the table of refractive indexes for various wavelengths, choosing the spectral interval between the yellow (5461 Å) and the blue (4861 Å) parts of the spectrum. Substituting $\omega = 2\pi c/n\lambda$ and $k = 2\pi/\lambda$ into the expression for the group velocity

$$U = \frac{\Delta\omega}{\Delta k} = \frac{\omega_2 - \omega_1}{k_2 - k_1}$$

we obtain

$$U = \frac{c (n_1\lambda_1 - n_2\lambda_2)}{n_1 n_2 (\lambda_1 - \lambda_2)}$$

The phase velocity is $u = c/n$.

41.16. Consider the energy balance in the case when light passes through a plate. Suppose a beam of intensity I_0 falls normally on the plate. Part of it will be reflected, the rest, of intensity $I' = TI_0$, where T is the transmittance (Fig. 41.16), will enter the plate. Because of absorption, the intensity of the light which reaches the other face will be $I'' = I'e^{-\mu d}$. Finally, the intensity of light passing out into the air will be $I = TI'' = T^2 I_0 e^{-\mu d}$. Hence

$$\frac{I_1}{I_2} = \frac{T^2 I_0 e^{-\mu d_1}}{T^2 I_0 e^{-\mu d_2}} = e^{\mu(d_2 - d_1)}$$

The half-thickness is $L = (\ln 2)/\mu$ (see Problem 37.9).

47.17. The transmittance of a material layer is the ratio of the intensity of a beam of light passing through the layer to the intensity

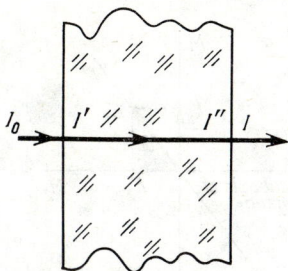

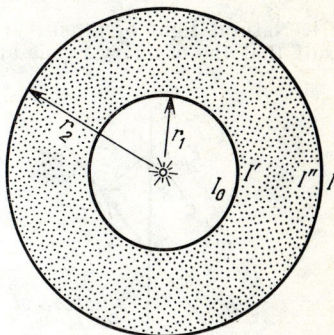

Fig. 41.16.   Fig. 41.17.

of the beam entering the layer: $k = I/I_0$ (Fig. 41.17). In the figure

$$I' = T I_0, \qquad I'' = I' \frac{r_1^2}{r_2^2} e^{-\mu(r_2 - r_1)}, \qquad I = T I'', \qquad T = \frac{4n}{(n+1)^2}$$

Substituting the appropriate data we obtain the result sought.

41.18. Suppose white light of intensity $I_{\text{in}} = A^2$ falls on the light filter. At the resonance wavelength λ_0 the intensity of the transmitted light will be $I_0 = A^2 e^{-\mu_0 d}$. The intensity of transmitted light of other wavelengths will be

$$I = A^2 e^{-\mu d} = A^2 e^{-\mu_0 d} e^{-\alpha d(\lambda_0 - \lambda)^2} = I_0 e^{-\alpha d(\lambda_0 - \lambda)^2}$$

We are interested in the case when

$$I \geqslant I_0/2, \qquad \text{i.e. when} \qquad e^{-\alpha d(\lambda_0 - \lambda)^2} \geqslant 2^{-1}$$

Taking logarithms, we obtain $\alpha d (\lambda_0 - \lambda)^2 \leqslant \ln 2$, giving $\lambda_b = \lambda_0 \pm \sqrt{\dfrac{\ln 2}{\alpha d}}$. The width of the spectral interval is $\Delta \lambda = 2 \sqrt{\dfrac{\ln 2}{\alpha d}}$. The transmittance at the resonance wavelength is $k_0 = I_0/A^2 = e^{-\mu_0 d}$.

41.19. From the law of absorption $I = I_0 \cdot 2^{-d/L}$ we obtain $\dfrac{d}{L} =$

$= \dfrac{\log Z}{\log 2}$, where $z = I_0/I$ is the attenuation of the beam of light.

41.20. The maximum half-thickness is $L_{max} = \dfrac{\ln 2}{\mu_{min}}$, where $\mu_{min} = 44$ m^{-1} is the absorption coefficient at the wavelength of 30×10^{-3} Å.

42. Polarization of Light

42.1. Natural light of intensity I_{in} falls on the polarizer with the result that the ordinary ray is absorbed completely and 10% of the

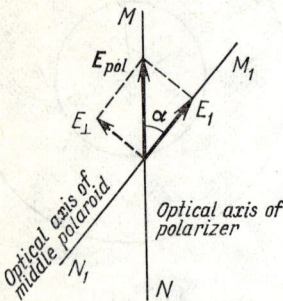

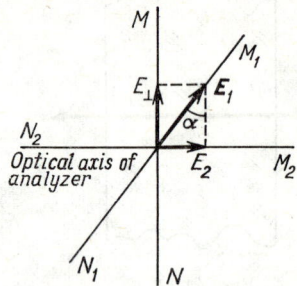

Fig. 42.2a.   Fig. 42.2b.

extraordinary ray is absorbed. Accordingly, the intensity of the polarized light passing out of the polarizer is $I_{pol} = 0.5 I_{in} \times 0.9 = 0.45 I_{in}$. In accordance with the Malus law the intensity of light transmitted by the polarizer will be $I = I_{pol} \cos^2 \alpha$. Since 10% of the light will be absorbed,

$$I_{trans} = 0.9 I_{pol} \cos^2 \alpha = 0.9 \times 0.45 I_{in} \cos^2 \alpha$$

The attenuation of light will be

$$z = \frac{I_{in}}{I_{trans}} = \frac{1}{0.9 \times 0.45 \times \cos^2 \alpha} = \frac{2.5}{\cos^2 \alpha}$$

42.2. The electric field vector of the extraordinary ray transmitted through the polarizer is parallel to the polarizer axis MN (see Fig. 42.2a). Let us resolve this vector into ordinary ray $E_\perp$ and extraordinary ray E_1 with respect to the middle polaroid. This polaroid will transmit only the extraordinary ray with electric field strength $E_1 = E_{pol} \cos \alpha$. Similarly, the analyzer will transmit the extraordinary ray, whose electric field strength is (Fig. 42.2b) $E_2 = E_1 \sin \alpha = E_{pol} \sin \alpha \cos \alpha$. The intensity of the wave is proportional to the square of the field strength vector. Therefore $I = I_{pol} \sin^2 \alpha \cos^2 \alpha$. Noting that the polarizer absorbs **half** the intensity of natural light, we obtain

$$I = \frac{1}{2} I_0 \sin^2 \alpha \cos^2 \alpha = \frac{1}{8} I_0 \sin^2 2\alpha$$

42.3. The frequencies and phases of the ordinary and extraordinary rays are identical, but their electric field vectors are mutually perpendicular, and hence there is no interference pattern.

42.4. The phase difference between the ordinary and the extraordinary rays in a direction perpendicular to the optical axis is

$$\Delta\varphi = \frac{2\pi d}{\lambda_0} - \frac{2\pi d}{\lambda_e} = \frac{2\pi d}{\lambda_0} (n_0 - n_e)$$

Putting $\Delta\varphi = (2m + 1)\,\pi/2$, i.e. equal to that introduced by a quarter-wave plate, we obtain

$$d = \frac{(2m + 1)\,\lambda_0}{4\,(n_0 - n_e)}$$

Knowing the thickness of the plate we find the phase difference for the violet light.

42.5. We have $\Delta\varphi' + \Delta\varphi'' = 0$, or

$$\frac{2\pi d'}{\lambda_0} (n_0' - n_e') + \frac{2\pi d''}{\lambda_0} (n_0'' - n_e'') = 0$$

Hence it follows

$$\frac{d''}{d'} = \frac{n_0' - n_e'}{n_0'' - n_e''}$$

where the prime refers to calcite and a double prime to quartz.

42.7. To brighten the field of view between crossed polaroids one should rotate the plane of oscillations of the light wave by 90°. We have

$$d = (2m + 1)\,\frac{90°}{[\alpha]}$$

43. Geometrical Optics

43.1. The paths of the rays are shown in Fig. 43.1. The separation of the rays is

$$x = OE \cos \alpha = d \cos \alpha\,(\tan \alpha_e - \tan \alpha_0)$$

The angles of refraction may be obtained from the relation

$$\sin \alpha = n_0 \sin \alpha_0 = n_e \sin \alpha_e$$

43.2. It may easily be seen that the angle of incidence of the ray on the second face is equal to the prism angle φ. The red rays will pass out of the prism, if $n_{red} \sin \varphi < 1$; the violet rays will be totally reflected, if $n_{\text{viol}} \sin \varphi \geqslant 1$. Hence it follows that

$$\frac{1}{n_{\text{viol}}} \leqslant \sin \varphi < \frac{1}{n_{\text{red}}}, \qquad 40°48' \leqslant \varphi < 41°30'$$

43.3. The path of the rays is shown in Fig. 43.3. It may easily be

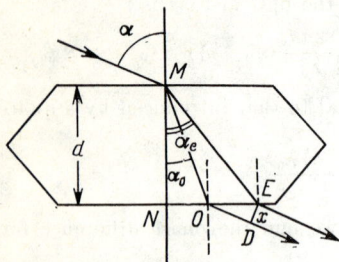

Fig. 43.1.

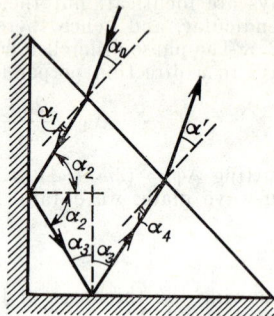

Fig. 43.3.

shown that

$$\alpha_2 = 45° + \alpha_1 \qquad \alpha_3 = 90° - \alpha_2 = 45° - \alpha_1$$
$$\alpha_4 = 45° - \alpha_3 = \alpha_1$$

Hence $\alpha' = \alpha_0$.

43.4. The path of the rays is shown in Fig. 65.2 (§ 65.2). Obviously

$$D = 2d \tan \alpha_{\lim} = \frac{2d}{\sqrt{n^2 - 1}}$$

where d is the depth of the pond.

43.5. The path of the rays is shown in Fig. 43.5. The angle of refraction of glass is $\alpha_2 = \varphi/2$; the angle of incidence α_1 may be found from the condition $n_1 \sin \alpha_1 = n_2 \sin \alpha_2$. The ray will be rotated through an angle $\varepsilon = 2(\alpha_1 - \alpha_2) = 2\alpha_1 - \varphi$.

43.7. The path of the rays is shown in Fig. 43.7*.

43.8. Make use of the diagram of the path of rays of the previous problem and bring the lenses closer together until they are in contact. Then the point F_1 will serve as the object for the system, the point F_2 being its image. Denoting the focal length of the left-hand lens by $a_1 = OF_1 = f_1$, the focal length of the right-hand lens by $a_2 = OF_2 = f_2$, and the focal length of the system by f, we obtain from the thin lens formula

$$\frac{1}{f_1} + \frac{1}{f_2} = \frac{1}{f}$$

---

* The converging and diverging lenses in the path diagrams of rays in this section are shown by symbols, as is the usual practice.

or

$$\Phi = \Phi_1 + \Phi_2$$

43.9. Choose a converging lens with a focal power greater than the magnitude of the focal power of the diverging lens, and using conventional methods find the focal power first of the converging lens and then of the system as a whole. We obtain $\Phi_{\text{div}} = \Phi_{\text{sys}} - \Phi_{\text{con}}$.

43.10. First find the focal power of the glass lens: $\Phi_1 = (n_1 - 1) \times$
$\times \left(\dfrac{1}{R_1} - \dfrac{1}{R_2} \right)$, where $R_1 = 1$ m,
$R_2 = 12$ cm. Then find the focal power of the plano-convex water lens: $\Phi_2 = (n_2 - 1)/R_2$. Finally

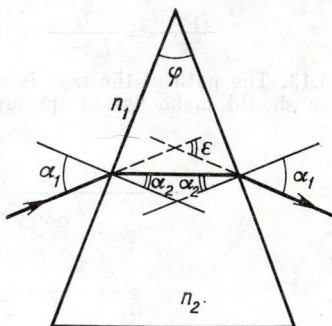

$$\Phi = \Phi_1 + \Phi_2 = \frac{n_1 - 1}{R_1} - \frac{n_1 - n_2}{R_2}$$

43.11. Of course, the required formula may be obtained from the general formula by putting one of the radii of curvature equal to infinity. But this formula may also be obtained independently by

Fig. 43.5.

using the diagram of Fig. 43.11. Here $f = FC \approx FM = h \cot \varphi$. In turn $h = R \sin \alpha$. For the paraxial ray ($h \ll R$) we have $\sin \alpha \approx$

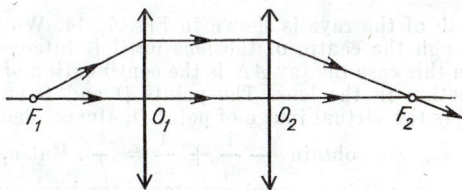

Fig. 43.7.

$\approx \alpha$, $\sin \beta \approx \beta$, $\tan \varphi \approx \varphi$. The law of refraction $n \sin \alpha = \sin \beta$ takes the form $n\alpha = \beta$. But $\beta = \alpha + \varphi$, where $\alpha = h/R$, $\varphi = h/f$. Substituting, we obtain

$$n\alpha = \alpha + \varphi, \quad (n-1)\,\alpha = \varphi, \quad (n-1)\,\frac{h}{R} = \frac{h}{f}, \quad \Phi = \frac{1}{f} = \frac{n-1}{R}$$

43.12. The path of the rays is shown in Fig. 43.12. The ray AB parallel to the optical axis is refracted and travels in the direction BC. Draw $DO_2 \parallel BC$ until it intersects with the focal plane of the second lens at point E. After the ray BC is refracted in the second lens it travels in the direction CE and intersects the principal optical axis of point F.

Denote the distance FO_2 by x. From the similarity of triangles, $\triangle CO_2F \backsim \triangle EF_2F$, $\triangle CO_2F_1 \backsim \triangle O_2F_2E$, we have

$$\frac{CO_2}{x} = \frac{F_2E}{f_2-x}, \qquad \frac{CO_2}{f_1-d} = \frac{F_2E}{f_2}$$

Dividing the first equation by the second, we obtain

$$\frac{f_1-d}{x} = \frac{f_2}{f_2-x}, \qquad \text{giving} \qquad x = \frac{f_2(f_1-d)}{f_1+f_2-d}$$

43.13. The path of the rays is shown in Fig. 43.13. To find x and h one should make use of the similarity of triangles.

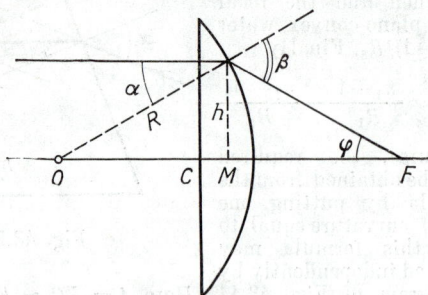

Fig. 43.11.

43.14. The path of the rays is shown in Fig. 43.14. We pass the ray $ON \parallel AB$ through the centre of the lens until it intersects with the focal plane. In this case the ray AN is the continuation of the ray MA after its refraction in the lens. The points D and B are conjugate; for instance B is the virtual image of point D. Hence, denoting $OB = a_1$, $OD = a_2$, we obtain $-\frac{1}{a_1} + \frac{1}{a_2} = \frac{1}{f}$. But $a_1 = R \cot \alpha$, $a_2 = R \cot \beta$, where R is the semidiameter of the lens, and we obtain

$$\tan \beta = \tan \alpha + \frac{R}{f}$$

43.15. The lateral magnification is $\beta = \frac{h'}{h} = \frac{a'}{a} = \frac{f}{a-f}$. The longitudinal magnification is $\alpha = x'/x$ (see Fig. 43.15). To calculate it, write the thin lens formula in the form

$$\frac{1}{a-x} + \frac{1}{a'+x'} = \frac{1}{f}, \qquad \text{hence} \qquad a'+x' = \frac{f(a-x)}{a-f-x}$$

But $a' = af/(a-f)$; therefore

$$x' = \frac{f(a-x)}{a-f-x} - \frac{af}{a-f} = \frac{xf^2}{(a-f)(a-f-x)}$$

Hence the longitudinal magnification is

$$\alpha = \frac{x'}{x} = \frac{f^2}{(a-f)(a-f-x)} = \frac{\beta^2(a-f)}{a-f-x} = \frac{\beta^2}{1-x/(a-f)}$$

For small longitudinal dimensions of the body ($x \ll a - f$) the longitudinal magnification is $\alpha = \beta^2$.

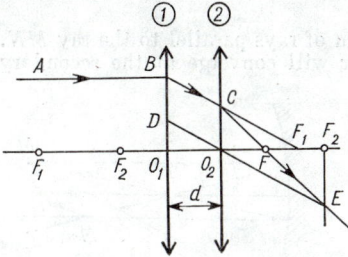

Fig. 43.12.

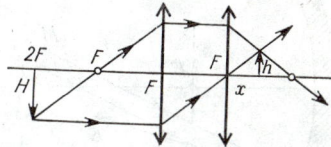

Fig. 43.13.

43.16. For $a = 2f$ the lateral magnification is $\beta = 1$ and the longitudinal magnification is $\alpha = \dfrac{1}{1-r/f}$, where r is the radius of the ball.

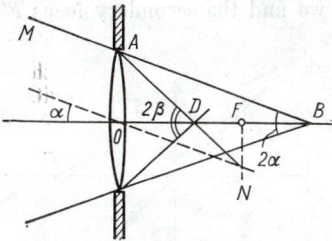

Fig. 43.14.

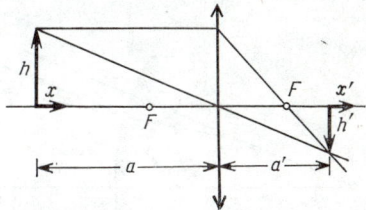

Fig. 43.15.

As can be seen, the longitudinal dimension of the image is greater than the lateral dimension, so the ball will look like an elongated rotational ellipsoid.

43.17. The focal length of a lens, both faces of which have identical radii of curvature, is $f = R/2 \, (n - 1)$. The chromatic aberration is

$$\Delta = f_{\text{red}} - f_{\text{viol}} = \frac{R}{2} \cdot \frac{n_{\text{viol}} - n_{\text{red}}}{(n_{\text{viol}} - 1)(n_{\text{red}} - 1)}$$

The ratio of the chromatic aberration to the average focal length is

$$\frac{\Delta}{f_{\text{av}}} = \frac{2(n_{\text{viol}} - n_{\text{red}})}{n_{\text{viol}} + n_{\text{red}} - 2}$$

43.18. The focal power of the mirror is $\Phi_1 = 2/R$. The focal power of the plano-convex lens containing water is $\Phi_2 = (n-1)/R$. The focal power of the system is $\Phi = \Phi_1 + 2\Phi_2$, since the light passes through the water twice. Hence

$$\Phi = \frac{2}{R} + \frac{2(n-1)}{R} = \frac{2n}{R}$$

43.19. *First solution.* Consider a beam of rays parallel to the ray MN. The beam reflected from the mirror will converge at the secondary

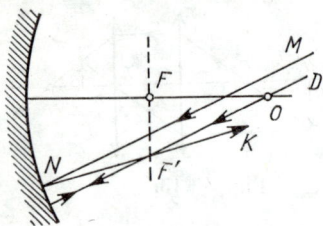

Fig. 43.19b.

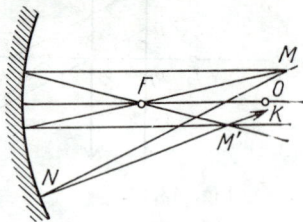

Fig. 43.19c.

focus F', which lies in the focal plane. Drawing the ray $DO \parallel MN$ parallel to the centre of the mirror, we find the secondary focus F'.

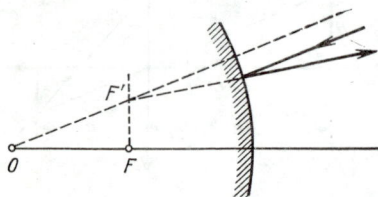

Fig. 43.20b.

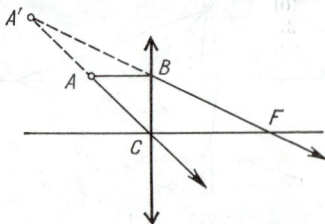

Fig. 43.21b.

The ray NK is the one we are looking for (Fig. 43.19b).

Second solution. Choose an arbitrary point M on the ray MN and with the aid of characteristic rays construct its image M'. The required ray NK passes through this point (see Fig. 43.19c).

43.20. The paths of the rays are shown in Fig. 43.20b.

43.21. The paths of the rays are shown in Fig. 43.21b. First draw the ray AA' until it intersects with the principal optical axis and find the centre of the lens C. Since the virtual image is magnified, the lens is convex. Draw the ray AB parallel to the principal optical axis. It is refracted by the lens so that it passes through its focus and

its continuation passes through the virtual image. The ray $A'B$ intersects the principal optical axis at point F, the focus of the lens.

43.22. The paths of the rays are shown in Fig. 43.22b.

43.23. The problem is solved in exactly the same way as Problem 10.4,
since the law of reflection is the
same in each case. We obtain the
result that a parabolic mirror focuses a beam of any width at its
focal point not only a paraxial
beam. This implies the absence of
spherical aberration.

43.24. Since ideal point sources do
not exist it is impossible to obtain
an ideally parallel beam. But for
practical purposes an almost parallel beam may be obtained. Take
into account the part played by
diffraction as well.

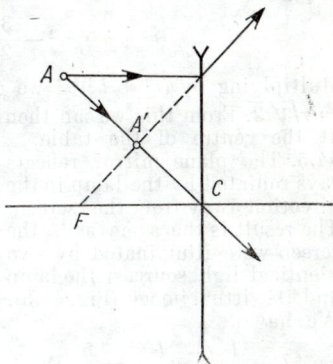

Fig. 43.22b.

44. Optical Instruments

44.1. At a wavelength of 555
nm the luminous flux corresponding
to a radiation power of 1.0 W is 683 lm. Hence we can find the power
of the flux of 1200 lm. To find the power of an identical luminous flux
at other wavelengths the value obtained should be divided by the
relative spectral sensitivity of the human eye also called visibility
factor (see § 66.1, Fig. 66.1).

44.2. To find the amplitude of the electric field strength, we can make
use of the expression for the intensity of a wave (59.8) from § 59.1:
$I = \overline{EH} = E_M H_M/2$, since a monochromatic wave is a sinusoidal
one. But $\mu_0 H^2 = \varepsilon_0 E^2$, so the wave intensity is $I = 1/2 E_M^2 \sqrt{\varepsilon_0/\mu_0}$.
On the other hand, the intensity of the wave is the power per unit
area:

$$I = \frac{P}{4\pi r^2} = \frac{\Phi}{683 K_\lambda \times 4\pi r^2} = \frac{I}{683 K_\lambda r^2}$$

Here I is the luminous intensity and K_λ is the relative spectral sensitivity of the human eye.

The magnetic field induction is found from the relation

$$B = \mu_0 H = \mu_0 E \sqrt{\varepsilon_0/\mu_0} = E \sqrt{\varepsilon_0 \mu_0} = E/c$$

44.4. The illuminance near the edge of the table is $E = \dfrac{I \cos \alpha}{R^2} =$
$= \dfrac{Ih}{(r^2 + h^2)^{3/2}}$, where h is the elevation of the lamp above the centre
of the table. Let us find the maximum of the function obtained. The

condition for a maximum is

$$\frac{d}{dh}\left[\frac{h}{(r^2+h^2)^{3/2}}\right]=0$$

We have

$$(r^2+h^2)^{-3/2}-\frac{3}{2}\,h\,(r^2+h^2)^{-5/2}\cdot 2h=0$$

Multiplying by $(r^2+h^2)^{5/2}$ we obtain $-3h^2+r^2+h^2=0$, so $h=$ $=r/\sqrt{2}$. From this we can then find the illuminance at the edge and at the centre of the table.

44.5. The plane mirror reflects rays radiated by the lamp in the direction away from the screen. The result is the same as if the screen were illuminated by two identical light sources: the lamp and its virtual image (Fig. 44.5). We have

$$E=\frac{I}{d^2}+\frac{I}{(2d)^2}=\frac{5}{4}\,E_0$$

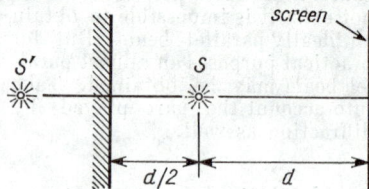

Fig. 44.5.

44.6. The luminous intensity of the lamp is expressed in terms of its brightness and the diameter of the sphere: $I=BS=\pi BD^2/4$. The illuminance at the point directly under each lamp is the sum of illu-

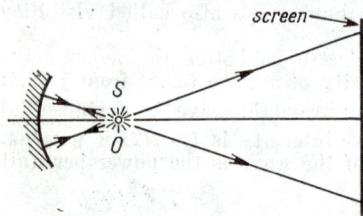

Fig. 44.7.

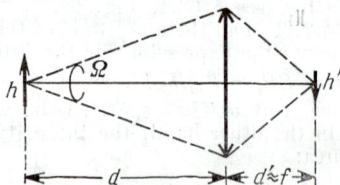

Fig. 44.8.

minances produced by this lamp and by the two adjacent lamps. The illuminance at the midpoint is the sum of illuminances produced by two adjacent lamps. The illuminances produced by the other lamps are very small and can be neglected.

44.7. The maximum illuminance will be at a point on the principal axis of the optical system (Fig. 44.7). In this case of a sufficiently narrow beam of light the role of the concave mirror is to double the luminous flux falling on the screen. Therefore, if the mirror is withdrawn, the illuminance will decrease by one half.

44.8. If the object is removed far from the lens, its image lies practically in the focal plane. The magnification is $\beta=h'/h=d'/d=f/d$.

The illuminance of the image is equal to the luminous flux $\Phi = I\Omega$ divided by the area of the image $S' = \pi h'^2/4$. Noting that the solid angle is $\Omega = \pi D^2/4d^2$, where D is the diameter of the lens, we obtain

$$E = \frac{\Phi}{S'} = \frac{4\pi D^2 I}{4\pi d^2 h'^2} = \frac{D^2 I d^2}{d^2 h^2 f^2} = \frac{I}{h^2} \cdot \frac{D^2}{f^2}$$

But $B = 4I/\pi h^2$ is the brightness of the object and $R = \pi B = 4I/h^2$ is its luminance. We have $E = \frac{R}{4} \cdot \frac{D^2}{f^2}$, where D^2/f^2 is the focal power of the lens. Note that we have neglected the light losses in the lens.

44.9. According to the sign convention formulated in § 65.6, the focal length f of diverging lens and the distance d' from the virtual image are both negative. Without the lens the luminous flux is distributed over an area $S_0 = \pi D_0^2/4$. With the lens the same flux is distributed over an area $S = \pi D^2/4$ (Fig. 44.9). Therefore $E/E_0 =$

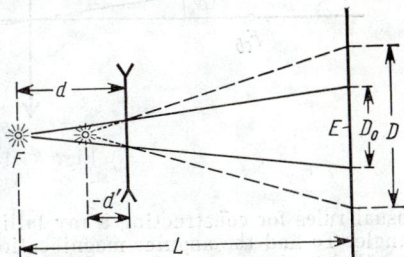

Fig. 44.9.

$= D_0^2/D^2$. But $D_0 = \varphi L/d$ and $D = \dfrac{\varphi(L - d - d')}{-d'}$, where φ is the lens diame-

ter. In our problem $d' = -f$, so $-\dfrac{1}{f} + \dfrac{1}{d'} = \dfrac{1}{f}$, i.e. $d' = f/2$. We have

$$\frac{D_0}{D} = \frac{L}{2L + f} \quad \text{and} \quad \frac{E}{E_0} = \frac{L^2}{(2L + f)^2}$$

44.10. For a short-sighted eye $\dfrac{1}{\Delta'} + \dfrac{1}{d'} = \Phi'$, where $\Delta' = 9$ cm, d' is the distance between the optical centre of the eye and the retina, and Φ' is the focal power of the eye. To correct the eye-sight, glasses with lens power Φ should be worn. We have $\dfrac{1}{\Delta} + \dfrac{1}{d'} = \Phi' + \Phi$, where $\Delta = 25$ cm. Subtracting the first equality from the second we find the focal power of the glasses:

$$\Phi = \frac{1}{\Delta} - \frac{1}{\Delta'}$$

44.11. From the Rayleigh criterion $\sin \theta = \lambda/D$ we obtain for a small angle

$$\theta = \frac{\lambda}{D} = \frac{555 \times 10^{-9} \times 180° \times 3600''}{2 \times 10^{-3}} = 57'' \approx 1'$$

(cf. § 66.4).

44.15. The paths of the rays are shown in Fig. 44.15. The ray coming from a distant source at a viewing angle α_0 should produce a real image h in the focal plane of the objective. But the eyepiece (ocular) is placed in its way, and the ray experiences secondary refraction, leaving the eyepiece at a viewing angle α. To find this we apply the

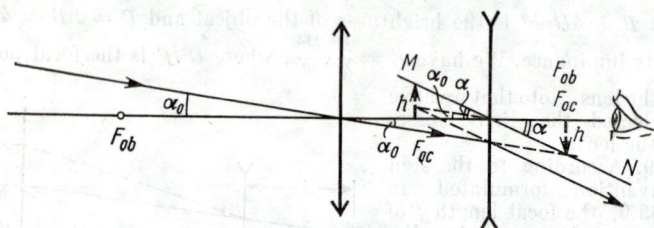

Fig. 44.15.

usual rules for constructing a ray falling on the lens at an arbitrary angle. To find the angular magnification we draw a straight line MN parallel to the ray and obtain a segment h in the left-hand focal plane of the eyepiece.

Clearly, $\tan \alpha_0 = \dfrac{h}{|f_{ob}|}$, $\tan \alpha = \dfrac{h}{|f_{oc}|}$ and for small angles

$$\gamma = \frac{\alpha}{\alpha_0} = \left| \frac{f_{ob}}{f_{oc}} \right|$$

44.18. The ratio of the velocity of the ray across the negative to the velocity of the runner is the same as the ratio of the dimensions of

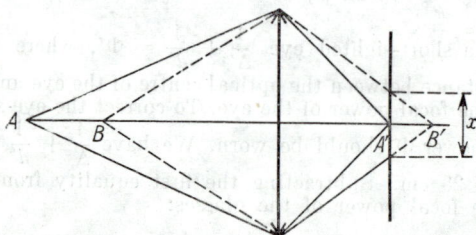

Fig. 44.19.

the image to that of the object. Denoting the lateral magnification by β, we obtain $v_{neg} = \beta v = v \dfrac{d'}{d} = v \dfrac{f}{d} = \dfrac{v}{\Phi d}$, since when the focal power of the objective is high the image will lie practically in the focal plane. The exposure time is found by dividing the blurring of the image by the velocity obtained: $\tau = \dfrac{x}{v_{neg}} = \dfrac{x\Phi d}{v}$.

44.19. A schematic diagram of the path of the rays is shown in Fig. 44.19. Suppose the image of a point A on the negative is sharp. Then the image on the negative of point B which is closer to the lens will be a small dot of width x. Let the distance from point A to the lens be a, and the distance from point B to the lens be b.

Then $a' = \dfrac{af}{a-f}$ and $b' = \dfrac{bf}{b-f}$. Obviously $\dfrac{x}{\varphi} = \dfrac{b'-a'}{b'}$, where φ is the diameter of the diaphragm. Hence $\varphi = \dfrac{xb'}{b'-a'} =$

$= \dfrac{bx(a-f)}{f(a-b)} = \dfrac{bx(a\Phi - 1)}{a-b}$.

44.20. First one should estimate the apparent depth of the pond d_1 (Fig. 44.20). Evidently

$d_1 = l \cot \beta$, $d = l \cot \alpha$ and $\dfrac{d_1}{d} = \dfrac{\tan \alpha}{\tan \beta}$

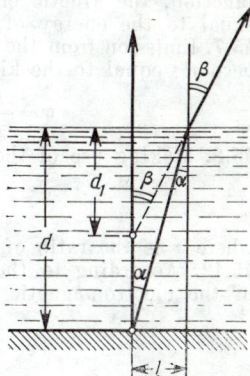

Fig. 44.20.

For small angles $\tan \alpha \approx \sin \alpha$, so $d_1 = \dfrac{d \sin \alpha}{\sin \beta} = \dfrac{d}{n}$. From the thin lens formula we obtain $\dfrac{1}{d_1} + \dfrac{1}{d'} = \dfrac{1}{f}$. Therefore the required distance between the objective lens and the film is

$$d' = df/(d - nf)$$

45. Photons

45.1. The total energy radiated by the Sun per unit time is $N = 4\pi J R^2$, where J is the solar constant and R is the radius of the Earth's orbit. The total emissive power of the Sun is

$$E_T = \frac{N}{4\pi R_\odot^2} = \frac{J R^2}{R_\odot^2}$$

where $R_\odot$ is the Sun's radius. Assuming the Sun to radiate as a black body, we obtain

$$E_T = \sigma T^4, \quad \text{whence} \quad T = \sqrt[4]{J R^2 / \sigma R_\odot^2}$$

45.4. The intensity of a wave is equal to the energy transmitted through unit area per unit time. We have

$$I = \frac{4Nh\nu}{\pi D^2} = \frac{4Nhc}{\pi \lambda D^2}$$

where N is the number of photons per unit time and D is the diameter of the pupil.

The power of the source is $P = 4\pi r^2 I$, where r is the distance from the source to the eye.

45.6. Since the energy of a gamma-quantum greatly exceeds the work function, the kinetic energy of a photoelectron will be practically equal to the energy of the photon, $K = hc/\lambda$.

45.7. Emission from the cathode will stop when the cut-off potential becomes equal to the kinetic energy (in electron-volts):

$$\varphi = \frac{K}{e} = \frac{h\nu - A_0}{e} = \frac{hc}{e\lambda} - \varphi_0$$

45.8. Making use of the result of the previous problem, we obtain

$$\varphi_0 = \frac{hc\,(x\lambda_1 - \lambda_2)}{e\lambda_1\lambda_2\,(x-1)}$$

where x is the ratio of cut-off potentials.

45.12. According to the Doppler effect (see § 59.8), the frequency of the electromagnetic wave in the laboratory reference frame is

$$\omega = \omega_0\,\frac{\sqrt{1 - \beta^2}}{1 - \beta\cos\theta}$$

where ω_0 is the proper frequency of the wave. But the energy and the momentum of a photon are proportional to the frequency of the wave $\mathscr{E} = \hbar\omega$ and $p = \hbar\omega/c$. Therefore the ratio between the energies (and the momenta) in the laboratory and in the source reference frames will be expressed by the same formula.

45.13. In the case of normal incidence of photons on the mirror surface, the light pressure is expressed by the formula $p = 2nh\nu/c = 2w$, where w is the volume energy density of the incident light. The factor 2 is due to the reversal of the momentum of a photon in the act of reflection. When the angle of incidence of photons is α, the *normal* component of the momentum undergoes a change of sign. The expression for the light pressure is $p = 2w\cos\alpha$.

Fig. 45.14.

45.14. The energy of a laser light is $\mathscr{E}$ and its momentum is $p = \mathscr{E}/c$. This momentum is transferred to the system (Fig. 45.14) and by the law of conservation of momentum $mv = p = \dfrac{\mathscr{E}}{c}$. By the law of conservation of energy $\dfrac{mv^2}{2} = mgl\,(1 - \cos\alpha)$, so $v = \sqrt{4gl\sin^2\dfrac{\alpha}{2}}$.

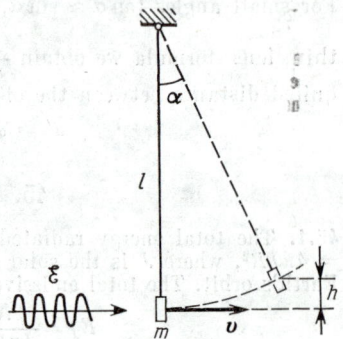

The energy of a laser light is

$$\mathcal{E} = mvc = mc \sqrt{4gl \sin^2 \frac{\alpha}{2}}$$

45.15. The force of light pressure on an absolute black spherical particle of radius r is

$$F_{\text{light}} = \pi r^2 w = \pi r^2 I/c$$

where I is the intensity of the electromagnetic wave at the given point. The gravitational force is

$$F_{\text{grav}} = \frac{\gamma m M_\odot}{R^2} = \frac{4\pi\gamma\rho r^3 M_\odot}{3R^2}$$

where R is the distance of the particle from the Sun. It follows from the equality of forces that

$$r = 3IR^2/4\gamma\rho c M_\odot$$

But $IR^2 = JR_0^2$, where J is the solar constant and R_0 is the distance from the Earth to the Sun. Hence

$$r = 3JR_0^2/4\gamma\rho c M_\odot$$

45.16. The shift in the wavelength in the Compton effect is $\Delta\lambda = \lambda' - \lambda = 2\lambda_C \sin^2 (\theta/2)$, where θ is the photon scattering angle. Substituting $\lambda = hc/\mathcal{E}$ and $\lambda_C = h/m_e c$, we obtain

$$\frac{hc}{\mathcal{E}'} - \frac{hc}{\mathcal{E}} = \frac{2h}{m_e c} \sin^2 \frac{\theta}{2}, \quad \text{or} \quad \frac{1}{\mathcal{E}'} - \frac{1}{\mathcal{E}} = \frac{2 \sin^2 (\theta/2)}{\mathcal{E}_0}$$

where $\mathcal{E}_0 = m_e c^2$ is the rest energy of the electron. In the course of the collision of the photon with the electron the latter acquires an energy

$$\Delta\mathcal{E} = \mathcal{E} - \mathcal{E}' = \frac{2\mathcal{E}^2 \sin^2 (\theta/2)}{\mathcal{E}_0 + 2\mathcal{E} \sin^2 (\theta/2)}$$

45.17. The problem can be solved with the aid of the laws of conservation of energy and the momentum (Fig. 45.17):

$$\mathcal{E}_{\text{ph}} + \mathcal{E}_0 = \mathcal{E}'_{\text{ph}} + \sqrt{\mathcal{E}_0^2 + p^2 c^2}$$

$$\frac{\mathcal{E}_{\text{ph}}}{c} = \frac{\mathcal{E}'_{\text{ph}}}{c} \cos\theta + p\cos\alpha, \quad 0 = \frac{\mathcal{E}'_{\text{ph}}}{c} \sin\theta - p\sin\alpha$$

where $\mathcal{E}_{\text{ph}}$ and $\mathcal{E}'_{\text{ph}}$ are photon energies prior to and after its collision with the electron, and $\mathcal{E}_0$ and p are the rest energy and the momentum of the electron. The unknown quantities $\mathcal{E}'_{\text{ph}}$ and p can be eliminated from this system, and we obtain

$$\mathcal{E}'_{\text{ph}} = pc \sin\alpha/\sin\theta$$

This gives a system of two equations:

$$\mathcal{E}_{\text{ph}} + \mathcal{E}_0 = \frac{pc \sin\alpha}{\sin\theta} + \sqrt{\mathcal{E}_0^2 + p^2 c^2}, \quad \mathcal{E}_{\text{ph}} = \frac{pc \sin(\alpha + \theta)}{\sin\theta}$$

Eliminating the momentum p of the recoil electron from this system, we obtain

$$\mathscr{E}_{\mathrm{ph}} + \mathscr{E}_0 = \frac{\mathscr{E}_{\mathrm{ph}} \sin \alpha}{\sin (\alpha + \theta)} + \sqrt{\mathscr{E}_0^2 + \frac{\mathscr{E}_{\mathrm{ph}}^2 \sin^2 \theta}{\sin^2 (\alpha + \theta)}}$$

After tedious but simple transformations, we obtain the desired expression for the energy of the photon prior to collision.

45.18. Since we are interested in the minimum energy of photons for which the formation of Compton recoil electrons with the specified

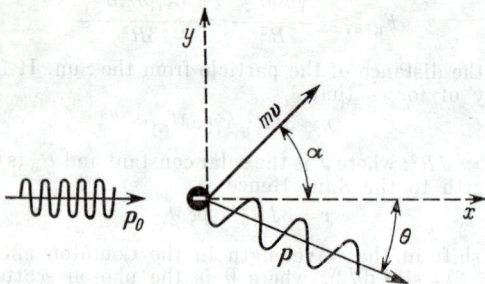

Fig. 45.17.

momentum is possible, we must consider the case of central impact, as in this case the momentum transmitted from the photon to the electron is a maximum. From the laws of conservation of energy and the momentum

$$\mathscr{E}_{\mathrm{ph}} + \mathscr{E}_0 = \mathscr{E}_{\mathrm{ph}}' + \sqrt{\mathscr{E}_0^2 + p^2 c^2}, \qquad \frac{\mathscr{E}_{\mathrm{ph}}}{c} = -\frac{\mathscr{E}_{\mathrm{ph}}'}{c} + p$$

we obtain the expression for the photon energy:

$$\mathscr{E}_{\mathrm{ph}} = \frac{1}{2} \left(pc - \mathscr{E}_0 + \sqrt{\mathscr{E}_0^2 + p^2 c^2} \right)$$

On the other hand, the momentum of the electron may be determined from the curvature of its track: $p = eBR$ (see § 41.2). The photon energy is

$$\mathscr{E}_{\mathrm{ph}} = \frac{1}{2} \left(ecBR - \mathscr{E}_0 + \sqrt{\mathscr{E}_0^2 + e^2 c^2 B^2 R^2} \right)$$

45.19. Suppose the stationary electron absorbs a photon with energy $\mathscr{E}_{\mathrm{ph}}$ and momentum $p_{\mathrm{ph}} = \mathscr{E}_{\mathrm{ph}}/c$. The laws of conservation of energy and momentum in this case can be written thus:

$$\mathscr{E}_{\mathrm{ph}} + \mathscr{E}_0 = \sqrt{\mathscr{E}_0^2 + p^2 c^2}, \qquad \frac{\mathscr{E}_{\mathrm{ph}}}{c} = p$$

Eliminating the energy of a photon we obtain $\mathscr{E}_0 + pc = \sqrt{\mathscr{E}_0^2 + p^2 c^2}$. After squaring and gathering like terms we obtain $2pc\mathscr{E}_0 = 0$, which is impossible. This proves that the assumption that the electron absorbed a photon was false.

45.20. The easiest way to solve the problem is to adopt an inertial reference frame in which the electron is at rest. Indeed, if a photon is in some reference frame, it is also in any other frame, although its energy and momentum are different in different frames (see Problem 45.12). Therefore for the purpose of solving the problem one can choose the reference frame in which the electron is at rest. But the mass (and the internal energy) of an electron at rest are a minimum. To emit a photon the electron must spend some of its internal energy, and its mass must become less than the minimum. Therefore the emission of a photon by an electron at rest contravenes the law of conservation of energy. The same conclusion remains valid in any other inertial reference frame.

45.21. In principle, the photon may be detected at arbitrary points behind the screen, but with different probabilities. If the counter is placed a long way from the slit, in a direction making an angle θ with the normal to the screen, the probability of the photon entering the counter will be proportional to the volume of the counter and to the intensity of the light wave corresponding to the photon. This intensity is expressed by the formula

$$I = I_0 \frac{\sin^2 \alpha}{\alpha^2}, \quad \text{where} \quad \alpha = \frac{\pi D \sin \theta}{\lambda}$$

(see § 57.9.) Expressing the wavelength in terms of the energy of a photon we obtain the expression for the probability of detecting a photon:

$$w \propto V_0 \frac{\sin^2 \alpha}{\alpha^2}, \quad \text{where} \quad \alpha = \frac{\pi D \mathscr{E} \sin \theta}{hc}$$

45.22. For a system of N slits each of width D spaced at a distance d, the probability of detecting a photon in a specified region is proportional to the intensity of the respective sinusoidal wave passing through the diffraction grating. It is substantially different from the probability of detecting at the same point a photon which had only one slit to pass through. Using the results of §§ 57.6-57.9, we can write the probability sought in the form

$$w \propto V_0 \frac{\sin^2 \alpha}{\alpha^2} \cdot \frac{\sin^2 N\beta}{\sin^2 \beta}$$

where V_0 is the volume of the counter, and the auxiliary angles α and β are expressed in terms of energy of a photon in the following way:

$$\alpha = \frac{\pi D \mathscr{E} \sin \theta}{hc}, \quad \beta = \frac{\pi d \mathscr{E} \sin \theta}{hc}$$

45.23. The photon will either pass through the polaroid, or it will be absorbed by it. The probability of a photon passing through the polaroid is $w_{pas} = \cos^2 \alpha$, while the probability of it being absorbed is $w_{abs} = \sin^2 \alpha$, where α is the angle between the optical axis of the polaroid and the direction of the electric field vector of the electromagnetic wave corresponding to the photon.

45.24. Prior to collision, the electron and the photon fly head-on towards each other; after collision they will move in the initial direction of the electron's motion. The laws of conservation of energy and the momentum will assume the form

$$p - \frac{h\nu}{c} = p' + \frac{h\nu'}{c}, \qquad \mathcal{E} + h\nu = \mathcal{E}' + h\nu'$$

Hence it follows

$$\mathcal{E} + pc = \mathcal{E}' + p'c + 2h\nu', \qquad \mathcal{E} - pc + 2h\nu = \mathcal{E}' - p'c$$

Multiplying, we obtain

$$\mathcal{E}^2 - p^2c^2 + 2h\nu\,(\mathcal{E} + pc) = \mathcal{E}'^2 - p'^2c^2 + 2h\nu'\,(\mathcal{E}' - p'c)$$

But $\mathcal{E}^2 - p^2c^2 = \mathcal{E}'^2 - p'^2c^2 = \mathcal{E}_0^2$. Hence

$$h\nu\,(\mathcal{E} + pc) = h\nu'\,(\mathcal{E}' - p'c), \quad \text{or} \quad h\nu\,(\mathcal{E} + pc) = h\nu'\,(\mathcal{E} - pc + 2h\nu)$$

Multiplying both sides of the equation by the expression $\mathcal{E} + pc$, we obtain

$$h\nu\,(\mathcal{E} + pc)^2 = h\nu'\,[\mathcal{E}_0^2 + 2h\nu\,(\mathcal{E} + pc)]$$

But in the ultra-relativistic case $\mathcal{E} \approx pc$ (see Problem 8.12). Hence

$$h\nu' = \frac{4\mathcal{E}^2 h\nu}{\mathcal{E}_0^2 + 4\mathcal{E}h\nu}$$

46. Elementary Quantum Mechanics

46.1. The kinetic energy of a particle is $K = \mathcal{E} - \mathcal{E}_0 = \sqrt{\mathcal{E}_0^2 + p^2c^2} - \mathcal{E}_0$ from which we obtain for the momentum $p = \frac{1}{c}\sqrt{K\,(2\mathcal{E}_0 + K)}$, and for the de Broglie wave

$$\lambda = \frac{h}{p} = \frac{hc}{\sqrt{K\,(2\mathcal{E}_0 + K)}}$$

For $K \ll \mathcal{E}_0$, we obtain the nonrelativistic approximation:

$$\lambda_{nonrel} = \frac{hc}{\sqrt{2\mathcal{E}_0 K}} = \frac{h}{\sqrt{2mK}}$$

The error due to the substitution of the nonrelativistic formula for the relativistic one is

$$\delta = \frac{\lambda_{nonrel} - \lambda}{\lambda} = \sqrt{\frac{2\mathcal{E}_0 + K}{2\mathcal{E}_0}} - 1, \quad \text{which gives}$$

$$\frac{K}{2\mathcal{E}_0} = (1 + \delta)^2 - 1 \approx 2\delta$$

since $\delta \ll 1$. Hence, the error introduced by the substitution of the nonrelativistic formula for the relativistic one will be less than δ, if $K \ll 4\delta\mathscr{E}_0$.

46.2. The kinetic energy of the particle is equal to its charge multiplied by the accelerating potential: $K = e\varphi$. Substituting this value for the kinetic energy into the formulae obtained in the previous problem, we express the de Broglie wavelength in terms of the accelerating potential.

46.3. We use the expression for the resolving power of a microscope (§ 66.8), putting $\sin u = 0.02$. We can find the wavelength from the nonrelativistic formula, since the kinetic energy of the electron of 10 keV is much less than its rest energy which is 510 keV.

46.4. If one assumes the apertures of the electron microscope and the ion projector to be approximately equal, the difference in the resolving powers will be determined by the difference in the wavelength. Assuming the accelerating potentials to be approximately equal as well, we see that the difference in the wavelengths is due mainly to the difference in the masses of the accelerated particles, the mass of the electron being about three orders of magnitude less than that of the ions.

46.5. The de Broglie wavelength for these electrons is $\lambda = h/\sqrt{2me\varphi} = 12.25/\sqrt{15} = 3.2$ Å. The first-order diffraction minimum is observed at an angle θ such that $\sin \theta = \lambda/D$, where D is the width of the slit (§ 57.9). Since the angle is very small the width of the principal maximum is

$$x = 2l \tan \theta = 2l\lambda/D$$

46.6. Using the Bragg law for the first-order maximum (see § 62.7), find the de Broglie wavelength for neutrons: $\lambda = 2d \sin \alpha$, where α is the glancing angle. From the wavelength we find the kinetic energy of neutrons (see Problem 46.1), their velocity and the corresponding temperature:

$$K = \frac{h^2}{2m\lambda^2}, \quad v = \frac{h}{m\lambda}, \quad T = \frac{h^2}{3mk\lambda^2}$$

46.7. The root-mean-square momentum of the molecule may be found from the condition $\frac{3}{2} kT = \overline{p^2}/2m$, from which $p_{\text{r.m.s.}} = \sqrt{3mkT}$ and the de Broglie wavelength $\overline{\lambda} = \dfrac{h}{p_{\text{r.m.s.}}} = \dfrac{h}{\sqrt{3mkT}}$.

46.8. (1) At the accelerating potential $\varphi_1 = 10^2$ V the electron is a nonrelativistic particle. Its momentum is $p_1 = \sqrt{2me\varphi_1}$ and the velocity is $v_1 = \sqrt{2e\varphi_1/m}$. But the group velocity of the de Broglie wave is equal to the particle's velocity: $U_1 = v_1$. The phase velocity is

$$u_1 = \frac{c^2}{v_1} = c^2 \sqrt{\frac{m}{2e\varphi_1}}$$

(2) At the accelerating potential $\varphi_2 = 10^5$ V the electron is a relativistic particle. Its momentum is found from the condition $\sqrt{\mathscr{E}_0^2 + p^2 c^2} = \mathscr{E}_0 + e\varphi_2$, from which it follows that $p_2 = \dfrac{1}{c}\sqrt{e\varphi_2\,(2\mathscr{E}_0 + e\varphi_2)}$. The mass is found from the condition $m_2 c^2 = \mathscr{E}_0 + e\varphi_2$, whence $m_2 = \dfrac{1}{c^2}\,(\mathscr{E}_0 + e\varphi_2)$. The group velocity is

$$U_2 = v_2 = \frac{p_2}{m_2} = \frac{c\,\sqrt{e\varphi_2\,(2\mathscr{E}_0 + e\varphi_2)}}{\mathscr{E}_0 + e\varphi_2}$$

The phase velocity is

$$u_2 = \frac{c^2}{v_2} = \frac{c\,(\mathscr{E}_0 + e\varphi_2)}{\sqrt{e\varphi_2\,(2\mathscr{E}_0 + e\varphi_2)}}$$

Note that in this case the energy is conveniently expressed not in joules, but in kiloelectron-volts, since $\mathscr{E}_0 = 510$ keV.

46.9. For a particle in the ground state one de Broglie half-wave fits into the length of the potential well: $L = \lambda/2$. The momentum of the particle is $p = h/\lambda = h/2L$. The recoil of the particle from the wall of the well is perfectly elastic, so the change in its momentum is $\Delta p = 2p = h/L$. The average force of pressure is equal to the product of the change in the momentum variation and the number of collisions per unit time:

$$F_{\mathrm{av}} = \Delta p \cdot z = 2p\,\frac{v}{2L} = \frac{p^2}{mL} = \frac{h^2}{4mL^3}$$

46.10. The energy of a particle is $\mathscr{E}_n = \dfrac{p^2}{2m} = \dfrac{n^2 h^2}{8mL^2}$, where the quantum number n, according to the conditions of the problem, assumes the values 1, 2, 3.

46.11. The zero-point energy is $\mathscr{E}_0 = 1/2 h\nu$. The energy of the first excited state is $\mathscr{E}_1 = \dfrac{3}{2} h\nu$, so the excitation energy is $\Delta\mathscr{E} = \mathscr{E}_1 - \mathscr{E}_0 = h\nu$. The vibrational degrees of freedom will no longer be excited when the energy of thermal motion becomes less than the excitation energy. The usual criterion is $\dfrac{3}{2} kT \leqslant h\nu$, which yields the minimum temperature

$$T_{\mathrm{vib}} = 2h\nu/3k = 4 \times 10^3 \text{ K}$$

This does not agree with experiment, since the lines of the vibrational spectrum of hydrogen molecules are observed at lower temperatures.

This is because of the Maxwellian molecular speed distribution (see § 25.2), which shows that a gas contains molecules whose speeds are far in excess of the average. For instance, about 2% of the molecules have speeds three times greater than the average. The energy of such molecules is more than 9 times the average kinetic energy.

46.12. The kinetic energy of an orbiting electron is $K = \frac{1}{2} m_e v^2 = \frac{1}{2} m_e \omega^2 r^2$, the zero-point energy is $\mathscr{E}_0 = \hbar\omega/2$. The natural frequency is $\omega = \sqrt{k_{el}/m_e} = \sqrt{F/m_e A}$, where F is a quasi-elastic force and A the amplitude of the oscillator. Assuming the quasi-elastic

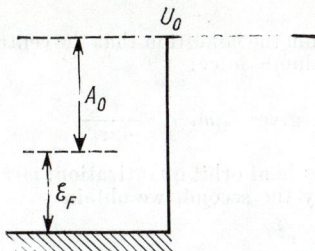

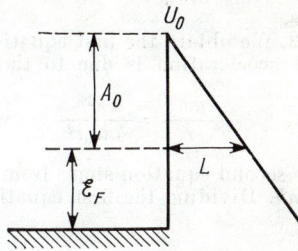

Fig. 46.14a.   Fig. 46.14b.

force to be of the Coulomb type and the amplitude to be equal to the radius, we obtain

$$\omega = \sqrt{\frac{e^2}{4\pi\varepsilon_0 m_e r^3}}$$

Putting $K = \mathscr{E}_0$ and substituting the circular frequency, we obtain after some simple transformations

$$r = \frac{4\pi\varepsilon_0 \hbar}{e^2 m_e}$$

Despite certain arbitrary assumptions, we have obtained a correct expression for the first Bohr radius.

46.13. The probability of tunnelling through a potential barrier is

$$w = D/D_0 = e^{-a}, \quad \text{where} \quad a = \frac{2L}{\hbar} \sqrt{2m(U_0 - e\varphi)}$$

(see § 70.6).

46.14. In the absence of an external electric field the electron in a metal is shielded by an infinitely wide potential barrier of height U_0 (Fig. 46.14a). In the presence of a strong electric field of intensity E the potential barrier assumes a triangular shape with height U_0 and width $L = \varphi/E = A_0/eE$ (Fig. 46.14b), where A_0 is the work function. Neglect the shape of the barrier and assume it to be rectangular. Since the energy of the electrons in the metal is $\mathscr{E}_F$, and their work function is $A_0 = U_0 - \mathscr{E}_F$ (see § 75.3), the parameter a which determines the probability of the electron tunnelling through the potential barrier assumes the form

$$a = \frac{2L}{\hbar} \sqrt{2m(U_0 - \mathscr{E}_F)} = \frac{2A_0}{eEh} \sqrt{2mA_0}$$

47. Atomic and Molecular Structure

47.1. The approach distance of an alpha-particle to the nucleus will be a minimum in the case of a central collision, when the entire kinetic energy of the alpha-particle is transformed into potential energy: $K = U = \dfrac{Z_1 Z_2 e^2}{4\pi\varepsilon_0 r}$, where Z_1 and Z_2 are the respective atomic numbers.

47.2. We obtain the first equation from the condition that the centripetal acceleration is due to the Coulomb force:

$$\frac{mv^2}{r} = \frac{e^2}{4\pi\varepsilon_0 r^2}, \quad \text{which gives} \quad mv^2 r = \frac{e^2}{4\pi\varepsilon_0}$$

The second equation stems from the rule of orbit quantization: $mvr = n\hbar$. Dividing the first equation by the second, we obtain

$$v = \frac{1}{n} \cdot \frac{e^2}{4\pi\varepsilon_0 \hbar}$$

The maximum speed corresponds to the first (principal) energy level. Its ratio to the speed of light in a vacuum is the fine structure constant:

$$\alpha = \frac{v_1}{c} = \frac{e^2}{4\pi\varepsilon_0 c\hbar} = 7.3 \times 10^{-3} = \frac{1}{137}$$

47.4. From the formula $\mathcal{E} = hcR\left(\dfrac{1}{1^2} - \dfrac{1}{n^2}\right) = 13.6\left(1 - \dfrac{1}{n^2}\right)$, we obtain the number of the excited level: $n = 3$. Direct transitions from the third level to the first, or second, and from the second to the first level are possible. We obtain three spectral lines.

47.5. The energy of transition from the excited to the ground state is shared by the photon and the atom: $\mathcal{E} = h\nu + D$, where $D = p^2/2M$ is the atom's recoil energy, and p is the momentum due to the emission of a photon. In accordance with the law of conservation of momentum, $p = p_{\text{ph}} = h\nu/c$. Hence $D = h^2\nu^2/2Mc^2$ and the transition energy is

$$\mathcal{E} = h\nu\left(1 + \frac{h\nu}{2Mc^2}\right)$$

Solving this quadratic equation, we obtain the expression for the energy of the photon:

$$h\nu = \frac{2\mathcal{E}}{1 + \sqrt{1 + 2\mathcal{E}/Mc^2}}$$

Since the transition energy in a hydrogen atom is below 13.6 eV, and its rest energy is 1 GeV, it follows that $2\mathcal{E}/Mc^2 \approx 10^{-8}$, and so this term in the denominator may be left out without appreciable loss in accuracy. Since, according to the statement of the problem, the transition is from the fifth to the first level, it follows that

$$\mathscr{E} = hcR \left(\frac{1}{1^2} - \frac{1}{5^2} \right) = \frac{24}{25} \, hcR$$

Hence $h\nu = \dfrac{24hcR}{25}$, the recoil energy is $D = \dfrac{24^2 h^2 R^2}{2 \times 25^2 M}$, the velocity of the atom is $v = \dfrac{24hR}{25M}$.

47.6. Noting that for a hydrogen-like ion $\mathscr{E}_n = -\dfrac{Z^2 hcR}{n^2}$, we obtain the generalized Balmer formula

$$\frac{1}{\lambda} = Z^2 R \left(\frac{1}{m^2} - \frac{1}{n^2} \right)$$

For helium $(Z = 2)$ we obtain

$$\frac{1}{\lambda} = 4R \left(\frac{1}{m^2} - \frac{1}{n^2} \right)$$

The principal line of the Lyman series is the result of the transition from the second to the first level $(m = 1, \; n = 2)$ and of the Balmer series (H_α) the result of the transition from the third to the second level $(m = 2, \; n = 3)$.

47.7. The diameter of the excited hydrogen atom is $d = 2n^2 a_0$, where n is the number of the energy level and a_0 the Bohr radius. The concentration of atoms is

$$n_0 \leqslant \frac{1}{d^3}, \quad \text{or} \quad n_0 \leqslant \frac{1}{8n^6 a_0^3}$$

Since the Balmer series is excited as the result of the transition of an electron to the second level, the maximum number of the level is two units more than the maximum number of observed lines. Hence in a gas-discharge tube $n = 14$, in a celestial body $n = 35$.

47.9. The spectral lines in question closely resemble the first three lines of the Balmer series of the hydrogen spectrum: 6563 Å, 4861 Å and 4340 Å. To make sure that they are in fact the lines, find the ratio of the wavelengths of the galaxy spectrum to the wavelengths radiated in the laboratory. We shall obtain identical ratios:

$$\frac{\lambda}{\lambda_0} = \frac{6877}{6563} = \frac{4989}{4861} = \frac{4548}{4340} = 1.045$$

The red shift is due, obviously, to the motion of the galaxy away from us (the Doppler effect). We have

$$\lambda = \lambda_0 \sqrt{\frac{1+\beta}{1-\beta}}, \quad \text{whence} \quad \sqrt{\frac{1+\beta}{1-\beta}} = 1.045$$

Solving this equation we find the speed at which the galaxy moves away from us.

47.10. Since the muon mass is only one ninth the mass of the proton, we should consider the proton and the muon as revolving about a common centre of mass (Fig. 47.10). To find the radii, we obtain a system of equations:

$$\frac{m_1 v_1^2}{r_1} = \frac{m_2 v_2^2}{r_2} = \frac{e^2}{4\pi\varepsilon_0 a^2} \qquad (1)$$

$$a = r_1 + r_2 \qquad (2)$$

$$m_1 v_1 r_1 + m_2 v_2 r_2 = n\hbar \qquad (3)$$

$$m_1 r_1 = m_2 r_2 \qquad (4)$$

It follows from the first and the fourth equations that $v_1/r_1 = v_2/r_2$, and from the third and the fourth that $v_1 + v_2 = \dfrac{n\hbar}{m_1 r_1} = \dfrac{n\hbar}{m_2 r_2}$.

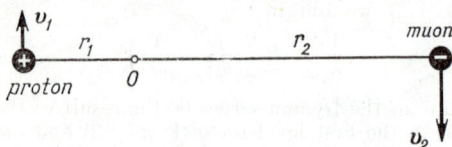

Fig. 47.10.

Hence we obtain the orbital speeds: $v_1 = n\hbar/am_1$, $v_2 = n\hbar/am_2$. Substituting this result into the first and the second equations, we obtain the radii:

$$r_1 = n^2 \frac{4\pi\varepsilon_0 \hbar^2}{m_1 e^2}, \qquad r_2 = n^2 \frac{4\pi\varepsilon_0 \hbar^2}{m_2 e^2}$$

Hence the Bohr radii of a mesoatom may be obtained:

$$a_n = n^2 \frac{4\pi\varepsilon_0 \hbar^2}{e^2} \cdot \frac{m_p + m_\mu}{m_p m_\mu}$$

The energy of an electron occupying an arbitrary energy level is

$$\mathscr{E}_n = \frac{m_1 v_1^2}{2} + \frac{m_2 v_2^2}{2} - \frac{e^2}{4\pi\varepsilon_0 a_n} = -\frac{e^2}{8\pi\varepsilon_0 a_n} = -\frac{e^2}{8\pi\varepsilon_0 a_0} \cdot \frac{a_0}{a_n}$$

$$= -\hbar c R \frac{a_0}{a_n}$$

where a_0 is the first Bohr radius of the hydrogen atom.

47.12. The solution is similar to that of Problem 47.10. One may make use of the formula obtained in Problem 47.10, putting $m_1 = m_2 = m_0$. We have $a_n = n^2 2a_0$, where a_0 is the first Bohr radius. The energy in the ground state ($n = 1$) assumes the form $\mathscr{E}_1 = -hcR/2$.

47.13. The first potential jump takes place when the electron goes over from the first to the second level:

$$\Delta\mathscr{E} = hcR \left(\frac{1}{1^2} - \frac{1}{2^2} \right)$$

47.14. The orbital quantum number corresponding to the s-state is $l = 0$. Therefore the appropriate magnetic quantum number is also $m = 0$. Hence the electrons may differ only in their spin projections: $s = 1/2$ and $s = -1/2$. Thus there are two possible sets of quantum numbers: $n, 0, 0, 1/2$ and $n, 0, 0, -1/2$.

The orbital quantum number corresponding to the p-state is $l = 1$. Therefore the magnetic quantum number can assume three values: $m = 1$, $m = 0$ and $m = -1$. Since there are two possible spin projections corresponding to each magnetic number, the possible sets of quantum numbers are six in all: $n, 1, 1, 1/2$; $n, 1, 1, -1/2$; $n, 1, 0, 1/2$; $n, 1, 0, -1/2$; $n, 1, -1, 1/2$ and $n, 1, -1, -1/2$.

47.16. The valency of an element is determined by the number of electrons occupying the upper partially filled electron level. All these elements have one electron on this level.

47.17. The Pauli exclusion principle does not hold for bosons. Therefore in a system in a state of minimum energy, all three particles will occupy the first energy level. Since in this case their momenta are equal, the force of pressure turns out to be three times greater.

47.18. Of the three fermions, only two (with opposite spins) can occupy the lowest energy levels. The third fermion must go over to the second level, and this will be the state with a minimum energy of the system. On the second level the length of a potential well holds two half-waves, i.e. $L = \lambda$. The particle's momentum turns out to be $p = h/\lambda = h/L$, i.e. it is twice that of a particle occupying the first level. The corresponding increase in force is four times (see Problem 46.9). For the resultant we obtain

$$F_{av} = \frac{2h^2}{4mL^3} + \frac{4h^2}{4mL^3} = \frac{3h^2}{2mL^3}$$

47.19. The shortwave threshold is determined by the kinetic energy of the electrons bombarding the anti-cathode: $hc/\lambda \leqslant K$. But the kinetic energy of the electrons is itself determined by the accelerating potential: $K = e\varphi$. Hence

$$\lambda \geqslant hc/e\varphi$$

47.20. Apply the Moseley law in the form $\dfrac{1}{\lambda} = R(Z-1)^2 \times$

$\times \left(\dfrac{1}{1^2} - \dfrac{1}{2^2} \right)$. Hence it follows

$$Z = 1 + \sqrt{\frac{4}{3\lambda R}}$$

Knowing the atomic number, we can easily find the material of the anti-cathode.

47.21. The wavelength of the K_α-line for vanadium ($Z = 23$) may be determined from the Moseley law. This line can be resolved only if it does not lie outside the continuous spectrum, i.e. if $\lambda_\alpha > hc/e\varphi$. Hence $\varphi > \dfrac{hc}{e\lambda_\alpha}$, or $\varphi > \dfrac{3(Z-1)^2 hcR}{4e}$.

47.22. From the conditions of the problem, $(\lambda_\alpha - \lambda)/\lambda_\alpha = 0.1$. Hence it follows that $\lambda = 0.9\lambda_\alpha$, or $hc/e\varphi = 0.9\lambda_\alpha$. We have $\varphi = \dfrac{hc}{0.9e\lambda_\alpha} =$

$= \dfrac{(Z-1)^2 hcR}{1.2e}$.

47.23. The angular momentum of a rotating quantum system, including a molecule, is $L = \sqrt{l(l+1)}\,\hbar$, where $l = 0, 1, 2, \ldots$. The kinetic energy will accordingly be

$$K_{\mathrm{rot}} = \frac{L^2}{2J} = \frac{l(l+1)\,\hbar^2}{2J}$$

where J is the moment of inertia. The kinetic energy in the first excited state is $K_1 = \hbar^2/J$, the angular momentum is $L_1 = \hbar\sqrt{2}$ and the angular velocity is

$$\omega_1 = \frac{L_1}{J} = \frac{2\hbar\sqrt{2}}{md^2}$$

Here $d = 0.74$ Å is the distance between the centres of the atoms in the molecule, and $m = 1.67 \times 10^{-27}$ kg is the mass of hydrogen atom.

47.24. The energy of the molecule on the first vibration-rotational level is

$$\mathscr{E}_1^{\mathrm{vib\text{-}rot}} = \mathscr{E}_0^{\mathrm{vib}} + \mathscr{E}_1^{\mathrm{rot}} = \frac{\hbar\omega}{2} + \frac{\hbar^2}{J}$$

The transition to the zero level results in the radiation of a photon of energy $\mathscr{E}_{\mathrm{ph}} = \mathscr{E}_1^{\mathrm{rot}} = \hbar^2/J$. Expressing the photon energy in terms of its wavelength, $\mathscr{E}_{\mathrm{ph}} = 2\pi\hbar c/\lambda$, we obtain

$$\lambda = 2\pi J c/\hbar$$

47.25. The diagram of vibration-rotational energy levels is shown in Fig. 47.25. There are only two purely vibrational levels: $\mathscr{E}_0^{\mathrm{vib}} = \hbar\omega/2$ and $\mathscr{E}_1^{\mathrm{vib}} = 3\hbar\omega/2$, and thirteen intermediate vibration-rotational levels:

$$\mathscr{E}_l = \mathscr{E}_0^{\mathrm{vib}} + \mathscr{E}_l^{\mathrm{rot}} = \frac{\hbar\omega}{2} + \frac{l(l+1)\,\hbar^2}{2J}, \qquad \text{where} \qquad l = 1, 2, \ldots, 13$$

It is clear from the diagram that the fourteenth vibration-rotational level coincides with the first purely vibrational level:

$$\mathscr{E}_{14} = \frac{\hbar\omega}{2} + \frac{14 \times 15\hbar^2}{2J} = \frac{3\hbar\omega}{2}, \qquad \text{whence} \qquad \frac{14 \times 15\hbar^2}{2J} = \hbar\omega$$

This makes it possible to determine the molecule's moment of inertia about its centre of mass: $J = 105\,\hbar/\omega$. On the other hand, the moment of inertia is $J = m_{\mathrm{H}}r_{\mathrm{H}}^2 + m_{\mathrm{F}}r_{\mathrm{F}}^2$, where $r_{\mathrm{H}} + r_{\mathrm{F}} = d$ is the distance sought between the centres of atoms and $m_{\mathrm{H}}r_{\mathrm{H}} = m_{\mathrm{F}}r_{\mathrm{F}}$. But $m_{\mathrm{F}} = 19m_{\mathrm{H}}$. Therefore $r_{\mathrm{H}} = 19r_{\mathrm{F}} = 19d/20$. Substituting into the expression for

the moment of inertia, we obtain

$$J = m_H r_H (r_H + r_F) = \frac{19}{20} m_H d^2$$

For the distance between the centres we obtain

$$d = \sqrt{\frac{2.1 \times 10^3 \hbar}{19 \omega m_H}}$$

47.27. The spectral lines of a helium atom are due exclusively to the electronic transitions from one energy level to another. These transitions result in a line spectrum.

In a hydrogen molecule there is a set of vibrational and rotational levels, in addition to the electronic levels (see § 74.4). Because of this the spectrum of a hydrogen molecule consists not of isolated lines, but of bands.

47.28. The orientations of the magnetic moments of the proton and the electron may be either parallel, or anti-parallel to one another. Therefore the total energy of interaction of the electron and the proton is

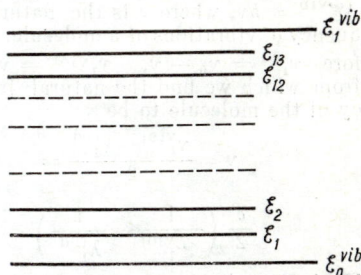

Fig. 47.25.

$$\mathscr{E} = \mathscr{E}_{Coul} \pm \mathscr{E}_{mag} = -\frac{e^2}{4\pi\varepsilon_0 r} \pm \frac{2\mu_0\mu_p\mu_e}{4\pi r^3}$$

(see §§ 40.6, 41.10 and Table 10 in the end of the book). The relative error is

$$\delta = \left| \frac{\mathscr{E} - \mathscr{E}_{Coul}}{\mathscr{E}} \right| \approx \left| \frac{\mathscr{E}_{mag}}{\mathscr{E}_{Coul}} \right| = \frac{2\mu_p\mu_e}{e^2 c^2 r^2} \leqslant \frac{2\mu_p\mu_e}{e^2 c^2 a_0^2}$$

where a_0 is the Bohr radius.

Every energy level is seen to split into two sub-levels: the upper $\mathscr{E}'_n = \mathscr{E} + | \mathscr{E}_{mag} |$, and the lower $\mathscr{E}''_n = \mathscr{E} - | \mathscr{E}_{mag} |$, where n is the number of the level and $| \mathscr{E}_{mag} |$ is the magnitude of the energy of magnetic interaction. Dashed lines in Fig. 47.28 show the first three energy levels stemming from Bohr's theory, while the solid lines show the sub-levels due to magnetic interaction. The diagram is, of course, not to scale.

47.29. The transition from the upper to the lower sub-level of the ground state in hydrogen results in the emission of a photon with an energy $\mathscr{E}_{ph} = \mathscr{E}'_1 - \mathscr{E}''_1 = 2 | \mathscr{E}_{mag} |$. The corresponding wavelength is

$$\lambda = \frac{hc}{\mathscr{E}_{\mathrm{ph}}} = \frac{4\pi hca_0^3}{4\mu_0\mu_{\mathrm{p}}\mu_{\mathrm{e}}} =$$

$$= \frac{4\pi \times 6.62 \times 10^{-34} \times 3.00 \times 10^8 \times 5.29^3 \times 10^{-33}}{4 \times 4\pi \times 10^{-7} \times 1.41 \times 10^{-26} \times 9.28 \times 10^{-24}} = 0.56 \ \mathrm{m} = 56 \ \mathrm{cm}$$

It follows that the classical calculation does not produce the correct wavelength, but the order of magnitude is right.

47.30. The frequency of the nearest red companion in the combination scattering spectrum is known to be $v_1^{\mathrm{red}} = v_0 - \Delta\mathscr{E}^{\mathrm{vib}}/h$, of the violet companion $v_1^{\mathrm{viol}} = v_0 + \Delta\mathscr{E}_{\mathrm{vib}}/h$, where v_0 is the frequency of light. But $\Delta\mathscr{E}^{\mathrm{vib}} = hv$, where v is the natural frequency of vibrations of a molecule. Therefore $v_1^{\mathrm{red}} = v_0 - v$, $v_1^{\mathrm{viol}} = v_0 + v$, from which we find the natural frequency of the molecule to be

$$v = \frac{v_1^{\mathrm{viol}} - v_1^{\mathrm{red}}}{2} =$$

$$= \frac{c}{2}\left(\frac{1}{\lambda_1^{\mathrm{viol}}} - \frac{1}{\lambda_1^{\mathrm{red}}}\right)$$

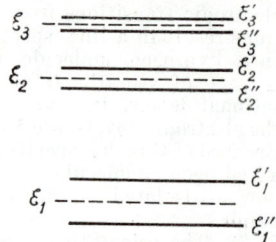

Fig. 47.28.

47.31. To make the operation of a laser possible, a mechanism of stimulated emission must be provided which produces absolutely identical photons. The photons must have identical frequencies (energies), identical phases and identical spins (i.e. their polarization must be identical). This is possible only because photons are bosons and there may be an unlimited number of them in the same quantum state. Fermions, on the other hand, obey the Pauli principle, which forbids the presence in a system even of two particles with identical quantum numbers. Consequently, there can be no induced radiation in a system made up of fermions. Therefore a laser operating on fermions is not feasible.

47.32. The lowest angular divergence can be found from the condition $2\theta \approx 2\lambda/D$.

48. Quantum Properties of Metals and of Semiconductors

48.3. Find the total energy of the electron gas $W = \frac{3}{5}n\mathscr{E}_{\mathrm{F}}V$, where V is the volume of the metal. Imagine the gas compressed by a small amount dV. This will require work against the forces of pressure equal to $\Delta W = -P\,dV$, where P is the pressure of the electron gas. This work is equal to the change in the energy of the electron gas $\Delta W = dW$. To find the differential of energy let us express the electron gas concentration in terms of its volume: $n = N/V$, where N is the total number of electrons. We have

$$W = \frac{3}{5} \, N \, \frac{h^2}{2m} \left(\frac{3}{8\pi} \right)^{2/3} N^{2/3} V^{-2/3}$$

Differentiating, we obtain

$$dW = -\frac{2}{3} \times \frac{3}{5} \frac{h^2}{2m} \left(\frac{3}{8\pi} \right)^{2/3} N^{5/3} V^{-5/3} \, dV =$$

$$= -\frac{2h^2}{5m} \left(\frac{3}{8\pi} \right)^{2/3} n^{5/3} \, dV = -\frac{2}{5} \, n \mathscr{E}_F \, dV$$

The pressure of the electron gas is $P = \dfrac{2}{5} \, n \mathscr{E}_F$

48.4. Making use of the result of the previous problem, we obtain

$$P = \frac{2h^2}{5m} \left(\frac{3}{8\pi} \right)^{2/3} N^{5/3} V^{-5/3}$$

which yields

$$PV^{5/3} = \text{const}$$

The "adiabatic index" is $\gamma = 5/3$.

48.5. The pressure in the "white dwarf" is due to gas consisting of free electrons and of helium nuclei. These particles are in a degenerate state, like free electrons in a metal. The mass of an electron is almost 1/8000 the mass of a helium nucleus. Therefore the Fermi energy of the electron and the pressure of the electron gas are 8000 times greater than the corresponding quantities for helium. Hence the helium pressure may be neglected. Making use of the result of the previous problem for the pressure of the electron gas, we obtain

$$PV^{5/3} = \frac{h^2}{5m_e} \left(\frac{3}{8\pi} \right)^{2/3} N_e^{5/3}$$

There are two electrons to each helium nucleus, so $N_e = 2N_\alpha = 2M/m_\alpha$ where M is the mass of the star, and $m_\alpha = 4.002 \times 1.66 \times 10^{-27}$ kg is the mass of a helium nucleus.

Hence $PV^{5/3} = AM^{5/3}$, or $P = A\rho^{5/3}$, where

$$A = \frac{h^2}{5m_e \, (m_\alpha/2)^{5/3}} \left(\frac{3}{8\pi} \right)^{2/3} = 3.2 \times 10^6 \ \text{Pa} \cdot \text{m}^5 \cdot \text{kg}^{5/3}$$

48.6. The number of electrons rising above the Fermi level is estimated with the aid of an approximate formula $\dfrac{\Delta n}{n} \approx \dfrac{kT}{2\mathscr{E}_F}$ (see § 75.7).

48.7. The specific heat of a kilomole of electron gas is $C_m^{el} = RkT/2\mathscr{E}_F$ (see § 75.8), the lattice heat is $C_m^{lat} = 3R$ (see § 45.2). We have $C_m^{el}/C_m^{lat} = kT/6\mathscr{E}_F$.

48.8. The mean free path is found from the quantum expression for the electric conductivity: $\gamma = e^2 n\lambda/p_F$ (see § 75.9). The Fermi momentum is found from the known concentration of conduction electrons.

The interatomic distance is found from the concentration of atoms:
$d = n_A^{-1/3} = 2.3$ Å (see § 44.2).

48.9. Let the concentration of pairs in the superconductor be $n' = n/2$.
Then the current will be $i = qn'Sv = 2e \dfrac{n}{2} S \dfrac{p}{2m_e}$, where p is the momentum of the pair. According to Bohr's rule, the angular momentum is quantized: $pr = N\hbar$, where $N = 1, 2, 3, \ldots$ (the principal quantum number). We have for the current

$$i = N \frac{nS}{r} \cdot \frac{e\hbar}{2m_e}$$

where S is the conductor's cross section, and r is the radius of the ring. Clearly the current is quantized: $i = N i_0$, where i_0 is the minimum current, $i_0 = \dfrac{nS}{r} \cdot \dfrac{e\hbar}{2m_2}$

Since the magnetic flux is proportional to the current, it too turns out to be quantized:

$$\Phi = Li = N L i_0 = N\Phi_0$$

where L is the inductance of the ring, and Φ_0 is the minimum magnetic flux. Rigorous theory yields $\Phi_0 = h/2e = 2.07 \times 10^{-15}$ Wb.

48.10. The electric conductivity of electronic (N-type) semiconductors is proportional to the number of electrons in the conduction band. In the assumption that the transition probability of the electron from the valence to the conduction band can be computed with the aid of a barometric distribution, we obtain $n = A e^{-\Delta\mathscr{E}/kT}$, where $\Delta\mathscr{E}$ is the forbidden band width (see §§ 26.11, 34.3, 35.1). Hence we obtain for the electric conductivity

$$\gamma = \frac{e^2 \lambda A}{p_F} e^{-\Delta\mathscr{E}/kT} = B e^{-\Delta\mathscr{E}/kT}$$

where B is a constant characteristic of the material (at a specified temperature).

48.11. The mean free path of the electron is much less dependent on the temperature than the exponential term, therefore the temperature dependence of the factor B can be neglected in the first approximation. We have

$$\frac{\gamma_2}{\gamma_1} = \frac{e^{-\Delta\mathscr{E}/kT_2}}{e^{-\Delta\mathscr{E}/kT_1}} = \exp\left\{\frac{\Delta\mathscr{E}\,(T_2 - T_1)}{kT_1 T_2}\right\}$$

48.12. In the case of intrinsic conductivity, the electron and the hole concentrations are equal. Therefore $\gamma = en\,(b_+ + b_-)$, where b_+ is the mobility of holes and b_- is the mobility of electrons. Hence $n = \dfrac{\gamma}{e(b_+ + b_-)}$.

To find the Hall coefficient, note that the Hall potential difference of the electron and the hole components are of opposite signs (see

§ 44.2). We have

$$R_H = R_H^{(-)} - R_H^{(+)} = \frac{b_- - b_+}{\gamma}.$$

48.13. Since indium is a trivalent element, the indium impurity acts as an acceptor and produces hole-type conductivity. Knowing the concentration of holes and their mobility (see Problem 48.12), we obtain $\gamma = en_+ b_+$. Antimony is a pentavalent element, so the antimony impurity acts as a donor. The electric conductivity is $\gamma = en_- b_-$.

49. Nuclear Structure

49.2. Solve the system of two equations:

$$10.013\, x + 11.009\, y = 10.811;\quad x + y = 1$$

where x and y are the fractions of the light and the heavy isotopes, respectively.

49.3. The radius of the nucleus can be estimated from the formula $R = R_0 \sqrt[3]{A}$ (see § 80.6), where $R_0 = 1.4 \times 10^{-15}$ m and A is the mass number. The height of the Coulomb potential barrier is $U_0 = \frac{Ze^2}{4\pi\varepsilon_0 R}$, where Z is the atomic number.

49.5. The binding energy of the tritium nucleus $_1H^3$ is $\mathscr{E}_{_1H^3} = (1.00783 + 2 \times 1.00867 - 3.01605) \times 931.5 = 8.5$ MeV. The binding energy of the helium nucleus $_2He^3$ is $\mathscr{E}_{_2He^3} = (2 \times 1.00783 + 1.00867 - 3.01603) \times 931.5 = 7.7$ MeV.

49.6. The number of alpha-disintegrations is obtained by dividing the change in the mass number by 4, which is the mass number of the alpha-particle. We have

$$N_\alpha = \frac{A_{Ra} - A_{Pb}}{A_{He}} = \frac{226 - 206}{4} = 5$$

After five alpha-disintegrations the decrease in the atomic number will be 10, and $Z_{Ra} - Z_{Pb} = 88 - 82 = 6$. It follows from this that there are in addition four beta-disintegrations, each of which results in a unit increase in the atomic number.

49.7. The transition energy is equal to the difference between the energy of the original nucleus and the rest energy of the reaction products:

$$\mathscr{E} = [209.98297 - (4.00260 + 205.97446)] \times 931.5 = 5.5 \text{ MeV}$$

This energy is equal to the sum of kinetic energies of the alpha-particle and the recoil nucleus (see § 17.2): $\mathscr{E} = K_\alpha + K_{Pb}$ and $K_\alpha / K_{Pb} = M_{Pb}/M_\alpha$.

49.8. The sum of the masses in the final stage of the possible reaction exceeds the mass of the original nucleus. The reaction is impossible because it contravenes the law of conservation of energy.

49.9. See the previous problem.

49.10. The mass of a silicon nucleus exceeds the mass of a phosphorus nucleus by $\Delta m = 30.97535 - 30.97376 = 0.00159$ amu, the corresponding energy being $\Delta \mathscr{E} = 0.00159 \times 931.5 = 1.48$ MeV. This exceeds the electron rest energy (0.51 MeV), and therefore beta-decay is possible:

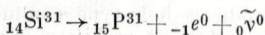

$$_{14}\text{Si}^{31} \rightarrow {}_{15}\text{P}^{31} + {}_{-1}e^0 + {}_0\widetilde{\nu}^0$$

The total energy of the beta-particle and the antineutrino is 1.48 MeV.

49.11. Let the kinetic energy of the extracted neutron be zero. Then the work needed to extract a neutron will be equal to the difference between the total energy of the reaction products and the rest energy of the original nucleus:

$$\Delta \mathscr{E} = (12.00000 + 1.00867 - 13.00335) \times 931.5 = 4.96 \text{ MeV}$$

49.12. To evaluate the probability, apply the formula

$$w = e^{-a}, \quad \text{where} \quad a = \frac{2R}{\hbar} \sqrt{2m\,(U_0 - K)}$$

Here U_0 is the height of the Coulomb barrier, and K is the kinetic energy of the alpha-particle. For data on the radius of the polonium nucleus and on the barrier height see Problem 49.3.

49.13. The activity of the specimen is equal to the number of decays per unit time:

$$Q = -\frac{dN}{dt} \lambda N \quad \text{(see § 81.4). The ratio of the activities is}$$

$$x = \frac{Q_2}{Q_1} = \frac{N_2}{N_1} = e^{-\lambda\,(t_2 - t_1)} = 2^{-\frac{t_2 - t_1}{T}}$$

Knowing the half-life, we can easily compute the decrease in the activity.

49.15. Knowing the activity $Q = \lambda N$ and noting that $\lambda = \frac{\ln 2}{T} = \frac{0.693}{T}$, we find the half-life $T = 0.693 N/Q$. The number of nuclei is $N = m N_\text{A}/A$, where m is the mass of the specimen, A is the mass number of the isotope and N_A is the Avogadro number. Finally $T = 0.693 m N_\text{A}/AQ$.

49.17. We might at first reason that the energy of gamma-photons is $\mathscr{E}_\gamma = 5.30 - 4.50 = 0.80$ MeV. However, this estimate is too rough, since it takes no account of the recoil energy of the nucleus. Certain problems in nuclear physics demand a much higher accuracy. Consider the energy level diagram for the case of polonium decay (Fig. 49.17). The letter Pb* with an asterisk denotes the excited lead nucleus which emits gamma-photons. The total energy of the transition is $\mathscr{E}_1 = K_{1\alpha} + R_1$, where $K_{1\alpha} = 5.30$ MeV, and R_1 is the recoil energy of the nucleus. Since $R_1 = 4K_{1\alpha}/206$ (see § 17.2), it follows that $\mathscr{E}_1 = 5.30 + (5.30 \times 4/206) = 5.40$ MeV

Similarly, the energy liberated in the course of the second transition is

$$\mathscr{E}_2 = 4.50 + (4.50 \times 4/206) = 4.58 \text{ MeV}$$

The energy of the gamma-photon is

$$\mathscr{E}_\gamma = \mathscr{E}_1 - \mathscr{E}_2 = 5.40 - 4.58 = 0.82 \text{ MeV}$$

Note that because the mass of the lead nucleus is large, we can neglect the recoil energy resulting from the emission of a gamma-photon.

49.18. This problem is similar to Problem 47.5, but because the energy of the gamma-photon is much higher than that of an ultraviolet photon, the recoil is in this case much greater. Since the energy of a gamma-photon is $\mathscr{E}_\gamma = 14.4$ keV, and the momentum is $p_\gamma = \mathscr{E}_\gamma/c$, the recoil energy is $\mathscr{E}_R = p_\gamma^2/2M = = \mathscr{E}_\gamma^2/2Mc^2$. Therefore the transition energy is

$$\mathscr{E} = \mathscr{E}_\gamma + \mathscr{E}_R = \mathscr{E}_\gamma \left(1 + \frac{\mathscr{E}_\gamma}{2Mc^2}\right)$$

The relative change in energy is

$$\delta = \frac{\Delta\mathscr{E}}{\mathscr{E}_\gamma} = \frac{\mathscr{E}_\gamma}{2Mc^2}.$$

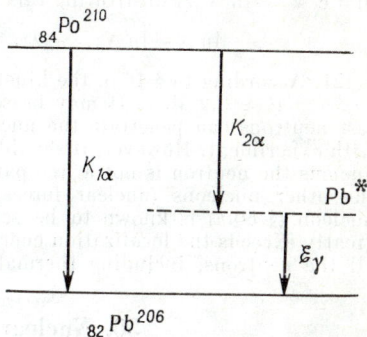

Fig. 49.17.

The natural relative line width is $\delta_{nat} = \hbar/\tau\mathscr{E}_\gamma$, where τ is the lifetime of the nucleus in the excited state.

49.19. The absorption of a gamma-photon by a free nucleus results in it acquiring a momentum equal to that of the photon and, consequently, a kinetic energy $\mathscr{E}_R = p_\gamma^2/2M = \mathscr{E}_\gamma^2/2Mc^2$. Therefore the energy of the absorbed photon is $\mathscr{E}_\gamma^{ab} = \mathscr{E} + \mathscr{E}_R$, where $\mathscr{E} = \mathscr{E}_\gamma + + \mathscr{E}_R$ is the energy of the transition, and $\mathscr{E}_\gamma$ is the energy of the emitted photons. Hence

$$\mathscr{E}_\gamma^{ab} = \mathscr{E}_\gamma + 2\mathscr{E}_R = \mathscr{E}_\gamma \left(1 + \frac{\mathscr{E}_\gamma}{Mc^2}\right)$$

This distorts the resonance absorption. If we start bringing the source and the absorbing substance closer together, the gamma-photon's energy increases because of the Doppler effect: $\mathscr{E}_\gamma' = \mathscr{E}_\gamma \sqrt{\dfrac{1+\beta}{1-\beta}} \approx$ $\approx \mathscr{E}_\gamma (1 + \beta)$. At a certain speed we obtain $\mathscr{E}_\gamma' = \mathscr{E}_\gamma^{ab}$, and resonance absorption sets in. We have

$$\mathscr{E}_\gamma \left(1 + \frac{\mathscr{E}_\gamma}{Mc^2}\right) = \mathscr{E}_\gamma (1+\beta), \quad \text{giving} \quad \beta = \frac{\mathscr{E}_\gamma}{Mc^2}, \quad \text{and} \quad v = \beta c = \frac{\mathscr{E}_\gamma}{Mc}$$

49.20. The decay probability is the ratio of the number of the nuclei that have experienced decay to the total number of nuclei: $w = -\dfrac{dN}{N}$.

It is proportional to the time of observation, $w = \lambda \, dt$, i.e. $\dfrac{dN}{N} =$
$= -\lambda \, dt$. We have

$$\int \frac{dN}{N} = -\lambda \int dt, \quad \text{so} \quad \ln N + C = -\lambda t$$

At the initial point of time $t = 0$, $N = N_0$, so $\ln N_0 + C = 0$ and $C = -\ln N_0$. Substituting this into the above formula, we obtain

$$\ln N - \ln N_0 = -\lambda t, \quad \text{or} \quad N = N_0 e^{-\lambda t}$$

49.21. According to § 16.6, the kinetic energy of the neutron is $K \geqslant$ $\geqslant \hbar^2/2ma^2 \approx 0.2$ MeV. It may be seen at first glance that only very fast neutrons can penetrate the nucleus, but this is in contradiction with experiment. However, it should be taken into account that in the nucleus the neutron is not a free particle, but interacts strongly with the other nucleons (nuclear forces). The mean binding energy per nucleon (§ 80.4) is known to be several mega-electron-volts, which greatly exceeds the localization energy calculated above. This enables all the neutrons, including thermal ones, to penetrate the nucleus.

50. Nuclear Reactions

50.1. The number of the nuclei that took part in the reaction is $N =$ $= mN_A/A$, where m is the mass of uranium reacted, N_A is the Avogadro number, and A the mass number. Multiplying the number of the nuclei by $\Delta \mathscr{E} = 200$ MeV, we obtain the energy of the explosion:

$$W = \frac{1.5 \times 6.02 \times 10^{26} \times 200 \times 1.6 \times 10^{-13}}{235} \text{ J} = 1.2 \times 10^{14} \text{ J}$$

Dividing by the calorific value of TNT, q, we obtain the TNT equivalent: $m_{TNT} = W/q$.

50.2. The energy released is found from the masses equation:

$$\Delta \mathscr{E} = (6.01513 + 2.01410 - 2 \times 4.00260) \times 931.5 = 22.4 \text{ MeV}$$

The energy release per nucleon is $22.4/8 = 2.8$ MeV. This is three times as much as is released in fission of uranium: $200/235 = 0.85$ MeV per nucleon.

50.3. To initiate the nuclear reaction, the deuterium nuclei must be brought together to within the radius of action of nuclear forces. To do this they must surmount the Coulomb potential barrier (see Problem 49.3). Take account of the Maxwellian distribution (see Problems 33.10 and 47.26).

50.4. Let the pi-meson be at rest in some reference frame. Then its momentum is zero. If a pi-meson decays into two photons, they will fly in opposite directions, so that in this reference frame the combined momentum will be zero although each photon separately has momentum. The transformation of a pion into a single photon is impossible, since it contravenes the law of conservation of momentum.

The energy of each photon is $\mathscr{E}_\gamma = 135/2 = 67.5$ MeV (see § 83.7).

50.5. From the uncertainty relation for the energy we obtain $\Delta\mathscr{E} \approx$ $\approx \hbar/\tau$, where τ is the lifetime of the particle. The accuracy with which the mass (and the energy) can be measured is

$$\delta = \frac{\Delta m}{m} = \frac{\Delta\mathscr{E}}{\mathscr{E}} \approx \frac{\hbar}{\mathscr{E}\tau}$$

50.6. From the law of conservation of energy we obtain for the gamma-photon $\mathscr{E}_\gamma \geqslant 2m_0c^2$, where m_0 is the rest mass of an electron.

50.7. Suppose that the photon produces a pair of particles with identical momenta (Fig. 50.7). In this case the laws of conservation of energy and the momentum will be written in the form

$$\mathscr{E}_{ph} = 2mc^2, \qquad \mathscr{E}_{ph}/c = 2mv\cos\alpha$$

Hence $2mc^2 = 2mvc\cos\alpha$, or $c = v\cos\alpha$, which is impossible.

50.8. Find the total energy released in the reaction:

$$\Delta\mathscr{E} = (m_\pi - m_\mu) \times 931.5 =$$
$$= 140 - 106 = 34 \text{ MeV}$$

The rest energy of a muon is

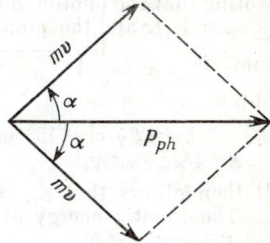

Fig. 50.7.

$\mathscr{E}_{0\mu} = 106$ MeV, the rest mass of a neutrino is zero. Assuming the dacaying pion to be at rest, we obtain that the muon and the neutrino momenta are equal in magnitude and opposite in direction. We have

$$p_\nu = \frac{\mathscr{E}_\nu}{c}, \qquad p_\mu = \frac{1}{c}\sqrt{K_\mu(2\mathscr{E}_{0\mu} + K_\mu)}$$

which yields

$$\mathscr{E}_\nu = \sqrt{K_\mu(2\mathscr{E}_{0\mu} + K_\mu)}$$

But, from the law of conservation of energy $\mathscr{E}_\nu = \Delta\mathscr{E} - K_\mu$, so $\Delta\mathscr{E} - K_\mu = \sqrt{K_\mu(2\mathscr{E}_{0\mu} + K_\mu)}$. Hence it follows that the kinetic energy of the muon is

$$K_\mu = \frac{(\Delta\mathscr{E})^2}{2(\mathscr{E}_{0\mu} + \Delta\mathscr{E})}$$

50.9. The decay of a neutron results in the release of energy

$$\Delta\mathscr{E} = (m_n - m_p) \times 931.5 = 939.6 - 938.2 = 1.4 \text{ MeV}$$

This energy is shared by the electron and the antineutrino: $\Delta\mathscr{E} =$ $= \mathscr{E}_e + \mathscr{E}_{\tilde{\nu}}$, where the total energy of the electron is the sum of its rest energy $\mathscr{E}_0$ and its kinetic energy K_e, i.e. $\mathscr{E}_e = \mathscr{E}_0 + K_e$. In accordance with the law of conservation of momentum for a proton at rest

$$p_e = p_\nu, \qquad \text{or} \qquad \frac{\mathscr{E}_\nu}{c} = \frac{1}{c}\sqrt{\mathscr{E}_e^2 - \mathscr{E}_0^2}$$

Substituting the value of the neutrino energy, we obtain after simple transformations

$$\mathscr{E}_e = \frac{(\Delta\mathscr{E})^2 + \mathscr{E}_0^2}{2\Delta\mathscr{E}}, \qquad K_e = \frac{(\Delta\mathscr{E} - \mathscr{E}_0)^2}{2\Delta\mathscr{E}}, \qquad \mathscr{E}_\nu = \frac{(\Delta\mathscr{E})^2 - \mathscr{E}_0^2}{2\Delta\mathscr{E}}$$

50.10. Let us denote the total energy of the neutral pion by $\mathscr{E}_\pi$ and its rest energy by $\mathscr{E}_0 = 135$ MeV. By the law of conservation of energy $\mathscr{E}_\pi = 2\mathscr{E}_\gamma$, where $\mathscr{E}_\gamma$ is the photon energy. From the law of conservation of momentum (see Fig. 50.10) we obtain $p_\pi = 2p_\gamma \cos 45°$. Noting that the photon momentum is $p_\gamma = \mathscr{E}_\gamma/c$ and the pion momentum is $p_\pi = \frac{1}{c}\sqrt{\mathscr{E}_\pi^2 - \mathscr{E}_0^2}$, we obtain

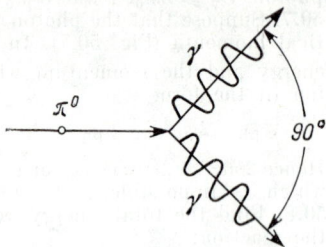

Fig. 50.10.

$\mathscr{E}_\pi^2 - \mathscr{E}_0^2 = 4\mathscr{E}_\gamma^2 \cos^2 45°$, or, $\mathscr{E}_\pi^2 - \mathscr{E}_0^2 = \mathscr{E}_\pi^2 \cos^2 45°$

It then follows that $\mathscr{E}_\pi = \mathscr{E}_0 \sqrt{2}$.
The kinetic energy of the pion is $K_\pi = \mathscr{E}_0 (\sqrt{2} - 1)$ and the photon energy is $\mathscr{E}_\gamma = \mathscr{E}_0/\sqrt{2}$.

50.11. The nuclear reaction takes the form $_1\text{H}^1 + _3\text{Li}^7 = 2\,_2\text{He}^4$. The kinetic energy of the alpha-particle is found from the law of conservation of energy which for this reaction is of the form

$$2K_\alpha = (M_\text{H} + M_\text{Li} - 2M_\alpha) \times 931.5 + K_\text{H} = 24.2 \text{ MeV}$$

Since the kinetic energy of the alpha-particle turns out to be much lower than its rest energy, the alpha-particles produced in the reaction are nonrelativistic. The separation angle is found from the law of conservation of momentum

$$p_\text{H} = 2p_\alpha \cos\frac{\theta}{2}$$

But for a nonrelativistic particle $p = \sqrt{2mK}$, so

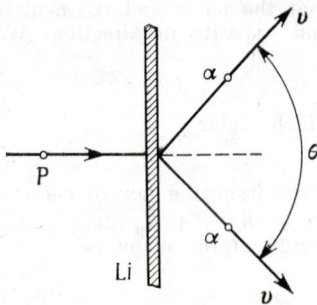

Fig. 50.11.

$$\cos\frac{\theta}{2} = \frac{1}{2}\sqrt{\frac{m_\text{H}K_\text{H}}{m_\alpha K_\alpha}}$$

50.12. The equation of the reaction is of the form $_{-1}e^0 + _1p^1 \rightarrow _0n^1 + _0\nu^0$. Since we assume the neutron produced in the reaction to be at rest, the electron momentum is completely transmitted to the neutrino. The laws of conservation of energy and the momentum will be written in the form

$$p_e = p_\nu, \quad \mathcal{E}_e + \mathcal{E}_{0p} = \mathcal{E}_{0n} + \mathcal{E}_\nu$$

Since the rest mass of a neutrino is zero, its energy is

$$\mathcal{E}_\nu = p_\nu c = p_e c = \sqrt{\mathcal{E}_e^2 - \mathcal{E}_{0e}^2}$$

Hence

$$\mathcal{E}_e + \mathcal{E}_{0p} = \mathcal{E}_{0n} + \sqrt{\mathcal{E}_e^2 - \mathcal{E}_{0e}^2}$$

Solving this equation, we obtain for the total energy of an electron

$$\mathcal{E}_e = \frac{(\mathcal{E}_{0n} - \mathcal{E}_{0p})^2 + \mathcal{E}_{0e}^2}{2(\mathcal{E}_{0n} - \mathcal{E}_{0p})}$$

The kinetic energy of the electron is

$$K_e = \mathcal{E}_e - \mathcal{E}_{0e} = \frac{(\mathcal{E}_{0n} - \mathcal{E}_{0p} - \mathcal{E}_{0e})^2}{2(\mathcal{E}_{0n} - \mathcal{E}_{0p})}$$

Substituting the respective values, we obtain the desired result.

ANSWERS AND HINTS

1. Kinematics of a Particle

1.1. $t = 7$ s; $x = 35$ m. **1.2.** $t = 60$ s; $x = 90$ m.

1.3. $t = 7.5$ h; $x = 600$ km. **1.4.** $\sin \alpha = u/v$; $t = l/v \cos \alpha$.

1.5. $\alpha = \beta - \arcsin \dfrac{n \cos \beta}{v}$. **1.6.** $\alpha = \pi/2$.

1.7. 35 min. **1.8.** 30 m/s; -2 m/s²; 4125 m.

1.9. *Hint.* Make use of the definitions of acceleration and average velocity in the case of motion with constant acceleration.

1.10. 1.6×10^5 m/s².

2. Force

2.1. $k = \dfrac{k_1 k_2}{k_1 + k_2}$. **2.3.** $x_0 = \dfrac{F_1 x_1 + F_2 x_2 + F_3 x_3 + \cdots}{F_1 + F_2 + F_3 + \cdots}$.

2.4. $d = F_2 a/(F_1 - F_2)$. **2.5.** $k = k_1 + k_2$.

2.6. $T_1 = \dfrac{P \cos \alpha_2}{\sin (\alpha_1 + \alpha_2)}$, $T_2 = \dfrac{P \cos \alpha_1}{\sin (\alpha_1 + \alpha_2)}$.

2.7. $F_1 = \dfrac{mg \sin \beta}{\sin (\alpha + \beta)}$, $F_2 = \dfrac{mg \sin \alpha}{\sin (\alpha + \beta)}$.

2.8. mg, mg and $2mg$.

3. Particle Dynamics

3.1. 8.4×10^7 Pa.

3.2. $a = g \dfrac{m_2 - m_1}{m_2 + m_1}$, $F = \dfrac{2m_1 m_2 g}{m_2 + m_1}$, $F_{pres} = 2F$.

3.3. It is greater in the second case.

3.4. (1) $a_1 = a_1' = \dfrac{mg}{m+M}$, $F_1 = Ma_1$;

(2) $a_2 = \dfrac{m(g+b)}{m+M}$, $a_2' = a_2 - b$, $F_2 = Ma_2$;

(3) $a_3 = \dfrac{m(g-b)}{m+M}$, $a_3' = a_3 + b$, $F_3 = Ma_3$.

3.5. $a = g\,\dfrac{m - M\sin\alpha}{m+M}$, $F = \dfrac{mMg\,(1+\sin\alpha)}{m+M}$.

3.6. $a_1 = -g\,\dfrac{m_2}{m_2\tan\alpha + m_1\cot\alpha}$, $a_2 = -g\,\dfrac{m_2\tan\alpha}{m_2\tan\alpha + m_1\cot\alpha}$,

$$Q = \dfrac{m_1 m_2 g\cos\alpha}{m_2\sin^2\alpha + m_1\cos^2\alpha}\ .$$

3.7. $a_x = g\,\dfrac{M\sin\alpha\cos\alpha}{M + m\sin^2\alpha}$, $a_y = -g\,\dfrac{(M+m)\sin^2\alpha}{M+m\sin^2\alpha}$

$$b_x = -g\,\dfrac{m\sin\alpha\cos\alpha}{M+m\sin^2\alpha}; \qquad Q = \dfrac{mMg}{M+m\sin^2\alpha}\ .$$

3.8. $T = 2\pi\sqrt{\dfrac{l\cos\alpha}{g}}$. **3.9.** $l = \dfrac{l_0}{1 - m\omega^2/k}$. **3.10.** $39°12'$.

3.11. In the lower point the overload is 8, in the upper it is 6.

3.12. $\dfrac{r}{H} = 2\cot^2\alpha$; $\dfrac{r}{L} = \dfrac{1}{2}\cot\alpha$.

3.13. $r = p\left(1 + \dfrac{x^2}{p^2}\right)^{3/2}$. **3.15.** $b = \dfrac{2v_0^2\sin\beta\cos(\alpha-\beta)}{g\cos^2\alpha}$.

3.16. $v_0 = \sqrt{gH(1 + l^2/H^2)}$; $\tan\alpha = H/l$.

4. Gravitation. Electrical Forces

4.1. 5.96×10^{24} kg. **4.2.** 6.03×10^{24} kg. **4.3.** 1.99×10^{30} kg.

4.4. The Sun attracts the Moon 2.1 times more strongly than does the Earth.

4.5. 0.63 astronomical units $= 1.08 \times 10^8$ km.

4.6. 0.414 of the planet's radius.

4.7. 8.52 m/s^2; 1.62 m/s^2; 270 m/s^2. **4.8.** 1 h 25 min.

4.9. 4×10^{-8} C. **4.10.** $E = 0$; $E = \dfrac{q\sqrt{2}}{\pi\varepsilon_0 a^2}$.

4.11. $E = \dfrac{qx}{4\pi\varepsilon_0\,(a^2+x^2)^{3/2}}$. **4.12.** 6.7×10^{-20} N.

4.13. $v_0 = \sqrt{\dfrac{eEL \cos \beta}{m \cos \alpha \sin (a - \beta)}}$.   **4.14.** 4.3×10^4 N/C.

4.15. $0 < \tan \alpha < \dfrac{4h}{l}$; $\dfrac{mv_0^2 \sin^2 \alpha}{2eh} < E < \dfrac{mv_0^2 \sin 2\alpha}{el}$.

5. Friction

5.1. 2 s; 4 m.

5.2. (1) $a_1 = \dfrac{(m - \mu M) g}{m + M}$, $F_1 = \dfrac{mMg (1 + \mu)}{m + M}$;

(2) $a_2 = \dfrac{m (g + b) - \mu Mg}{m + M}$, $F_2 = \dfrac{mM [g (1 + \mu) + b]}{m + M}$;

(3) $a_3 = \dfrac{m (g - b) - \mu Mg}{m + M}$, $F_3 = \dfrac{mM [g (1 + \mu) - b]}{m + M}$.

5.3. $a = g \dfrac{m - M (\sin \alpha \pm \mu \cos \alpha)}{m + M}$. [*Hint.* In solving the problem one should take into account the initial velocity of the block.]

5.4. $Q = \dfrac{m_1 m_2 g \cos (\alpha - \varphi)}{m_1 \cos^2 \alpha \cos \varphi + m_2 \sin \alpha \sin (\alpha - \varphi)}$; $\varphi = \arctan \mu$.

[*Hint.* The force of sliding friction of the wedge against the table should be included in the equation of motion of the wedge (Problem 3.6).]

5.5. $Q = \dfrac{mMg \cos \alpha \cos \varphi}{M \cos \varphi + m \sin \alpha \sin (\alpha - \varphi)}$.

5.6. $Q = \dfrac{mMg \cos (\alpha - \varphi)}{M \cos \varphi + m \sin \alpha \sin (\alpha - \varphi)}$. [*Hint.* See Problems 5.4 and 5.5.]

5.7. $g \tan (\alpha - \varphi) \leqslant a \leqslant g \tan (\alpha + \varphi)$, where $\varphi = \arctan \mu$. [*Hint.* Note that the direction of the force of static friction is not known.]

5.8. At a distance less than 8 cm from the centre of the disk.

5.9. Over 11 m/s.

5.10. $\sqrt{\dfrac{g \tan (\alpha - \varphi)}{R \sin \alpha}} \leqslant \omega \leqslant \sqrt{\dfrac{g \tan (\alpha + \varphi)}{R \sin \alpha}}$, where $\varphi = \arctan \mu$.

[*Hint.* Take into account the fact that the direction of the force of static friction is not known.]

5.11. 98 m; 57°. **5.12.** 23 cm/s; 5.1 m/s²; 0.09 s; 1 cm.

5.13. *Hint.* Making use of the results of the previous problem, express the instantaneous acceleration in terms of the instantaneous velocity.

5.4. 0.2 m/s; 15 s. **5.15.** 11 m/s.

6. Theory of Relativity

6.1. *Hint.* Compare the dimensions of the rod and of the hole which at rest are precisely the same.

6.2. $\varepsilon = uv/c^2$. **6.3.** $0.99995c$.

6.4. *Hint.* Does the result obtained have the meaning of the law of addition of velocities?

6.5. *Hint.* Consider the reference frame fixed to the medium which moves at a speed v with respect to the source of light.

6.6. *Hint.* Make use of the results of the previous problem.

6.7. 55 m; 7.7 m. **6.8.** 6.3×10^{-5} s. **6.9.** 2.83×10^8 m/s.

6.10. $\rho = \rho_0/(1 - \beta^2)$, where $\beta = v/c$.

6.11. *Hint.* Make use of the Lorentz transformations.

6.12. 2.6×10^8 m/s; 5.3×10^8 m/s.

6.13. The particle moves in a circle. The expression for the force will be formally the same as in Newtonian mechanics.

6.15. $l = l_0 \sqrt{1 - \beta^2}$.

7. The Law of Conservation of Momentum. Centre of Mass

7.1. 670 m/s. **7.2.** -3.25 m/s; 9.3 m/s. **7.3.** 87 cm.

7.4. 20 m/s².

7.5. 8.1 km/s; 5.3 km/s. [*Hint.* Make use of the Tsiolkovsky formula.]

7.6. *Hint.* Write equation (15.7) of § 15.5 in differential form and integrate it, keeping in mind that the velocity of the exhaust gases is a constant.

7.7. *Hint.* Take into account the change in the rocket's mass as the fuel burns.

7.8. *Hint.* Make use of the properties of the centre of mass (§ 15.8).

7.10. The centre of mass is at a distance of 4.3 units from the left-hand edge of the plate.

7.11. At a distance of $x = \dfrac{r^2}{R + r} = 1.13$ cm to the left of the centre of the large circle.

7.16. $T^2/R^3 = 4\pi/\gamma\,(m_1 + m_2)$.

8. Total and Kinetic Energy

8.1. Electron: 8.19×10^{-14} J $= 0.511$ MeV; proton: 1.504×10^{-10} J $= 938.3$ MeV; neutron: 1.506×10^{-10} J $= 939.6$ MeV.

8.2. 2.6×10^8 m/s.

8.3. 1.28×10^{-13} J $= 0.8$ MeV; 6.4×10^{-22} kg·m/s.

8.4. 5.8×10^{-18} kg·m/s; $u = \beta c = 0.996c$.

8.5. $u = \beta c = 0.976c$. **8.6.** 0.8%; 69%; 92%.

8.7. 3.8 m/s. **8.8.** $\alpha = \arctan \dfrac{1}{\mu}$. **8.9.** 2.7×10^2 kW.

8.10. *Hint.* The work done by the electrical forces is equal to the change in the kinetic energy.

8.11. Less than $\mathscr{E}_0^2/2pc$.

9. Uncertainty Relation

9.1. *Hint.* Express the kinetic energy of the electron in terms of the radius of its orbit; assume the characteristic dimension of the region of localization to be equal to the radius.

9.2. 200 MeV. **9.3.** 1 eV. **9.4.** 9 MeV.

10. Elementary Theory of Collisions

10.1. Horizontally at a speed of 3.1 m/s. **10.2.** 0.14 MeV.

10.4. The distance from the vertex of the parabolic mirror to the focus is $f = p/2$. [*Hint.* Use the result of Problem 3.14.]

10.6. 83°; 43°.

10.7. $v_1 = vd/2r$; $v_2 = v \sqrt{1 - (d^2/4r^2)}$; $\sin \alpha_2 = d/2r$; $\alpha_1 + \alpha_2 = \pi/2$; [*Hint.* Use the result of Problem 10.5.]

10.8. $\sin \alpha_2 = \dfrac{d}{r_1 + r_2}$; $v_2 = \dfrac{2m_1 v \cos \alpha_2}{m_1 + m_2}$;

$$v_1 = v \sqrt{1 - \frac{4m_1 m_2 \cos^2 \alpha_2}{(m_1 + m_2)^2}} .$$

[*Hint.* See solution of the previous problem.]

10.9. $p = 2nmv^2 \cos^2 \alpha$. **10.10.** 5 m².

10.11. The ratio of the distances is $l_2/l_1 = 1 + 2 \sin^2 \alpha$.

11. Potential Energy. Potential

11.1. *Hint.* A field is said to be uniform, if the forces acting on an object have the same magnitude and the same direction at all points of the field.

11.3. $U = -\dfrac{\gamma mM}{r} = -\dfrac{\gamma mM}{R+h}$; $U_{\text{sur}} = -\dfrac{\gamma mM}{R} = -mgR$.

11.4. $U = \dfrac{\gamma mMh}{R(R+h)} = mgh \dfrac{R}{R+h}$; $U_\infty = \dfrac{\gamma mM}{R} = mgR$.

11.5. $U = -p_e^2/4\pi\varepsilon_0 d^3$. **11.6.** 1.65 MJ. **11.7.** 27.2 V.

11.8. −13.6 eV. **11.9.** $p = \sqrt{2mq\varphi}$; $p = \dfrac{1}{c} \sqrt{q\varphi(2\mathscr{E}_0 + q\varphi)}$.

11.10. For the electron 10^5 V, for the proton 2×10^8 V.

11.11. 1 MeV/c = 5.33×10^{-22} kg·m/s. For the electron 10^7 V, for the proton 2×10^{10} V.

12. The Law of Conservation of Energy in Newtonian Mechanics

12.1. 5.20×10^2 m/s. **12.2.** 17 m/s. **12.4.** $\sqrt{5gl}$.

12.5. $\sqrt{4gl}$. **12.6.** $mg(3\cos\alpha - 2\cos\alpha_0)$.

12.7. $mg(3\cos\alpha - 2)$; $\alpha_{ref} = \arccos\dfrac{2}{3} = 48°$.

12.8. $3mg(1 + \cos\alpha)$.

12.9. $(1 + \sqrt{2})R \leqslant H \leqslant 2.5R$; 45°, 60°.

12.10. $R_0 = -\dfrac{2r_0K_0}{U_0}$; $r_a = -\dfrac{r_0K_v}{W}$; $v_a = \dfrac{v_0W}{K_0}$.

12.11. *Hint.* Use the results of Problems 10.4 and 2.18.

12.12. *Hint.* Consider the change in the kinetic and potential energies of the interacting bodies for any possible displacement (the principle of virtual displacements).

12.13. See Problem 12.12. **12.14.** 0.83 tonne; 15.6 tonnes.

12.15. 9 km.

13. The Law of Conservation of Energy

13.1. 2.5 km/s. **13.2.** 89%.

13.3. 3.8×10^{26} W; 4.2×10^9 kg/s; 1.5×10^{12} years $= 4.7 \times 10^9$ s.

13.4. A half of the initial kinetic energy is transformed into internal energy.

13.5. $0.218M_0$. **13.6.** (1) 4.7 GeV, 7.2 GeV; (2) 12.1 GeV, 65.8 GeV.

13.7. 3.46. TeV [*Hint.* Use the results of the previous problem.]

13.8. 1 GeV.

13.9 *Hint.* Compare the accelerating potentials needed to obtain the same internal energies of the bunch.

13.10. 157 GeV; 886 MeV.

14. Rotational Dynamics of a Rigid Body

14.1. *Hint.* Draw the axis of rotation perpendicularly to the plane through an arbitrary point in the plane of the forces. Compute the moment of each force about this axis and find their sum.

14.3. 1.3×10^2 N·m. **14.4.** 4 kJ. **14.5.** $\dfrac{3}{2}MR^2$.

14.6. $\dfrac{45}{32}mR^2$. [*Hint.* The cut is considered as a negative mass.]

14.7. *Hint.* Divide the disk into thin concentric rings.

14.8. $0.4MR^2$.

14.9. $0.3MR^2$. [*Hint.* Divide the body into thin disks perpendicular to the axis of rotation.]

14.12. $v = \sqrt{3gl(\cos\alpha - \cos\alpha_0)}$. **14.13.** 2.7 m/s; 3.4 m/s.

14.14. 2.3 m/s. **14.15.** 2.5×10^2 N. **14.16.** 3.5 s; 0.58 m/s.

14.17. $a = g\dfrac{m_2 - m_1}{m_1 + m_2 + I/r^2}$. **14.18.** $\alpha = \arccos 0.59 = 54°$.

14.19. 83 r.p.m. **14.20.** 21.6 r.p.m.; 380 J.
14.21. 15 km; 10^{-3} s. **14.22.** 3.6×10^{45} J; 1.6×10^{36} J.

15. Non-inertial Frames of Reference and Gravitation

15.2. *Hint.* In a rotating frame of reference a centrifugal force of inertia acts on a body at rest in this frame, the force being equal to the product of the mass and the centripetal acceleration, taken with the opposite sign: $I_{cf} = -m\omega^2 r$.

15.6. $\omega \geqslant \sqrt{\gamma M/R^3}$. **15.7.** 28 s.

15.8. $\tan \dfrac{\alpha}{2} = \sqrt{\dfrac{m\omega^2}{2k}}$; $\omega_{max} \leqslant \sqrt{\dfrac{2k}{19m}}$.

15.9. *Hint.* Introduce a rotating frame of reference and use the result of Problem 3.14.

15.11. 7 r.p.m. **15.12.** 330 ns.

15.13. The Sun: 2.1×10^{-6}; the white dwarf: 1.5×10^{-3}; the pulsar: 16%.

16. An Ideal Gas

16.3. On the Moon 1 mm Hg = 22.1 Pa; on Venus 1 mm Hg = = 116 Pa.

16.4. 5.1 mm; 40%. **16.5.** 5830 r.p.m.; 64 m/s; 9%.

16.6. *Hint.* Compare the velocity of thermal motion of the hydrogen atoms with the escape velocity.

16.7. 180 km [*Hint.* Use the result of Problem 4.7.]

16.8. 10^4 Pa; 0.24 mm. **16.9.** 6×10^{13} Pa; 6×10^6 K; 10^{30} m^{-3}.

16.10. See hint for Problem 16.6.

16.11. 1.3×10^{-5} kg/m^3; 0.8 Pa = 6×10^{-3} mm Hg.

16.12. 2×10^5 N; 7×10^4 N. **16.13.** NH_3.

16.15. 1.2×10^6 Pa. **16.16.** 72.5% nitrogen and 27.5% oxygen.

16.17. $N_A = (5.9 \pm 0.3) \times 10^{26}$ kmole^{-1}. [*Hint.* The Brownian particles behave like gigantic molecules, and the barometric distribution is valid for them.]

16.18. $n = n_0 e^{\frac{m\omega^2 r^2}{2kT}}$.

16.19. $n_2 : n_1 = 176 : 1$; $x = \exp\left\{\dfrac{(M_2 - M_1)\,\omega^2 r^2}{2RT}\right\} = 1.27$.

16.20. 20 times. [*Hint.* See § 27.9.].

16.21. *Hint.* Note that by definition $e = \lim\limits_{x \to 0}(1 + x)^{1/x}$.

16.22. *Hint.* Find the forces acting on a vertical gas column of infinitesimal height and integrate the equation obtained.

16.23. *Hint.* Using the barometric distribution find the molar mass of the gas.

17. The First Law of Thermodynamics

17.1. By 9 kJ; 6 kJ. **17.2.** 1.52 kJ.

17.3. Helium:
$3.10 \times 10^3 \leqslant c_V \leqslant 3.20 \times 10^3$ J/(kg·K); $5.17 \times 10^3 \leqslant c_p \leqslant$ $\leqslant 5.28 \times 10^3$ J/(kg·K).
Neon:
$6.14 \times 10^2 \leqslant c_V \leqslant 6.34 \times 10^2$ J/(kg·K); $1.03 \times 10^3 \leqslant c_p \leqslant$ $\leqslant 1.05 \times 10^3$ J/(kg·K).

17.4. $7.21 \times 10^2 \leqslant c_V \leqslant 7.60 \times 10^2$ J/(kg·K); $1.02 \times 10^3 \leqslant c_p \leqslant$ $\leqslant 1.06 \times 10^3$ J/(kg·K).

17.5. 1.38 kJ; 4.83 kJ; 1.9 m.

17.6. 1.8×10^5 J; 4.8×10^5 J; 6.6×10^5 J; 1.71 kJ/(kmole·K); $C_{mV} < C_m < C_{mp}$.

17.11. *Hint.* Make use of the first law of thermodynamics for an adiabatic process and eliminate the temperature with the aid of the Mendeleev-Clapeyron equation.

17.12. $(p/p_0)^{\gamma-1} = (T/T_0)^\gamma$; $(V/V_0)^{\gamma-1} = T_0/T$.

17.13. 2.8×10^6 Pa; 1.6×10^6 Pa; it is more difficult to compress the gas adiabatically.

17.14. 3.2×10^4 Pa; 6.7×10^4 Pa. **17.15.** $V_1/V_2 = 21$.

17.16. 1.4×10^{-46} kg·m²; 6 K. [*Hint.* See § 27.9.]

17.17. 2.2×10^3 K [*Hint.* See § 27.9.]

18. The Second Law of Thermodynamics

18.1. 1/4; 1/2; 1/9. **18.2.** 1/3; 1/6. **18.3.** 1/81; 1/105.

18.4. $1:4:6:4:1$. **18.7.** $w_n = (V/V_0)^n$.

18.11. $Q = \int\limits_{S_1}^{S_2} T \, dS$. **18.12.** $Q_T = T(S_2 - S_1)$.

18.13. $S_2 - S_1 = \dfrac{m}{M} \left(C_{mV} \ln \dfrac{T_2}{T_1} + R \ln \dfrac{V_2}{V_1} \right)$.

18.17. $\eta = 1 - x^{\gamma-1}$

18.18. 52%. The fact that the real efficiency is below the ideal is due to irreversible energy losses (friction, heat exchange with the environment, etc.).

18.19. $S = k \ln W + \text{const.}$

19. Fundamentals of Fluid Dynamics

19.1. 1.1 m. **19.2.** 1.6×10^5 Pa = 1.58 atm.

19.3. $\mu = \dfrac{\pi D^2 d^2}{4} \sqrt{\dfrac{2\rho\rho_0 gh}{D^4 - d^4}} = 1.7 \times 10^{-2}$ kg/s.

19.4. *Hint.* Note that in this case the work done by the forces of pressure is equal to the change in the total mechanical energy $\left(p + \dfrac{\rho v^2}{2} + \rho g h = \text{const}\right)$.

19.5. $v = \sqrt{2gh}$. **19.6.** $\dfrac{v_1^2}{2} + \dfrac{a_1^2}{\gamma - 1} = \dfrac{v_2^2}{2} + \dfrac{a_2^2}{\gamma - 1}$.

19.7. 4.7×10^3 m/s.

19.8. $p/p_0 = 5.68$; $T/T_0 = 1.89$ (adiabatic compression for a shock); $p/p_0 = 4.67$; $T/T_0 = 1.56$ (adiabatic compression for a quasi-static process).

19.9. 2 km.

19.10. $\Delta S_{sp} = \dfrac{m}{M} C_{mV} \ln \dfrac{\dfrac{\gamma + 1}{\gamma - 1} \cdot \dfrac{\rho_2}{\rho_1} - 1}{\left(\dfrac{\gamma + 1}{\gamma - 1} - \dfrac{\rho_2}{\rho_1}\right)\left(\dfrac{\rho_2}{\rho_1}\right)^{\gamma}}$.

[*Hint.* Consider a cycle made up of three processes: shock compression, quasi-static adiabatic expansion and isochoric (constant volume) cooling of the gas to its original state (see § 30.9).]

19.11. 6.8×10^2 m/s; 1.4×10^3 m/s. **19.12.** 3300 K; 73%.

19.13. 588 kg/s; 2.34 kg/m³; 3.86×10^5 Pa = 3.8 atm.

19.14. 1.65×10^4 Pa = 124 mm Hg. **19.15.** 6 m/s.

19.16. 2.26×10^5 Pa = 2.2 atm; 172 kW. **19.17.** Yes; no; no.

20. Solids

20.1. 7.6×10^4 N. **20.2.** $F = ES \left| \dfrac{\Delta l}{l} \right|$; $k = \dfrac{ES}{l}$.

20.3. 3.3 mm; 2.4 tonnes. **20.4.** $F = 0.82 F_0$.

20.5. 3.8×10^{10} Pa; 1.4×10^{11} Pa.

20.6. Due to the presence of defects in the crystal lattice.

20.7. 3700 r.p.m.; 7500 r.p.m. **20.8.** 2.8×10^6 Pa = 28 atm.

20.10. 1.3×10^8 Pa. **20.11.** 1.2×10^9 Pa; the shell suffers plastic deformation.

20.12. 2.4×10^8 Pa = 2.4×10^3 atm. **20.13.** 1.0×10^{-3} K⁻¹.

20.14. One atom. **20.15.** Four atoms. **20.16.** Six atoms.

21. Liquids

21.1. In the temperature range from 0 °C to 100 °C the law is valid; the activation energy is $\varepsilon_0 = 4.2 \times 10^{-21}$ J = 2.6×10^{-2} eV.

21.2. 3.7 cm.

21.3. *Hint.* Find the contact angle for the case when water rises to the upper end of the capillary.

21.4. Energy of 0.12 mJ in the form of heat will be liberated.

21.5. 0.11 m/s.
21.6. Warm water runs more quickly. [*Hint.* Compare flow rates at two different temperatures, for instance, at 20 °C and 80 °C.]
21.7. A column of double the height.
21.8. $h = 2\sigma/\rho g d$. [*Hint.* Compare with the solution of Problem 20.9.]
21.9. 0.144 N. **21.10.** $R = R_1 R_2/(R_1 - R_2)$; 120°.

22. Vapours

22.1. Yes, it may. [*Hint.* Check several points.]
22.2. Does not contravene. [*Hint.* Investigate the change in the density of the saturated vapour caused by the change in the temperature.]
22.3. Less than 7.6 l. **22.4.** More than 125 l. **22.5.** 7.8 g/m³; 51%.
22.6. The precipitation will be 5.6 g of dew for every cubic meter of air.
22.7. 37%. **22.8.** Do not satisfy.
22.9. 304.4 K; 7.39 MPa; 464 kg/m³.

23. Phase Transitions

23.1. 1.69×10^5 J/kg $= 40$ kcal/kg; 22.6×10^5 J/kg $= 499$ kcal/kg.
23.2. *Hint.* Find the dependence of the melting point of ice on pressure from the phase diagram.
23.3. A mixture of 6.8 kg of water and 1.4 kg of ice is formed.
23.4. Water at 54 °C is produced.
23.5. A mixture of 1.2 kg of water and 0.3 kg of ice is produced.
23.6. Water at 4.5 °C is produced.
23.7. 11%. **23.8.** 4.7 m/s. **23.9.** 2.7%. **23.10.** 854 g.
23.11. (a) 216.5 K $< T <$ 304.4 K; (b) the pressure is less than 5.18×10^5 Pa; the temperature is below 216.5 K.

24. A Field of Fixed Charges in a Vacuum

24.1. 23%.
24.2. A circle whose centre lies on the straight line connecting the charges, at a distance $2a$ to the right of the positive charge. The radius of the circle is $4a$.
24.3. N·m $=$ C·V $=$ J. **24.4.** 3.2×10^{-18} C.

24.7.
$$\varphi = \frac{q}{4\pi\varepsilon_0 \sqrt{a^2 + x^2}}.$$

24.8. (a) $F_r = 0$; $M = \dfrac{Qp_e}{4\pi\varepsilon_0 r^2}$; (b) $F_r = -\dfrac{-2Qp_e}{4\pi\varepsilon_0 r^3}$; $M = 0$.

24.9.
$$C = C_1 + C_2.$$

24.10. $\dfrac{1}{C} = \dfrac{1}{C_1} + \dfrac{1}{C_2}$.   **24.11.** $n\varphi_0$;   it will not change.

24.13. *Hint.* Make use of considerations of symmetry and the fact that there are no charges inside the sphere.

24.14. *Hint.* Surround the sphere with another sphere carrying a charge of opposite sign and make use of the results of § 37.5.

24.15. $E_{int} = \rho r/3\varepsilon_0$. [*Hint.* Use the results of the previous problems.]

24.16. $C = \dfrac{4\pi\varepsilon_0 R R_1}{R - R_1}$; $\delta = \dfrac{R_1 - R}{R} = \dfrac{d}{R}$.

24.17. $W = \dfrac{e^2}{8\pi\varepsilon_0 a}$; $a = \dfrac{e^2}{8\pi\varepsilon_0 m_e c^2} = 1.4 \times 10^{-5}$ m.

24.18. $p = \dfrac{q^2}{32\pi^2\varepsilon_0 R^4}$.   **24.19.** 10^{-8} C.

24.20. $m = \dfrac{\varepsilon_0 S\varphi^2}{2gd^2} = 3.6 \times 10^{-3}$ kg.

24.21. $\varphi_{bat} = \dfrac{1}{2}(\varphi_1 + \varphi_2)$; $\Delta W = \dfrac{1}{4} C (\varphi_1 - \varphi_2)^2$.

25. Dielectrics

25.1. From 4.4×10^{-5} C/m^2 to 5.3×10^{-5} C/m^2 depending on the value of ε for mica.

25.2. From 7.4×10^{-6} C/m^2 to 5.6×10^{-5} C/m^2.

25.3. 0.03 μF, breakdown voltage is 4 kV.

25.4. $C = \dfrac{\varepsilon\varepsilon_0 S}{\varepsilon d_0 - (\varepsilon - 1) d}$.

25.5. $C = \dfrac{\varepsilon_0 S [l_0 + (\varepsilon - 1) l]}{dl_0}$.

25.6. 26 cm. **25.7.** $h = -\dfrac{a}{2(\varepsilon - 1)} + \sqrt{\dfrac{a^2}{4(\varepsilon - 1)^2} + \dfrac{\varepsilon_0 a\varphi_0^2}{\rho gd^2}}$.

25.8. $h = \dfrac{(\varepsilon - 1)\,\varepsilon_0\varphi^2}{\rho gd^2}$.

25.9. 6.45×10^{-30} C·m.   **25.10.** 1.78×10^{-36} C·m.

26. Direct Current

26.1. $R = \dfrac{4\rho x (l - x)}{\pi D^2 l}$;   11 cm.

26.2. 26   mohm. **26.3.** $x = 2r \sin 18° = 0.62r$. **26.4.** r.

26.5. $R = \dfrac{r}{3} + \dfrac{r}{6} + \dfrac{r}{3} = \dfrac{5r}{6}$.

26.6. $R_x = R l_1/l_2 = Rl/(L - l)$, where $L = AB$, $l = BD$.

26.7. In the middle of the slide wire.

26.8. (a) 3.5×10^6 A/m²; 6.2×10^{-2} V/m; (b) 1.3×10^6 A/m²; 2.2×10^{-2} V/m.

26.9. 7.4 μohm; 0.74 mV.

26.10. (a) $\mathscr{E} = ne$, $R_i = nr$; (b) $\mathscr{E} = e$; $R_i = r/n$; (c) $\mathscr{E} = me$, $R_i = mr/k = m^2r/n$.

26.11. 1 ohm. **26.12.** $P_{tot} = \mathscr{E}^2/(R + r)$; $P_{ext} = \mathscr{E}^2R/(R + r)^2$.

26.13. *Hint.* Find the extrema of the expressions obtained in Problem 26.12.

26.14. 14.4 W; 51.6 W.

26.15. 33.3 kohm; 0.3 Mohm; 3 Mohm; 0.181 ohm; 0.036 ohm.

26.16. 31 bulbs.

26.17. *Hint.* Use a four-position switch which can connect both windings either independently, or in parallel.

26.18. 9.6 m. **26.19.** 0.1 MJ.

26.20. $i = i_0 e^{-t/\tau}$ where $\tau = RC$.

26.21. (a) If $\mathscr{E} < \varphi_0$, $i = 0$, $\varphi_S = \mathscr{E}$, $\varphi_R = 0$.
(b) If $\mathscr{E} > \varphi_0$, $i = (\mathscr{E} - \varphi_0)/R$, $\varphi_S = \varphi_0$, $\varphi_R = \mathscr{E} - \varphi_0$.

26.22. $i = i_0$, $\varphi_R = i_0R$, $\varphi_B = \mathscr{E} - i_0R$.

27. Magnetic Field in a Vacuum

27.1. *Hint.* Consider whether or not the spring constant is invariant.

27.2. $F = 0.141F_{coul}$. [*Hint.* Use the law of transformation of the lateral force.]

27.3. *Hint.* Consider the interaction of a charge moving parallel to the conductor with the charges in the conductor, making use of different reference frames.

27.4. 3.1×10^{-5} T; 1.1×10^{-5} T. **27.5.** 6.3×10^{-2} T; 3.1×10^{-2} T.

27.6. The field is almost homogeneous, within a relative error of 6%.

27.7. The radius of the ring 0.57 m. **27.8.** 3.0×10^{-5} C.

27.9. 2.5×10^{-3} A/m; 4.9×10^{-7} A·m²; 4.1×10^{-4} C/kg.

27.10. $\dfrac{dB}{dx} = -\dfrac{6\mu_0 p_m x}{4\pi r^5}$, where $r = \sqrt{a^2 + x^2}$.

28. Charges and Currents in a Magnetic Field

28.1. 2.8×10^7 m/s; 16 MeV. **28.2.** $0.856c = 2.57 \times 10^8$ m/s; 99 MeV.

28.3. (a) Nonrelativistic particle: $R_1/R_2 = \sqrt{K_1/K_2}$.

(b) Relativistic particle: $R_1/R_2 = \sqrt{\dfrac{K_1(2\mathscr{E}_0 + K_1)}{K_2(2\mathscr{E}_0 + K_2)}}$.

28.4. 7 ns.

28.5. A helix winding around the lines of induction. The radius of the circle is 23 mm, the pitch is 39 mm.

28.6. *Hint.* Use the results of the previous problem.

28.7. 51 mm.

28.8. 1.38×10^4 V/m. [*Hint.* Use the result of Problem 4.14.]

28.9. 4; 42; 3.0 MHz. **28.10.** 6.3×10^{-3} T; 87 kHz; 1.1 T; 0.2 MHz.

28.11. 10^8 m/s; no.   **28.12.** 2.3 mm.

28.13. 4.02 amu ($_2He^4$) and 3.01 amu ($_2He^3$, or $_1H^3$).

28.14. 1.2×10^{-5} N·m.   **28.15.**   22.5°; 10^{-10} N·m/deg = 5.7 × $\times 10^{-9}$ N·m/rad.

28.16. $F = -\dfrac{6\mu_0 p_m^2}{4\pi r^4}$.   **28.17.** 2.9×10^{-5} N.

28.18. *Hint.* Find the orientation of the velocity vector of the circulating charge with respect to the induction vector.

28.19. *Hint.* Determine how the magnetic field acts on the circulating charge, if its orbital magnetic moment is directed against the field.

28.20. Less than 2.5 MeV.

29. Magnetic Materials

29.1. 1.5×10^{-9} A·m^2; against the field. **29.2.** 1.5×10^{-9} A·m^2; along the field. **29.3.** 9.0×10^{-9} A/m.

29.4. (a) 1.1% greater; (b) 4.2% greater.

29.5. 33 A/m; 130 A/m.

29.6. *Hint.* Compare the energy of thermal motion with the energy of interaction of two Bohr magnetons, separated by the interatomic distance.

29.7. Above 9.0×10^{-2} eV. [*Hint.* Estimate the energy of thermal motion at the Curie temperature.]

29.8. 1.27×10^{-5} m ≈ 0.01 mm. **29.9** $\mu_{max} = 9.6 \times 10^3$ at $H = 75$ A/m.

29.10. 100 A/m; 1.26 T; 10^6 A/m; 1.8×10^5 A/m.

29.11.

H, A/m	50	75	100	200	500	1000	1500
μ'	∞	6.4×10^2	1.6×10^2	8×10^2	4×10^2	10	5

30. Electromagnetic Induction

30.1. 0.2 V; it will not. **30.2.** $\Delta\varphi = \mathscr{E} = Bl \sqrt{2g(H-h)}$.

30.3. It will move downwards at a stationary velocity $v_{stat} = mgR/B^2l^2$.

30.4. $\Delta\varphi = B\omega l^2/2$. **30.5.** 0.01 N.

30.6. $|\mathscr{E}| = \dfrac{3\pi\mu_0 iwa^2r^2v\,(x_0-vt)}{2\,[a^2+(x_0-vt)^2]^{5/2}}.$

30.7. 1.8×10^{-2} Wb. **30.8.** 2.5 T.

30.9. The dielectric is polarized. **30.10.** 1.25 µC.

30.11. 25 W. **30.12.** 5.9 mH. **30.13.** 29.5 V.

30.14. 41 H; 0.82 J; 1.36×10^2 J/m³. **30.15.** 3.1×10^{-2} J/m³; 1.8×10^{-5} J.

30.16. 4.5×10^3 N; 1.5×10^2 N. **30.17.** 1.5 H.

30.18. $i = I_\mathrm{M}\,(1 - e^{-t/\tau})$, where $I_\mathrm{M} = \mathscr{E}/R$, $\tau = L/R$.

30.19. $t = 2.3L/R.$

31. Classical Electron Theory

31.1. $\dfrac{q}{m} = \dfrac{\pi^2d^2nN}{QR} = 1.8 \times 10^{11}$ C/kg.

31.2. 1.1×10^{-8} V; will not change. **31.3.** 1.1×10^{29} m⁻³; 3.2×10^{-3} m²/(V·s).

31.4. 1.07×10^{-10} m³/C.

31.5. 6.2×10^{20} m⁻³; 4.0 m²/(V·s). **31.6.** 0.24 mm/s.

31.7. 4×10^{-14} s; 400 Å. **31.8.** 131 °C. **31.9.** 65 C.

31.10. 3.6×10^3 m/s. **31.11.** 38 kW/m². **31.12.** 90 MJ.

31.13. 4 Å. **31.14.** 4.1×10^2 W/(m·K); 68 W/(m·K). [*Hint.* Use the Wiedemann-Franz law.]

32. Electrical Conductivity of Electrolytes

32.1. 78%. **32.2.** 65 µm. **32.3.** 200 mg. **32.4.** 5 g.

32.5. 1.52 V. **32.6.** 6.25×10^{-11} kg; 9.1×10^{-3} J.

32.7. Over 10^3 kW·h; more than 40 roubles.

33. Electric Current in a Vacuum and in Gases

33.1. 160 mA. **33.2.** Increases 21 times.

33.3. 4.1×10^{-5} N.

33.4. A coated cathode is 3.3 times more efficient.

33.5. 2 kohm; 20. **33.6.** 1.15×10^{14} m⁻³; 4.3×10^{-12}.

33.7. 5.0×10^{-8} ohm⁻¹·m⁻¹.

33.8. *Hint.* Consider separately the phenomena that take place when the current is much less than the saturation current and when the current is saturated.

33.9. 2.5×10^{14} m⁻³·s⁻¹. **33.11.** 5.2 mm; 0.12 mm.

33.12. It will. [*Hint.* Find the Stewart number.]

33.13. It will not. **33.14.** 2.2×10^4 T. **33.15.** 4×10^{14} Pa; 3×10^{32} Pa.

34. Harmonic Vibrations

34.1. 20 cm; 48 Hz; 2.1×10^{-2} s; 2 rad $= 114°39'$.

34.2. $v = 1.6\pi \cos \left(20\pi t + \dfrac{3\pi}{4} \right)$; $a = 32\pi^2 \cos \left(20\pi t + \dfrac{5\pi}{4} \right)$;

$F = 6.4\pi^2 \cos \left(20\pi t + \dfrac{5\pi}{4} \right)$;   5.0 m/s; 3.2×10^2 m/s²; 64 N.

34.3. $K = 2.5 \cos^2 \left(20\pi t + \dfrac{3\pi}{4} \right)$; $U = 2.5 \cos^2 \left(20\pi t + \dfrac{5\pi}{4} \right)$;

$W = 2.5$ J.

34.4. 20 Hz; 50 ms. **34.5.** $s = 0.064 \cos \left(\pi t + \dfrac{3\pi}{2} \right) = 0.064 \sin \pi t$.

34.6. $s = 0.05 \cos (126 t + 0.53)$; 1.6 m. **34.7.** 30 m/s.

34.8. $B = \dfrac{3A \sqrt{5}}{8} = 0.84 A$; $\varphi = \arctan \dfrac{1}{2} = 0.464$ rad $= 26.6°$.

34.9. 0.5 s; 0.4 ms.
34.10. *Hint.* Write the product of the sinusoidal functions as a sum.

35. Free Vibrations

35.1. $\omega_0 = \sqrt{k/m} = \sqrt{g/l}$. [*Hint.* The spring constant is $k = F/x = mg/l$.]

35.2. 1.6 Hz; 2.1×10^2; 21 s.

35.3. 11 swings, i.e. almost 3 complete oscillations. [*Hint.* Do the calculations using the law of conservation of energy in the presence of external friction.]

35.4. $\omega_0^{\text{isot}} = \sqrt{2pV/md^2}$. **35.5.** $\omega_0^{\text{ad}} = \sqrt{2\gamma pV/md^2} = \omega_0^{\text{isot}} \sqrt{\gamma}$.

35.6. 1.6 Hz; 0.63 s. **35.7.** $\nu_0 = \dfrac{1}{2\pi} \sqrt{\dfrac{\rho_0 g}{\rho h}} = 1.7$ Hz; 0.6 s.

35.8. By 4 s. **35.9.** 1.42 s; 26°36'. **35.10.** 2.08 s. **35.11.** $\varepsilon = 1\%$.

35.12. $T = 2\pi \sqrt{2l/3g}$; $L = 2l/3$. **35.13.** 1.5 s.
35.14. 2.0 MHz; 5.0×10^{-7} s; 800.

36. Forced Vibrations. Alternating Current

36.1. 2.7 mm; 60 mm; 0.7 mm. **36.3.** 80 cm.

36.4. $\tau_{\text{sp}} = \dfrac{2QT_0}{\pi} = 2 \times 10^3 T_0 = 2$ ms; not greater than $N = \dfrac{\omega_0}{16Q} = 125$ pulses/s.

36.5. *Hint.* Write the voltage in the form $u = U_M \cos \omega t$, the current in the form $i = I_M \cos (\omega t + \varphi)$ and use the data of § 54.2 to find the voltage drop across the inductive reactance.

36.6. *Hint.* Write the voltage and the current in the same form as in Problem 36.5. Note that the current is the time derivative of the charge.

36.7. $Z = \sqrt{R^2 + L^2\omega^2}$; $\varphi = -\arctan(L\omega/R)$.

36.8. $Z = \sqrt{R^2 + \dfrac{1}{C^2\omega^2}}$; $\varphi = \arctan\dfrac{1}{RC\omega}$.

36.9. $Z = \dfrac{R}{\sqrt{1 + R^2C^2\omega^2}}$; $\varphi = \arctan RC\omega$.

36.10. $Z = R\sqrt{1 + \dfrac{Q^2}{\gamma^2}(\gamma^2 - 1)^2}$.

36.11. The current in the unbranched section of the circuit is

$$I = U\sqrt{\frac{R^2C^2\omega^2 + (LC\omega^2 - 1)^2}{R^2 + L^2\omega^2}} = \frac{U}{R}\sqrt{\frac{\gamma^2/Q^2 + (\gamma^2 - 1)^2}{1 + Q^2\gamma^2}}$$

It is minimum at resonance $\left(\gamma = \dfrac{\omega}{\omega_0} = 1\right)$.

$$\cos\varphi = \frac{R}{\sqrt{(R^2 + L^2\omega^2)[R^2C^2\omega^2 + (LC\omega^2 - 1)^2]}}$$

$$\cos\varphi_{res} = \frac{1}{C\omega\sqrt{R^2 + L^2\omega^2}}$$

36.12. 61 W. **36.13.** 80 Hz; 24 W.

36.14. *Hint.* Consider the operating principles of the instrument, and find the parameters which determine the average torque acting on the moving part of the instrument.

36.15. 28°40′; 10.5 ohm; 9.3 ohm. **36.16.** It will glow.

36.17. It cannot. **36.18.** 230 kV.

36.19. 33 turns; 73 mm²; 6×10^{-3} ohm; 260 W; 97%.

36.21. *Hint.* Use the fact that the ohmic resistance of the solid copper ring is much less than its inductive reactance.

36.22. $\cos\varphi = 0.8$; $\varphi = 37°$.

37. Elastic Waves

37.1. $a/\bar{v} = \sqrt{\gamma/3} = 0.68$. **37.2.** 7.0×10^{10} Pa.

37.3. 1.4×10^3 m/s; 4.9×10^{-10} Pa⁻¹. **37.4.** 1.42.

37.5. 3.5×10^{-5} J/m³; 2.7 μm. **37.6.** 1.4 μm; 0.9 μm.

37.7. 3.5 dB. **37.8.** 1.1 nW/m²; 4.4 dB.

37.9. $\mu = \dfrac{\ln 2}{L} = \dfrac{2.3\log 2}{L} = \dfrac{0.693}{L}$.

37.10. $\mathscr{L}_0 - \mathscr{L} = 4.34\mu x = 4.2 \times 10^{-2}$ dB.

37.11. 1.5 m/s. **37.12.** 593 Hz; 456 Hz.

37.13. 302 Hz; 1.1 m; 332 m/s; $\lambda/A = 1.8 \times 10^5$; $u/V_M = 2.9 \times 10^4$. **37.14.** 0.55 m; 2.1 rad = 121°.

37.15. From 17 m to 17 mm; from 70 m to 70 mm.
37.16. 28%. **37.17.** 12%.
37.18. *Hint.* Estimate the value of the reflection coefficient at the boundary between the supersonic transducer surface and the air.
37.19. About 60 mm.

38. Interference and Diffraction

38.1. *Hint.* Consider the sign of the amplitude of the reflected wave.
38.2. 0.41 MHz; will not change. **38.3.** 9.7 cm.
38.4. The third; 0.5 kHz. **38.5.** 18.6°C or 15.4°C.
38.6. 330 $\pm$ 3 m/s; $\varepsilon = 0.8\%$. **38.7.** 12°. **38.8.** 6 cm.

39. Electromagnetic Waves

39.1. 5 m; 3.4 m. **39.2.** $\nu_0 = \dfrac{c}{2l}$; $\nu = (2n+1)\dfrac{c}{2l}$.

39.3. 5.1 m. **39.4.** $\varepsilon = 4.7$ (kerosene); 8.3×10^{-7} Pa; 115 J.
39.5. 25 W; 197 ohm. **39.6.** 97 W. **39.7.** $R \approx 0.1$ ohm; $L \approx 8$ μH; $C \approx 22$ μμF.
39.8. *Hint.* Apply expression (59.22) from § 59.8.
39.9. *Hint.* Note that the electromagnetic field is not a reference frame. Hence in electrodynamics the motion of the source and the motion of the observer are equivalent and the change in the frequency is the same in each case.
39.10. $(\Delta\nu/\nu)_{\text{Dop}} = 5 \times 10^{-5}$; $(\Delta\nu/\nu)_{\text{grav}} = 20 \times 10^{-5}$.
39.11. 42 nm. **39.12.** 2.19×10^6 s $= 25.3$ days.
39.13. When the source moves away from the observer,

$$z = \sqrt{\frac{1+\beta}{1-\beta}} - 1$$

and when it approaches,

$$z = 1 - \sqrt{\frac{1-\beta}{1+\beta}}$$

where $\beta = v/c$.

39.14. (1) $\beta = 0.0334$, $v = 10^7$ m/s; (2) $\beta = 0.362$, $v = 1.1 \times 10^8$ m/s; (3) $\beta = 0.67$, $v = 2.0 \times 10^8$ m/s.
39.15. 18 km/s. **39.16.** 1.6×10^{32} kg; 2.7×10^{10} m.

40. Interference and Diffraction of Light

40.1. 0.9 mm; 0.7 mm
40.2. There are three maxima—the zero-order maximum and two first-order maxima; 0.56 mm.
40.3. 6.0×10^2 nm. **40.4.** 2.73×10^{-2} mm.
40.5. 1.00014. **40.6.** 0.61 μm.

40.8. $3°35'$; $7°11'$. [*Hint.* Use the condition for the minima in the case of diffraction on a single slit.]

40.9. $15°$; there are altogether seven maxima.

40.10. 534 nm. **40.11.** $18''$; 1.6×10^4. **40.12.** 20 mm; 8 mm.

40.13. We shall be able to see them; $25''$.

40.14. *Hint.* Consider the condition for the maximum of two adjacent rays, expressing it in terms of the glancing angles.

40.15. 24 Å.

40.16. 2.85 Å. [*Hint.* Apply the Bragg condition.]

41. Dispersion and Absorption of Light

41.1. $49°19'$; $50°10'$. **41.2.** 3.5 MeV.

41.3. $\varepsilon = 1 - \dfrac{e^2 n_0}{\varepsilon_0 m_e \omega^2}$. [*Hint.* One should apply the dispersion law for gases, noting that the natural frequency of oscillations of a free electron is zero.]

41.4. $U = \dfrac{c}{n + \omega \dfrac{dn}{d\omega}}$.

41.5. *Hint.* Consider separately the parts of the spectrum for which $n > 1$ and $n < 1$.

41.6. $n = 1 - \dfrac{e^2 n_0}{2\varepsilon_0 m_e \omega^2}$; $u = c/n$; $U = cn$.

41.7. The signal travels not at the phase velocity, but at the group velocity, which is below the limiting velocity.

41.8. It cannot. **41.9.** 2.4×10^{13} m^{-3}.

41.10. $n = 1 - \dfrac{e^2 n_0 \lambda^2}{8\pi^2 \varepsilon_0 m_e c^2} = 1 - 2.3 \times 10^{-7}$.

41.11. $R = \left(\dfrac{e^2 n_0}{4\varepsilon_0 m_e \omega^2} \right)^2$.

41.12. 0.345; 0.361; $R_{\text{viol}}/R_{\text{red}} = 1.05$. **41.13.** 3.0×10^8 m/s.

41.14. *Hint.* Use the results of Problem 41.6.

41.15. $U = 1.9 \times 10^8$ m/s; $u = 2.0 \times 10^8$ m/s.

41.16. 35 m^{-1}; 2.0 cm.

41.17. $k = \dfrac{I}{I_0} = \dfrac{r_1^2}{r_2^2} \cdot \dfrac{16n^2}{(n+1)^4} \, e^{-\mu(r_2 - r_1)}$.

41.18. 98%; 10 Å. **41.19.** 6 layers. **41.20.** 1.6 cm.

42. Polarization of Light

42.1. It will be reduced to one fifth of its initial value.

42.2. $I = \dfrac{1}{2} I_0 \sin^2 \alpha \cos^2 \alpha$; $45°$.

42.3. There will be no interference pattern.

42.4. $(2m + 1) \times 0.856$ µm; $(2m + 1) \times 0.78\pi$ rad $= (2m + 1) \times$ $\times 140°$.

42.5. $d_{quartz}/d_{calcite} = 19$. **42.6.** 2.1×10^2 kg/m³.

42.7. $(2m + 1) \times 5.19$ mm; $(2m + 1) \times 2.75$ mm.

43. Geometrical Optics

43.1. 2.6 mm. **43.2.** 41°. **43.4.** 1.8 m. **43.5.** 18.7°; 7.4°.

43.6. 2.2 diopters; —1.0 diopter.

43.7. In the posterior focus of the right-hand lens.

43.8. *Hint.* Bring the lenses in Fig. 43.7 together until they are in contact.

43.9. *Hint.* Use the result of the previous problem.

43.10. —3.8 diopters; —1.1 diopters. **43.11.** $\Phi = (n - 1)/R$.

43.12. 2.4 cm. **43.13.** $x = f/2$; $\beta = h/H = 1/2$. **43.14.** 81°40'.

43.15. $\alpha = \beta^2$ (for $x \ll a - f$).

43.16. An elongated ellipsoid of rotation.

43.17. 2.4 cm; 6%. **43.18.** 13.3 diopters.

43.19. *Hint.* See § 65.5, Fig. 65.9.

43.21. A convex lens. **43.22.** A concave lens.

43.23. *Hint.* See Problem 10.4. **43.24.** No.

44. Optical Instruments

44.1. 1.76 W; 8.8 W; 2.9 W. **44.2.** 11 V/m; 3.7×10^{-8} T.

44.3. $\dfrac{E_{wall}}{E_{floor}} = \dfrac{D}{2h}$. **44.4.** $E_{edge} = \dfrac{2I}{3r^2 \sqrt{3}} = \dfrac{0.38I}{r^2}$; $E_{centre} = \dfrac{2I}{r^2}$.

44.5. $E = 5/4 E_0$. **44.6.** 10 lx; 2.8 lx.

44.7. 5.0 lx; 2.5 lx. **44.8.** $E = \dfrac{R}{4} \cdot \dfrac{D^2}{f^2}$.

44.9. It will decrease to 1/3.2.

44.10. —7 diopter glasses.

44.11. $57'' \approx 1'$ (see § 66.4). **44.12.** 370.

44.13. 0.6 µm. **44.14.** 24 diopters; 8.3 mm; 1.2''; 830 km. **44.15.** $\gamma = = \left| \dfrac{f_{ob}}{f_{oc}} \right|$.

44.16. 35 m; 5.2 km. **44.17.** $A_{radio} = 2.5 \times 10^3$; $A_{opt} = 5.4 \times 10^6$.

44.18. Not greater than 6 ms. **44.19.** 55 mm; 0.18.

44.20. 14.5 cm.

45. Photons

45.1. 5.8×10^3 K. **45.2.** 6.16×10^3 K. **45.3.** 290 nm.

45.4. 4.3×10^{-13} W/m²; 5.4×10^{-4} W. **45.5.** 540 nm; 295 nm; 275 nm.

45.6. 41 keV; 1.1×10^8 m/s. **45.7.** 0.2 V.

45.8. 1.3 eV. **45.9.** 1.8 eV. **45.10.** 4.4 eV; 7.8 × 10⁻³⁶ kg; 2.3 × × 10⁻²⁷ kg·m/s. **45.11.** 2.5 × 10⁻² Å.

45.12. $\mathscr{E} = \mathscr{E}_0 \dfrac{\sqrt{1-\beta^2}}{1-\beta \cos \theta}$; $p = p_0 \dfrac{\sqrt{1-\beta^2}}{1-\beta \cos \theta}$.

45.13. $p = 2w \cos \alpha$, where w is the volumetric density of the energy of luminous flux.

45.14. 14 J. **45.15.** 0.3 μm.

45.16. $\Delta \mathscr{E} = \dfrac{2\mathscr{E}^2 \sin^2 (\theta/2)}{\mathscr{E}_0 + 2\mathscr{E} \sin^2 (\theta/2)}$; 1%.

45.17. $\mathscr{E}_{ph} = \dfrac{\mathscr{E}_0 \cos (\alpha + \theta/2)}{\sin \alpha \sin (\theta/2)}$; 0.37 MeV.

45.18. 83 keV; 0.15 Å.

45.19. *Hint.* Apply the laws of conservation of energy and the momentum in relativistic form.

45.20. *Hint.* Use the inertial reference frame in which the electron is at rest.

45.21. *Hint.* See § 68.7. **45.22.** It will change.

45.24. 370 MeV.

46. Elementary Quantum Mechanics

46.1. $\lambda = \dfrac{hc}{\sqrt{K (2\mathscr{E}_0 + K)}}$; $K < 0.04\mathscr{E}_0$.

46.2. $\lambda = \dfrac{hc}{\sqrt{e\varphi (2\mathscr{E}_0 + e\varphi)}}$; $\lambda_{nonrel} = \dfrac{h}{\sqrt{2me\varphi}}$.

46.3. 3 Å.

46.4. *Hint.* Compare the de Broglie wavelengths of the electron and the ion for equal accelerating potential.

46.5. 4.8 μm. **46.6.** 1.1 × 10⁻¹⁹ J = 0.68 eV; 1.1 × 10⁴ m/s; 5.4 × × 10³ K. **46.7.** 1.5 Å.

46.8. (1) $U_1 = v_1 = 5.9 \times 10^6$ m/s = 0.019c; $u_1 = c^2/v_1 = 51c =$ = 1.5 × 10¹⁰ m/s.

(2) $U_2 = v_2 = 0.549c = 1.6 \times 10^8$ m/s; $u_2 = c^2/v_2 = 1.83c =$ = 5.5 × 10⁹ m/s.

46.9. $F = h^2/4m_e L^3 = 1.2 \times 10^{-7}$ N.

46.10. 38 eV; 1.5 × 10² eV; 3.4 × 10³ eV.

46.11. 0.26 eV. They can.

46.12. $r = 4\pi \varepsilon_0 \hbar^2/e^2 m_e$.

46.13. $w = e^{-1.6} = 0.2 = 20\%$.

46.14. $a = \sqrt{8mA_0^3/eE\hbar}$; $w = e^{-a}$.

46.15. $a = 2$; $w = e^{-2} = 0.13 = 13\%$.

47. Atomic and Molecular Structure

47.1. 3.4×10^{-13} m.

47.2. $v = v_1/n$, where $v_1 = \dfrac{e^2}{4\pi\varepsilon_0 \hbar}$; $\alpha = \dfrac{v_1}{c} = \dfrac{1}{137}$.

47.3. $\mathscr{E} = \dfrac{3}{4} hcR = \dfrac{3}{4} \times 13.6$ eV $= 10.2$ eV.

47.4. $n = 3$; 1025 Å; 6560 Å; 1215 Å.

47.5. 4.2 m/s; 9.1×10^{-8} eV.

47.6. $r_1 = \dfrac{a_0}{Z} = 0.264$ Å; $\dfrac{1}{\lambda} = 4R\left(\dfrac{1}{m^2} - \dfrac{1}{n^2}\right)$

$$\lambda_1 = \frac{1}{3R} = 304.0 \text{ Å}; \quad \lambda_2 = \frac{9}{5R} = 1640 \text{ Å}.$$

47.7. (a) 1.1×10^{23} m^{-3}; 3.5 mmHg; 1.9×10^{-4} kg/m^3.
(b) 4.6×10^{20} m^{-3}; 1.4×10^{-2} mmHg; 7.7×10^{-7} kg/m^3.

47.8. $\mathscr{E} = Z^2 hcR = 9 \times 13.6 = 122.4$ eV.

47.9. Hydrogen; $v = 0.0436c = 1.3 \times 10^4$ km/s.

47.10. $a_n = n^2 \dfrac{4\pi\varepsilon_0 \hbar^2}{e^2} \cdot \dfrac{m_\mathrm{p} + m_\mu}{m_\mathrm{p} m_\mu} = n^2 a_0 \dfrac{2043}{1836 \times 207} = \dfrac{n^2 a_0}{186}$;

$$\mathscr{E}_n = -\frac{hcR}{n^2} \times 186 = -\frac{1}{n^2} \times 2.53 \text{ keV}.$$

47.11. $\dfrac{1}{\lambda} = 186R\left(\dfrac{1}{m^2} - \dfrac{1}{n^2}\right)$; $\lambda_1 = \dfrac{4}{3 \times 186R} = 6.54$ Å;

$$\lambda_2 = \frac{36}{5 \times 186R} = 35.3 \text{ Å}; \quad \lambda_3 = \frac{144}{7 \times 186R} = 109 \text{ Å}.$$

47.12. $a_1 = 2a_0 = 1.06$ Å; $\mathscr{E}_1 = -hcR/2 = -13.6/2 = -6.8$ eV.

47.13. 10.2 V.

47.15. (a) Boron: 1, 0, 0, 1/2; 1, 0, 0, −1/2; 2, 0, 0, 1/2; 2, 0, 0, −1/2; 2, 1, 0, 1/2.
(b) Sodium: 1, 0, 0, 1/2; 1, 0, 0, −1/2; 2, 0, 0, 1/2; 2, 0, 0, −1/2; 2, 1, 0, 1/2; 2, 1, 0, −1/2; 2, 1, 1, 1/2; 2, 1, 1, −1/2; 2, 1, −1, 1/2; 2, 1, −1, −1/2; 3, 0, 0, 1/2.

47.16. *Hint.* Find the number of electrons on the upper partially filled energy level.

47.17. $F_{\mathrm{av}} = 3h^2/4mL^3$.   **47.18.** $F_{\mathrm{av}} = 3h^2/2mL^3$.

47.19. 0.31 Å.   **47.20.** $Z = 41$—niobium.   **47.21.** Above 5 kV.

47.22. 8.3 kV.   **47.23.** 3.2×10^{13} rad/s.   **47.24.** 41 μm.

47.25. 0.95 Å.   **47.26.** There is no contradiction. [*Hint.* See Problems 33.10 and 46.11.]

47.28. $\dfrac{2\mu_\mathrm{p}\mu_\mathrm{e}}{e^2 c^2 a_0^2} = 4 \times 10^{-8}$.

47.29. 56 cm.   **47.30.** 3.2×10^{13} Hz.   **47.31.** It is not.

47.32. $2\theta = 1.2'$.

48. Quantum Properties of Metals and of Semiconductors

48.1. Aluminium: 12.8 eV; 1.9×10^{-24} kg·m/s;
sodium: 3.1 eV; 9.5×10^{-25} kg·m/s; copper: 8.6 eV; 1.6×10^{-24} kg·m/s. [*Hint*. See § 44.2.]

48.2. 9.9×10^4 K; 2.4×10^4 K; 6.6×10^4 K.

48.3. $P = 2/5 n_0 \mathscr{E}_F = 1.7 \times 10^{11}$ Pa. **48.4.** $PV^{5/3} = $ const; $\gamma = 5/3$.

48.5. $A = \dfrac{h^2}{20 m_e (m_\alpha / 2)^{5/3}} \approx 3.2 \times 10^6$ Pa·m^5·kg$^{5/3}$.

48.6. 0.2%. **48.7.** $C_m^{\text{el}} = 12.5$ J/(kmole·K); $C_m^{\text{el}} / C_m^{\text{lat}} = 5 \times 10^{-4}$.

48.8. $\lambda = 3 \times 10^2$ Å; $\lambda / d \approx 150$.

48.9. $i = N \dfrac{nS}{r} \cdot \dfrac{e\hbar}{2 m_e}$, where n is the concentration of electrons;
$N = 1. \ 2, \ 3, \ \ldots;$ $\Phi = Li$, where L is the inductance of the ring.

48.10. $\gamma = B e^{-\Delta \mathscr{E}/kT}$. **48.11.** $\gamma_2 / \gamma_1 = 6.6 \times 10^5$.

48.12. $n = 2.4 \times 10^{19}$ m^{-3}; $R_{\text{H}} = 9.4 \times 10^{-2}$ m^3/C.

48.13. 5.8×10^2 ohm^{-1}·m^{-1}; 3.0×10^2 ohm^{-1}·m^{-1}.

48.14. 0.55 V; 8.6 V. [*Hint*. For the expression for the internal contact potential difference see § 78.1.]

49. Nuclear Structure

49.1. Helium $_2\text{He}^3$—two protons, one neutron; tritium $_1\text{H}^3$—one proton, two neutrons.

49.2. 20% of the light isotope and 80% of the heavy one.

49.3. Deuterium: $R = 1.8 \times 10^{-15}$ m; $U_0 = 0.8$ MeV.
Polonium: $R = 8.3 \times 10^{-15}$ m; $U_0 = 14.6$ MeV.

49.4. 2.23 MeV; 1.12 MeV per nucleon.

49.5. 2.84 MeV/nucleon; 2.56 MeV/nucleon.

49.6. Five alpha-disintegrations and four beta-disintegrations.

49.7. $K_\alpha = 4.45$ MeV; $K_{\text{Pb}} = 1.05$ MeV.

49.8. It cannot. **49.9.** It cannot.

49.10. It can; an electron and an antineutrino; 1.48 MeV.

49.11. 4.96 MeV.

49.12. $w = e^{-21} = 2.8 \times 10^{-10}$.

49.13. Will decrease to 1/1.3 of its value.

49.14. 3.7 days.

49.15. 1.4×10^{17} s $= 4 \times 10^9$ years.

49.16. 8800 years.

49.17. 0.82 MeV. **49.18.** $\delta_{\text{rec}} = \mathscr{E}_\gamma / 2Mc^2 = 1.4 \times 10^{-7}$; $\delta_{\text{nat}} = \hbar / \tau \mathscr{E}_\gamma = 3.2 \times 10^{-13}$.

49.19. $v = \mathscr{E}_\gamma / Mc = 81$ m/s.

49.20. $N = N_0 e^{-\lambda t}$. **49.21.** 0.2 MeV.

50. Nuclear Reactions

50.1. 3×10^7 kg = 30 000 tonnes.
50.2. 22.4 MeV; 2.8 MeV per nucleon.
50.3. They can.
50.4. It contradicts the law of conservation of momentum; 67.5 MeV.
50.5. $\delta = \hbar/\tau \mathscr{E} = 6 \times 10^{-8}$. **50.6.** $\mathscr{E}_\gamma \geqslant 1.02$ MeV.
50.8. $K_\mu = 4.1$ MeV; $\mathscr{E}_\nu = 29.9$ MeV; $\mathscr{E}_\nu/K_\mu = 7.3$.
50.9. $K_e = 0.28$ MeV; $\mathscr{E}_\nu = 0.61$ MeV.
50.10. $K_\pi = 56$ MeV; $\mathscr{E}_\gamma = 95$ MeV. **50.11.** 12.1 MeV; 158.4°.
50.12. $_{-1}e^0 + {}_1p^1 \rightarrow {}_0n^1 + {}_0\nu^0$; 0.24 MeV.

TABLES

1. Astronomical Data

	Equatorial half-diameter, 10^6 m	Mass, kg	Average distance from the Sun, 10^9 m	Period of revolution about the Sun
The Sun	700	1.98×10^{30}	—	—
Venus	6.2	4.9×10^{24}	108.11	227.70 days
The Earth	6.4	5.98×10^{24}	149.46	365.26 days
Mars	3.4	6.5×10^{23}	227.7	686.98 days
The Moon	1.7	7.4×10^{22}	—	—

2. Mechanical Properties of Solids

Material	Bulk modulus K, 10^{10} Pa	Young's modulus E, 10^{10} Pa	Permissible stress σ_{per}, 10^7 Pa	Breaking stress for extension σ_{br}, 10^8 Pa	Density ρ, 10^3 kg/m³
Steel, soft	17	20	14	4-6	7.8
Steel, chrome-nickel	17	22	30	10-15	7.8
Silver	10.4	8.0	3-8	0.9-1.5	10.5
Aluminium	7.6	7.0	3-8	0.9-1.5	2.7
Copper	14	13	3-12	1.2-4.0	8.9
Nickel	16	20			8.9
Lead	4.1	1.7		0.2	11.3
Ice (−2 °C)		0.28			0.92

3. Thermal Properties of Solids

Material	Specific heat c, kJ/(kg·K) (from 0 to 100 °C)	Specific heat of fusion λ, 10^5 J/kg	Melting point t_m, °C	Linear expansion coefficient α, K^{-1} 10^{-6}	Coefficient of thermal conductivity K, W/(m·K)
Steel	0.45	2.7	1440	10–11	50–70
Silver	0.23	0.88	980.6	20.5	4.2×10^2
Aluminium	0.84	4.0	660	27	2.3×10^2
Copper	0.38	2.1	1080	20	3.8×10^2
Nickel	0.46	3.0	1453	18	0.9×10^2
Lead	0.126	0.25	327	30	35
Ice (−2 °C)	2.1	3.4	0.00	—	2.2

4. Properties of Liquids

Material	Density ρ, 10^3 kg/m³ (at 0 °C)	Viscosity η, mPa·s (at 20 °C)	Surface tension σ, mN/m (at 20 °C)	Volume expansion coefficient β, 10^{-4} K^{-1}	Coefficient of thermal conductivity K, W/(m·K) (at 20 °C)	Boiling point, °C (at normal atmospheric pressure)	Specific heat of vapourization L, MJ/kg (at normal atmospheric pressure)	Specific heat c, kJ/(kg·K)
Oil	0.8	1–10	—	—	—	—	—	—
Water	0.9999	1.00	72.8	2.1	0.61	100	2.28	4.18
Water (80 °C)	0.9718	0.36	62.8	—	—	—	—	—
Mercury	13.595	1.55	475.0	1.8	10	356.6	0.25	0.14
Castor oil	0.95	986	—	—	—	—	—	2.13
H_2SO_4, 30%	1.02	2.44	—	—	—	—	—	1.4

5. Properties of Gases

Material	Effective cross section σ, 10^{-20} m^2	Viscosity η, μPa·s (at standard conditions)	Heat conductivity K, 10^{-2} W/(m·K) (at standard conditions)	Specific heat c_p, KJ/(kg·K) (from 0 to 100 °C)	$\gamma = \dfrac{c_p}{c_V}$	Density ρ, kg/m^3 (at standard conditions)
Helium	3.1	18.6	14.15	0.523	1.630	0.1785
Neon	7.0	29.8	4.65	1.05	1.642	0.8999
Nitrogen (N_2)	10.8	16.6	2.43	1.04	1.401	1.2505
Hydrogen (H_2)	5.7	8.4	16.84	14.3	1.407	0.0899
Hydrogen* (H)	3.5	—	—	—	1.667	—
Oxygen (O_2)	9.6	19.2	2.44	0.913	1.400	1.4289
Air	10	17.1	2.4	1.01	1.40	1.293
Steam (100 °C)	6.0	12.8	2.6	1.951	1.334	0.598
Carbon dioxide (CO_2)	16.2	13.8	1.38	0.91	1.300	1.9769
CO_2, 100 °C		18.6		0.90	1.30	
CO_2, 300 °C		26.7		0.85	1.22	
CO_2, 500 °C				0.83	1.20	

* Computed with the aid of the formula $\sigma = 4\pi a_0^2$, where $a_0 = 0.5$ Å is the Bohr radius.

6. Electrical Properties of Materials (20 °C)

Material	Dielectric constant ε	Breakdown field strength E_M, MV/m
Paraffin paper	2	40-60
Mica	6-7	80-200
Glass	4-10	20-30
Transformer oil	2.2	
Ethyl alcohol	26	

7. Velocity of Sound (Longitudinal Waves)

Material	u, km/s	Material	u, km/s
Quartz, (X-cut)	5.72	Water (17 °C)	1.407
Nickel (in a magnetic field of 0.3 T induction)	4.86	Sea water	1.446
		Castor oil	1.50

8. Refractive Indexes

Light	Wavelength λ, nm	Fluorite	Molten quartz	Rock salt NaCl	Sylvite KCl	Water (20 °C)	Glass crown	Glass flint
Infra-red	1256.0	1.4275	—	1.5297	1.4778	1.3210	1.5042	1.6268
	670.8	1.4323	1.4561	1.5400	1.4866	1.3308	1.5140	1.6434
Red	656.3	1.4325	1.4564	1.5407	1.4872	1.3311	—	—
	643.8	1.4327	1.4568	1.5412	1.4877	1.3314	1.5149	1.6453
Orange	589.3	1.4339	1.4585	1.5443	1.4904	1.3330	1.5170	1.6499
Yellow	546.1	1.4350	1.4602	1.5475	1.4931	1.3345	—	—
Green	508.6	1.4362	1.4619	1.5509	1.4961	1.3360	—	—
Blue	486.1	1.4369	1.4632	1.5534	1.4983	1.3371	1.5230	1.6637
Dark blue	480.0	1.4371	1.4636	1.5541	1.4990	1.3374	—	—
Violet	404.7	1.4415	1.4697	1.5665	1.5097	1.3428	1.5318	1.6852
	303.4	1.4534	1.4869	1.6085	1.5440	1.3581	1.5552	—
Ultraviolet	214.4	1.4846	1.5339	1.7322	1.6618	1.4032	—	—
	185.2	1.5099	1.5743	1.8933	1.8270	—	—	—

9. Masses of Some Neutral Atoms (amu)

	Mass		Mass
Hydrogen $_1H^1$	1.00783	Carbon $_6C^{10}$	10.00168
Deuterium $_1H^2$	2.01410	$_6C^{12}$	12.00000
Tritium $_1H^3$	3.01605	$_6C^{13}$	13.00335
Helium $_2He^3$	3.01603	$_6C^{14}$	14.00324
$_2He^4$	4.00260	Aluminium $_{13}Al^{30}$	29.99817
Lithium $_3Li^6$	6.01513	Silicon $_{14}Si^{31}$	30.97535
$_3Li^7$	7.01601	Phosphorus $_{15}P^{31}$	30.97376
Berillium $_4Be^7$	7.01693	Lead $_{82}Pb^{206}$	205.97446
$_4Be^9$	9.01219	Polonium $_{84}Po^{210}$	209.98297

10. Fundamental Physical Constants

Constant	Notation	Value*
1. Magnetic constant	μ_0	$4\pi \cdot 10^{-7}$ G·m^{-7}
2. Electric constant	$\varepsilon_0 = 1/\mu_0 c^2$	$8.85418782 \times 10^{-12}$ F·m^{-1}
3. Velocity of light in a vacuum	c	299 792 458 m·s^{-1}
4. Elementary charge	e	$1.6021892 \times 10^{-19}$ C
5. Planck's constant	h	6.626176×10^{-34} J·s
	$\hbar = h/2\pi$	$1.0545887 \times 10^{-34}$ J·s
6. Avogadro number	N_A	6.0220943×10^{26} kmole^{-1}
7. Atomic mass unit	1 amu	$1.6605655 \times 10^{-27}$ kg
8. Rest mass of:		
electron	m_e	9.109534×10^{-31} kg
		5.4858026×10^{-4} amu
muon	m_μ	1.883566×10^{-28} kg
		0.11342920 amu
proton	m_p	$1.6726485 \times 10^{-27}$ kg
		1.007276470 amu
neutron	m_n	$1.6749543 \times 10^{-27}$ kg
		1.008665012 amu
9. Specific charge of electron	e/m_e	1.7588047 C·kg^{-1}
10. Faraday number	$F = eN_A$	9.648456×10^7 C·kmole^{-1}
11. Rydberg's constant	R_∞	1.097373143×10^7 m^{-1}
12. Bohr radius	a_0	$0.52917706 \times 10^{-10}$ m
13. Compton wavelength of electron	$\lambda_C = \hbar/m_e c$	$2.4263089 \times 10^{-12}$ m
14. Bohr magneton	$\mu_B = e\hbar/2m_e$	9.274078×10^{-24} J·T^{-1}
15. Magnetic moment:		
electron	μ_e	9.284832×10^{-24} J·T^{-1}
proton	μ_p	$1.4106171 \times 10^{-26}$ J·T^{-1}
16. Gas constant	R	8.31441×10^3 J/(kmole·K)
17. Volume of 1 kilomole of an ideal gas	V_m	22.41383 m^3·kmole^{-1}
18. Boltzmann constant	$k = R/N_A$	1.380662×10^{-23} J·K^{-1}
19. Stephan constant	σ	5.67032×10^{-8} W/(m^2·K^4)
20. Gravitational constant	γ, G	6.6720×10^{-11} N·m^2/kg^2
21. Energy equivalent of 1 amu		931.5016 MeV

* The above constants are from the paper "Recommended approved values of fundamental physical constants — 1973" (the periodical "Uspekhi fizicheskikh nauk", v. 115, No. 4, April 1975, pp. 623-633).

TO THE READER

Mir Publishers would be grateful for your comments on the contents, translation and design of this book. We would also be pleased to receive any other suggestions you may wish to make.
Our address is: Mir Publishers
2 Pervy Rizhsky Pereulok,
I-110, GSP, Moscow, 129820,
USSR

Printed in the Union of Soviet Socialist Republics

Basic Concepts of Quantum Mechanics

L. TARASOV, Cand.Sc.

This book gives a detailed and systematic exposition
of the fundamentals of non-relativistic quantum mechanics for those who are not acquainted with the subject.
The character of the physics of microparticles and the
problems of the physics of microprocesses (interference
of amplitudes, the principle of superposition, the specific nature of measuring processes, casuality in quantum
mechanics) are considered on the basis of concepts about
probability amplitudes. Besides, the quantum mechanical systems—microparticles with two basic states—are
analyzed in detail. The apparatus of quantum mechanics
is considered as a synthesis of concepts about physics
and the theory of linear operators. A number of specially
worked out problems and examples have been included
in order to demonstrate the working of the apparatus.
This book is meant for use by students of engineering
and teachers-training institutes. It may also be used
by engineers of different profiles.
Contents. Physics of Micro-particles. Physical Founda-
tions of Quantum Mechanics. Linear Operators in Quantum Mechanics. Brief Historical Survey.

Handbook of Physics

B. YAVORSKY, D. Sc. and A. DETLAF, Cand. Sc.

A companion volume to Vygodsky's *Handbook of Higher Mathematics*, designed for use by engineers, technicians, research workers, students, and teachers of physics. Includes definitions of basic physical concepts, brief formulations of physical laws, concise descriptions of phenomena, tables of physical quantities in various systems of units, universal physical constants, etc. This is a third English 'edition.

Contents. Physical Basis of Classical Mechanics. Fundamentals of Thermodynamics and Molecular Physics. Fundamentals of Fluid Mechanics. Electricity and Magnetism. Wave Phenomena. Atomic and Nuclear Physics.